THE PEARSON CUSTOM LIBRARY FOR
CHEMISTRY

CHEMISTRY & the CITIZEN
Dr. Ellen Kehres

PEARSON

This special edition published in cooperation with Pearson Learning Solutions.

Printed in the United States of America.

V092

Please visit our website at *www.pearsonlearningsolutions.com*.

Attention bookstores: For permission to return unused stock, contact us at *pe-uscustomreturns@pearson.com*.

Pearson Learning Solutions, 501 Boylston Street, Suite 900, Boston, MA 02116
A Pearson Education Company
www.pearsoned.com

ISBN 10: 1-269-24220-2
ISBN 13: 978-1-269-24220-2

Table of Contents

PERIODIC TABLE OF THE ELEMENTS

Main groups

Main groups

Transition metals

Metals   Nonmetals   Noble gases

1 a / 1A b	2 / 2A	3 / 3B	4 / 4B	5 / 5B	6 / 6B	7 / 7B	8 / 8B	9 / 8B	10 / 8B	11 / 1B	12 / 2B	13 / 3A	14 / 4A	15 / 5A	16 / 6A	17 / 7A	18 / 8A
1 **H** Hydrogen 1.00794																	2 **He** Helium 4.002602
3 **Li** Lithium 6.941	4 **Be** Beryllium 9.012182											5 **B** Boron 10.811	6 **C** Carbon 12.0107	7 **N** Nitrogen 14.00674	8 **O** Oxygen 15.9994	9 **F** Fluorine 18.998403	10 **Ne** Neon 20.1797
11 **Na** Sodium 22.989770	12 **Mg** Magnesium 24.3050											13 **Al** Aluminum 26.981538	14 **Si** Silicon 28.0855	15 **P** Phosphorus 30.973762	16 **S** Sulfur 32.066	17 **Cl** Chlorine 35.4527	18 **Ar** Argon 39.948
19 **K** Potassium 39.0983	20 **Ca** Calcium 40.078	21 **Sc** Scandium 44.95591	22 **Ti** Titanium 47.867	23 **V** Vanadium 50.9415	24 **Cr** Chromium 51.9961	25 **Mn** Manganese 54.938049	26 **Fe** Iron 55.845	27 **Co** Cobalt 58.933200	28 **Ni** Nickel 58.6934	29 **Cu** Copper 63.546	30 **Zn** Zinc 65.39	31 **Ga** Gallium 69.723	32 **Ge** Germanium 72.61	33 **As** Arsenic 74.92160	34 **Se** Selenium 78.96	35 **Br** Bromine 79.904	36 **Kr** Krypton 83.80
37 **Rb** Rubidium 85.4678	38 **Sr** Strontium 87.62	39 **Y** Yttrium 88.90585	40 **Zr** Zirconium 91.224	41 **Nb** Niobium 92.90638	42 **Mo** Molybdenum 95.94	43 **Tc** Technetium [98]	44 **Ru** Ruthenium 101.07	45 **Rh** Rhodium 102.90550	46 **Pd** Palladium 106.42	47 **Ag** Silver 107.8682	48 **Cd** Cadmium 112.411	49 **In** Indium 114.818	50 **Sn** Tin 118.710	51 **Sb** Antimony 121.760	52 **Te** Tellurium 127.60	53 **I** Iodine 126.90447	54 **Xe** Xenon 131.29
55 **Cs** Cesium 132.90545	56 **Ba** Barium 137.327	57 ***La** Lanthanum 138.9055	72 **Hf** Hafnium 178.49	73 **Ta** Tantalum 180.9479	74 **W** Tungsten 183.84	75 **Re** Rhenium 186.207	76 **Os** Osmium 190.23	77 **Ir** Iridium 192.217	78 **Pt** Platinum 195.078	79 **Au** Gold 196.96655	80 **Hg** Mercury 200.59	81 **Tl** Thallium 204.3833	82 **Pb** Lead 207.2	83 **Bi** Bismuth 208.98038	84 **Po** Polonium [209]	85 **At** Astatine [210]	86 **Rn** Radon [222]
87 **Fr** Francium [223]	88 **Ra** Radium 226.025	89 **†Ac** Actinium 227.028	104 **Rf** Rutherfordium [261]	105 **Db** Dubnium [262]	106 **Sg** Seaborgium [266]	107 **Bh** Bohrium [267]	108 **Hs** Hassium [269]	109 **Mt** Meitnerium [268]	110 **Ds** Darmstadtium [281]	111 **Rg** Roentgenium [272]	112 **Cn** Copernicium [285]	113 c [284]	114 [285]	115 [288]	116 [289]	117 d [294]	118 [294]

*Lanthanide series	58 **Ce** Cerium 140.116	59 **Pr** Praseodymium 140.90765	60 **Nd** Neodymium 144.24	61 **Pm** Promethium [145]	62 **Sm** Samarium 150.36	63 **Eu** Europium 151.964	64 **Gd** Gadolinium 157.25	65 **Tb** Terbium 158.92534	66 **Dy** Dysprosium 162.50	67 **Ho** Holmium 164.93032	68 **Er** Erbium 167.26	69 **Tm** Thulium 168.93421	70 **Yb** Ytterbium 173.04	71 **Lu** Lutetium 174.967
†Actinide series	90 **Th** Thorium 232.0381	91 **Pa** Protactinium 231.03588	92 **U** Uranium 238.0289	93 **Np** Neptunium 237.048	94 **Pu** Plutonium [244]	95 **Am** Americium [243]	96 **Cm** Curium [247]	97 **Bk** Berkelium [247]	98 **Cf** Californium [251]	99 **Es** Einsteinium [252]	100 **Fm** Fermium [257]	101 **Md** Mendelevium [258]	102 **No** Nobelium [259]	103 **Lr** Lawrencium [262]

Atomic masses in brackets are the masses of the longest-lived or most important isotope of certain radioactive elements.

a The labels on top (1, 2, 3 ... 18) are the group numbers recommended by the International Union of Pure and Applied Chemistry (IUPAC).

b The labels on the bottom (1A, 2A, ... 8A) are the group numbers commonly used in the United States and the ones we use in this text.

c The names and symbols of elements 113 and above have not been assigned.

d Discovered in 2010, element 117 is under review by IUPAC.

Further information is available at the Web site of WebElements™.

TABLE OF ATOMIC MASSES BASED ON CARBON-12

Name	Symbol	Atomic Number	Atomic Mass	Name	Symbol	Atomic Number	Atomic Mass
Actinium	Ac	89	227.028	Meitnerium	Mt	109	(268)
Aluminum	Al	13	26.9815	Mendelevium	Md	101	(258)
Americium	Am	95	(243)	Mercury	Hg	80	200.59
Antimony	Sb	51	121.760	Molybdenum	Mo	42	95.94
Argon	Ar	18	39.948	Neodymium	Nd	60	144.24
Arsenic	As	33	74.9216	Neon	Ne	10	20.1797
Astatine	At	85	(210)	Neptunium	Np	93	237.048
Barium	Ba	56	137.327	Nickel	Ni	28	58.6934
Berkelium	Bk	97	(247)	Niobium	Nb	41	92.9064
Beryllium	Be	4	9.01218	Nitrogen	N	7	14.0067
Bismuth	Bi	83	208.980	Nobelium	No	102	(259)
Bohrium	Bh	107	(267)	Osmium	Os	76	190.23
Boron	B	5	10.811	Oxygen	O	8	15.9994
Bromine	Br	35	79.904	Palladium	Pd	46	106.42
Cadmium	Cd	48	112.411	Phosphorus	P	15	30.9738
Calcium	Ca	20	40.078	Platinum	Pt	78	195.078
Californium	Cf	98	(251)	Plutonium	Pu	94	(244)
Carbon	C	6	12.0107	Polonium	Po	84	(209)
Cerium	Ce	58	140.116	Potassium	K	19	39.0983
Cesium	Cs	55	132.905	Praseodymium	Pr	59	140.908
Chlorine	Cl	17	35.4527	Promethium	Pm	61	(145)
Chromium	Cr	24	51.9961	Protactinium	Pa	91	231.036
Cobalt	Co	27	58.9332	Radium	Ra	88	226.025
Copernicium	Cn	112	(285)	Radon	Rn	86	(222)
Copper	Cu	29	63.546	Rhenium	Re	75	186.207
Curium	Cm	96	(247)	Rhodium	Rh	45	102.906
Darmstadtium	Ds	110	(281)	Roentgenium	Rg	111	(272)
Dubnium	Db	105	(262)	Rubidium	Rb	37	85.4678
Dysprosium	Dy	66	162.50	Ruthenium	Ru	44	101.07
Einsteinium	Es	99	(252)	Rutherfordium	Rf	104	(261)
Erbium	Er	68	167.26	Samarium	Sm	62	150.36
Europium	Eu	63	151.964	Scandium	Sc	21	44.9559
Fermium	Fm	100	(257)	Seaborgium	Sg	106	(266)
Fluorine	F	9	18.9984	Selenium	Se	34	78.96
Francium	Fr	87	(223)	Silicon	Si	14	28.0855
Gadolinium	Gd	64	157.25	Silver	Ag	47	107.868
Gallium	Ga	31	69.723	Sodium	Na	11	22.9898
Germanium	Ge	32	72.61	Strontium	Sr	38	87.62
Gold	Au	79	196.967	Sulfur	S	16	32.066
Hafnium	Hf	72	178.49	Tantalum	Ta	73	180.948
Hassium	Hs	108	(269)	Technetium	Tc	43	(98)
Helium	He	2	4.00260	Tellurium	Te	52	127.60
Holmium	Ho	67	164.930	Terbium	Tb	65	158.925
Hydrogen	H	1	1.00794	Thallium	Tl	81	204.383
Indium	In	49	114.818	Thorium	Th	90	232.038
Iodine	I	53	126.904	Thulium	Tm	69	168.934
Iridium	Ir	77	192.217	Tin	Sn	50	118.710
Iron	Fe	26	55.845	Titanium	Ti	22	47.867
Krypton	Kr	36	83.80	Tungsten	W	74	183.84
Lanthanum	La	57	138.906	Uranium	U	92	238.029
Lawrencium	Lr	103	(262)	Vanadium	V	23	50.9415
Lead	Pb	82	207.2	Xenon	Xe	54	131.29
Lithium	Li	3	6.941	Ytterbium	Yb	70	173.04
Lutetium	Lu	71	174.967	Yttrium	Y	39	88.9059
Magnesium	Mg	12	24.3050	Zinc	Zn	30	65.39
Manganese	Mn	25	54.9380	Zirconium	Zr	40	91.224

Atomic masses in this table are relative to carbon-12 and limited to six significant figures, although some atomic masses are known more precisely. For certain radioactive elements the numbers listed (in parentheses) are the mass numbers of the most stable isotopes.

Atoms

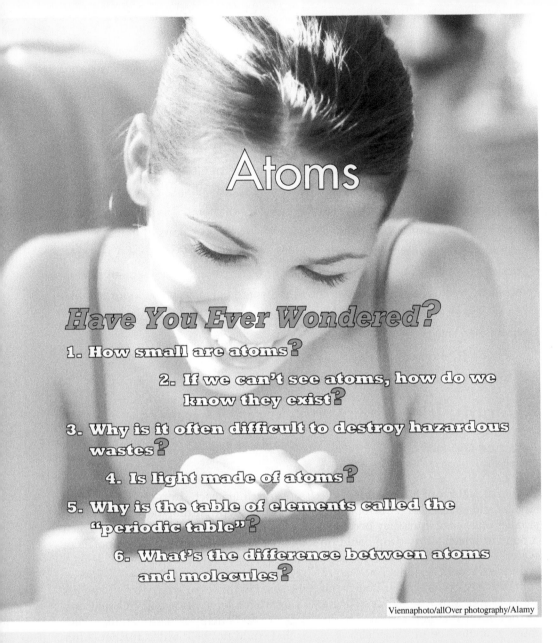

Have You Ever Wondered?

1. **How small are atoms?**

2. **If we can't see atoms, how do we know they exist?**

3. **Why is it often difficult to destroy hazardous wastes?**

4. **Is light made of atoms?**

5. **Why is the table of elements called the "periodic table"?**

6. **What's the difference between atoms and molecules?**

Viennaphoto/allOver photography/Alamy

Stockbyte/Getty Images, Inc

Learning Objectives

> Explain the ancient Greeks' ideas about the characteristics of matter. (1)

> Describe the significance of the laws of conservation of mass and definite proportions. (2)

> Calculate the amounts of elements from the composition of a compound. (2)

> Explain why the idea that matter is made of atoms is a theory. (3)

> Understand how atomic theory explains the law of conservation of mass. (3)

> Describe how the elements are arranged in the periodic table and why the arrangement is important. (4)

> Distinguish atoms from molecules. (5)

> Identify elements that could be classified as hazardous or rare.

> Explain how green chemistry can change technologies that rely on hazardous or rare elements.

Are They for Real?

We hear something about atoms almost every day. The twentieth century saw the start of the so-called Atomic Age. The terms *atomic power*, *atomic energy*, and *atomic bomb* are a part of our ordinary vocabulary. But just what are atoms?

Every material thing in the world is made up of atoms, tiny particles that are much, much too small to see even with the finest optical microscope. The smallest speck of matter that can be detected by the human eye is made up of many billions of atoms. There are more than 10^{22} (10,000,000,000,000,000,000,000) atoms in a penny. Imagine that the

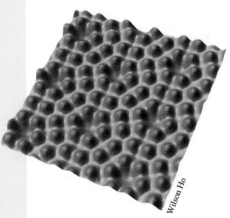

Wilson Ho

At the heart of every tablet computer (above), printer, telephone, television, MP3 player, and virtually every other electronic device lies a wafer of silicon (above right) in one or more integrated circuits (ICs or "chips"). The silicon used for electronics must be so pure that these devices were not possible until zone-refining purification was developed, about sixty years ago. Silicon is an *element*, made of a single type of atom. For making ICs, only about one atom of impurity can be present for every billion atoms of silicon. But how do we even know that atoms exist? The false-color image at the right shows individual silicon atoms in a hexagonal arrangement, using a recently developed technique called *scanning tunneling microscopy*. However, the behavior of matter led scientists to the atomic nature of matter over two hundred years ago. In this chapter, we will see some of that history, and we will explore the properties of atoms.

From Chapter 2 of *Chemistry for Changing Times*, Thirteenth Edition. John W. Hill, Terry W. McCreary, Doris K. Kolb.

atoms in a penny were enlarged until they were barely visible, like tiny grains of sand. The atoms in a single penny would then make enough "sand" to cover the entire state of Texas several feet deep. Comparing an atom to a penny is like comparing a grain of sand to a Texas-size sandbox.

Why should we care about something as tiny as an atom? Because our world is made up of atoms, and atoms are a part of all we do. *Everything* is made of atoms, including you and me. And because chemistry is the study of the behavior of matter, it observes the behavior of atoms. The behavior and interactions of atoms determine the behavior and interactions of matter.

Atoms are not all alike. Each element has its own kind of atom. On Earth, about 90 elements occur in nature. About two dozen more have been synthesized by scientists. As far as we know, the entire universe is made up of these same few elements. An **atom** is the smallest particle that is characteristic of a given element.

▲ A marble statue of Democritus, who first formulated the atomic nature of matter.

1 Atoms: Ideas from the Ancient Greeks

Learning Objective ❯ Explain the ancient Greeks' ideas about the characteristics of matter.

A pool of water can be separated into drops, and then each drop can be split into smaller and smaller drops. Suppose that you could keep splitting the drops into still smaller ones even after they became much too small to see. Would you ever reach a point at which a tiny drop could no longer be separated into smaller droplets of water? Is water infinitely divisible, or would you eventually come to a particle that, if divided, would no longer be water?

The Greek philosopher Leucippus, who lived in the fifth century B.C.E., and his pupil Democritus (ca. 460–ca. 370 B.C.E.) might well have discussed this question as they strolled along the beach by the Aegean Sea. Leucippus reasoned that there must ultimately be tiny particles of water that could not be divided further. After all, from a distance the sand on the beach looked continuous, but closer inspection showed it to be made up of tiny grains (Figure 1).

Democritus expanded on Leucippus's idea. He called the particles *atomos* (meaning "cannot be cut"), from which we derive the modern name *atom* for the tiny, discrete particle of an element. Democritus thought that each kind of atom was distinct in shape and size (Figure 2). He thought that real substances were mix-

▶ **Figure 1** A sandy beach.

Q: *Sand looks continuous—infinitely divisible—when you look at a beach from a distance. Is it really continuous? Water looks continuous, even when viewed up close. Is it really continuous? Is a cloud continuous? Is air?*

tures of various kinds of atoms. The Greeks at that time believed that there were four basic elements: earth, air, fire, and water. These "elements" were related by four "principles"—hot, moist, dry, and cold—as shown in Figure 3. These ideas seem strange to us today, but they persisted for two millennia.

Four centuries after Democritus, the Roman poet Lucretius (ca. 95–ca. 55 B.C.E.) wrote a long didactic poem (a poem meant to teach), *On the Nature of Things*, in which he presented strong arguments for the atomic nature of matter. Unfortunately, a few centuries earlier, the famous Greek philosopher Aristotle (ca. 384–ca. 322 B.C.E.) had declared that matter was continuous (infinitely divisible) rather than discrete (consisting of tiny indivisible particles). The people of that time had no way to determine which view was correct. To most of them, Aristotle's continuous view of matter seemed more logical and reasonable, and so it prevailed for 2000 years, even though it was wrong.

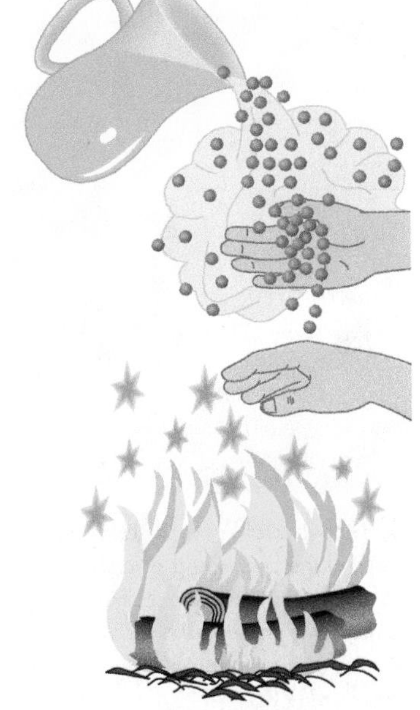

Self-Assessment Questions

1. Consider how the qualities *discrete* and *continuous* apply to materials at the macroscopic (visible to the unaided eye) level. Which of the following is continuous?
   a. apple juice
   b. a ream of paper
   c. a bowl of cherries
   d. chocolate chips

2. The view that matter is continuous rather than atomic prevailed for centuries because it was
   a. actually correct
   b. not considered important
   c. not tested by experiment
   d. tested and found to be true

Answers: 1, a; 2, c

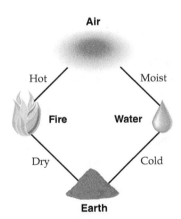

▲ **Figure 2** Democritus imagined that "atoms" of water might be smooth, round balls and that atoms of fire might have sharp edges.

2 Scientific Laws: Conservation of Mass and Definite Proportions

Learning Objectives ❯ Describe the significance of the laws of conservation of mass and definite proportions. ❯ Calculate the amounts of elements from the composition of a compound.

The eighteenth century saw the triumph of careful observation and measurement in chemistry. Antoine Lavoisier (1743–1794) perhaps did more than anyone to establish chemistry as a quantitative science. He found that when a chemical reaction was carried out in a closed container, the total mass of the system was not changed. Perhaps the most important chemical reaction that Lavoisier performed was decomposition of a red compound containing mercury to form metallic mercury and a gas he named *oxygen*. Both Carl Wilhelm Scheele (1742–1786), a Swedish apothecary, and Joseph Priestley (1733–1804), a Unitarian minister who later fled England and settled in America in 1794, had carried out the same reaction earlier, but Lavoisier was the first to weigh all the substances present before and after the reaction. He was also the first to interpret the reaction correctly.

The Law of Conservation of Mass

Lavoisier carried out many quantitative experiments. He found that when coal was burned, it united with oxygen to form carbon dioxide. He experimented with animals, observing that when a guinea pig breathed, oxygen was consumed and carbon dioxide was formed. Lavoisier therefore concluded that respiration was related

Air

Hot / Moist

Fire **Water**

Dry \ Cold

Earth

▲ **Figure 3** The Greek view of matter was that there were only four elements (in bold) connected by four "principles."

The work of Antoine Lavoisier marked the beginning of chemistry as a quantitative science. Here, Lavoisier is shown with his wife, Marie, in a painting by Jacques Louis David in 1788.

100.00 grams of mercuric oxide	92.61 grams of mercury	7.39 grams of oxygen
100.00 =	92.61 +	7.39

▲ **Figure 4** Although mercuric oxide (a red solid) has none of the properties of mercury (a silver liquid) or oxygen (a colorless gas), when 100.00 g of mercuric oxide is decomposed by heating, the products are 92.61 g of mercury and 7.39 g of oxygen. Properties are completely changed in this reaction, but there is no change in mass.

Q: *When 10.00 g of mercuric oxide decomposes, 0.739 g of oxygen forms. What mass of mercury forms?*

2. If we can't see atoms, how do we know they exist?

If matter had no "smallest particles," the law of conservation of mass, the law of definite proportions, and the law of multiple proportions would be almost impossible to explain. Atomic theory provides a simple explanation for these laws and for many others.

to combustion. In each of these reactions, he found that matter was *conserved*—the amount remained constant.

Lavoisier summarized his findings as the **law of conservation of mass**, which states that matter is neither created nor destroyed during a chemical change (Figure 4). The total mass of the reaction products is always equal to the total mass of the reactants (starting materials). For now, some simple examples and discussion will illustrate the conservation of mass.

Scientists by this time had abandoned the Greek idea of the four elements and were almost universally using Robert Boyle's working definition of an element presented in his book *The Sceptical Chymist* (published in 1661). Boyle said that a supposed *element* must be tested. If a substance could be broken down into simpler substances, it was not an element. The simpler substances might be elements and should be regarded as such until the time (if it ever came) when they in turn could be broken down into still simpler substances. On the other hand, two or more elements might combine to form a more complex substance called a *compound*.

Using Boyle's definition, Lavoisier included a table of elements in his book *Elementary Treatise on Chemistry*. (The table included some substances that we now know to be compounds, as well as light and heat, which are actually forms of energy.) Lavoisier was the first to use systematic names for chemical elements. He is often called the "father of modern chemistry," and his book is usually regarded as the first chemistry textbook.

The law of conservation of mass is the basis for many chemical calculations. This law states that we cannot create materials from nothing. We can make new materials only by changing the way atoms are combined. For example, we can obtain iron metal from iron ore only because the ore contains iron atoms. Furthermore, we cannot get rid of wastes by the destruction of matter. We must put wastes somewhere. However, through chemical reactions, we can change some kinds of potentially hazardous wastes to less harmful forms. Such transformations of matter from one form to another are what chemistry is all about.

The Law of Definite Proportions

By the end of the eighteenth century, Lavoisier and other scientists noted that many substances were compounds, composed of two or more elements. Each compound had the same elements in the same proportions, regardless of where

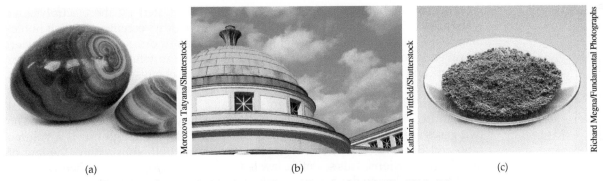

(a)   (b)   (c)

▲ **Figure 5** The compound known as *basic copper carbonate* has the formula $Cu_2(OH)_2CO_3$ and occurs in nature as the mineral *malachite* **(a)**. It is formed as a patina on copper roofs **(b)**. It can also be synthesized in the laboratory **(c)**. Regardless of its source, basic copper carbonate always has the same composition. Analysis of this compound led Proust to formulate the law of definite proportions.

it came from or who prepared it. The painstaking work of Joseph Louis Proust (1754–1826) convinced most chemists of the general validity of these observations. In one set of experiments, for example, Proust found that basic copper carbonate, whether prepared in the laboratory or obtained from natural sources, was always composed of 57.48% by mass copper, 5.43% carbon, 0.91% hydrogen, and 36.18% oxygen (Figure 5).

To summarize these and many other experiments, Proust formulated a new scientific law in 1799. The **law of definite proportions** states that a compound always contains the same elements in certain definite proportions and in no others. (This generalization is also sometimes called the *law of constant composition*.)

An early illustration of the law of definite proportions is found in the work of the noted Swedish chemist J. J. Berzelius, illustrated in Figure 6. Berzelius heated a quantity (say, 10.00 g) of lead with various amounts of sulfur to form lead sulfide. Lead is a soft, grayish metal, and sulfur is a yellow solid. Lead sulfide is a shiny, black solid. Therefore, it was easy to tell when all the lead had reacted. Excess sulfur was washed away with carbon disulfide, a solvent that dissolves sulfur but not lead sulfide. As long as he used at least 1.55 g of sulfur with 10.00 g of lead, Berzelius got exactly 11.55 g of lead sulfide. Any sulfur in excess of 1.55 g was left over; it did not react. If Berzelius used more than 10.00 g of lead with 1.55 g of sulfur, he got 11.55 g of lead sulfide, with some lead left over.

▲ Jöns Jacob Berzelius (1779–1848) was the first person to prepare an extensive list of atomic weights. Published in 1828, it agrees remarkably well with most of today's accepted values.

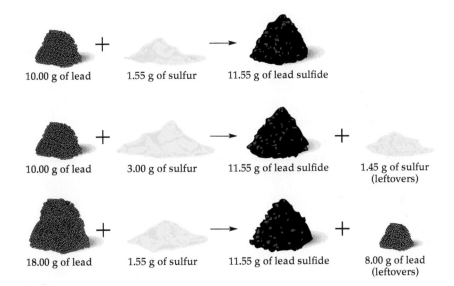

10.00 g of lead   1.55 g of sulfur   11.55 g of lead sulfide

10.00 g of lead   3.00 g of sulfur   11.55 g of lead sulfide   1.45 g of sulfur (leftovers)

18.00 g of lead   1.55 g of sulfur   11.55 g of lead sulfide   8.00 g of lead (leftovers)

◀ **Figure 6** An example showing how Berzelius's experiments illustrate the law of definite proportions.

Q: *What mass of sulfur can react completely with 20.00 g of lead? What mass of lead sulfide forms?*

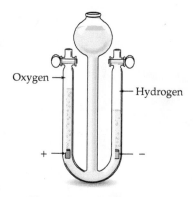

▲ Figure 7 Electrolysis of water. Hydrogen and oxygen are always produced in a volume ratio of 2:1.

Q: *If 24 cubic feet of hydrogen gas is produced by electrolysis, how much oxygen gas will be produced?*

The law of definite proportions is further illustrated by the electrolysis of water. In 1783, Henry Cavendish (1731–1810), a wealthy, eccentric English noble-man, found that water forms when hydrogen burns in oxygen. (It was Lavoisier, however, who correctly interpreted the experiment and who first used the names *hydrogen* and *oxygen*.) Later, in 1800, the English chemists William Nicholson and Anthony Carlisle decomposed water into hydrogen and oxygen gases by passing an electric current through the water (Figure 7). (The Italian scientist Alessandro Volta had invented the chemical battery only six weeks earlier.) The two gases are always produced in a 2:1 volume ratio. Although this is a volume ratio and Berzelius's experiment gave a mass ratio, both substantiate the law of definite proportions. This scientific law led to rapid developments in chemistry and dealt a death blow to the ancient Greek idea of water as an element.

The law of definite proportions is the basis for chemical formulas, such as H_2O for water. Constant composition also means that substances have constant properties. Pure water always dissolves salt or sugar, and at normal pressure it always freezes at 0 °C and boils at 100 °C.

Self-Assessment Questions

1. In any chemical change, compared to the mass of the reactants, the mass of the products is
   a. always equal
   b. always greater
   c. always less
   d. often different

2. In an experiment in which 36.04 g of liquid water is decomposed into hydrogen gas and oxygen gas, the total mass of the products is
   a. 0 g
   b. 18.02 g
   c. 36.04 g
   d. uncertain

3. The ancient Greeks thought that water was an element. In 1800, Nicholson and Carlisle decomposed water into hydrogen and oxygen. Their experiment proved that
   a. electricity causes decomposition
   b. the Greeks were correct
   c. hydrogen and oxygen are elements
   d. water is not an element

4. The fact that salt (sodium chloride) from any place on Earth is always 39.34% sodium and 60.66% chlorine by mass illustrates
   a. Dalton's atomic theory
   b. Democritus's atomic theory
   c. the law of definite proportions
   d. the law of conservation of mass

5. Ammonia produced in an industrial plant contains 3.0 kg of hydrogen for every 14.0 kg of nitrogen. The ammonia dissolved in a window-cleaning preparation contains 30.0 g of hydrogen for every 140.0 g of nitrogen. What law does this illustrate?
   a. Dalton's atomic theory
   b. Democritus's atomic theory
   c. the law of definite proportions
   d. the law of conservation of mass

6 When 60.0 g of carbon is burned in 160.0 g of oxygen, 220.0 g of carbon dioxide is formed. What mass of carbon dioxide is formed when 60.0 g of carbon is burned in 750.0 g of oxygen?
   a. 60.0 g
   b. 160.0 g
   c. 220.0 g
   d. 810.0 g

Answers: 1, a; 2, c; 3, d; 4, c; 5, c; 6, c

3 John Dalton and the Atomic Theory of Matter

Learning Objectives ❯ Explain why the idea that matter is made of atoms is a theory.
❯ Understand how atomic theory explains the law of conservation of mass.

Lavoisier's law of conservation of mass and Proust's law of definite proportions were repeatedly verified by experiment. This work led to attempts to develop theories to explain these laws.

In 1803, John Dalton, an English schoolteacher, proposed a model to explain the accumulating experimental data. By this time, the composition of a number of substances was known with a fair degree of accuracy. (To avoid confusion, we will use modern values, terms, and examples rather than those actually used by Dalton.) For example, all samples of water have an oxygen-to-hydrogen mass ratio of 7.94:1.00. Similarly, all samples of ammonia have a nitrogen-to-hydrogen mass ratio of 4.63:1.00 (14:3). Dalton explained these unvarying ratios by assuming that matter is made of atoms.

As Dalton continued his work, he discovered another law that his theory would have to explain. Proust had stated that a compound contains elements in certain proportions and only those proportions. Dalton's new law, called the **law of multiple proportions**, stated that elements might combine in *more* than one set of proportions, with each set corresponding to a different compound. For example, carbon combines with oxygen in a mass ratio of 1.00:2.66 (or 3.00:8.00) to form carbon dioxide, a gas that is a product of respiration and of the burning of coal or wood. But Dalton found that carbon also combines with oxygen in a mass ratio of 1.00:1.33 (or 3.00:4.00) to form carbon monoxide, a poisonous gas produced when a fuel is burned in the presence of a limited air supply.

Dalton then used his **atomic theory** to explain the various laws. Following are the important points of Dalton's atomic theory, with some modern modifications that we will consider later.

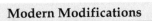

▲ John Dalton (1766–1844), who, in addition to developing the atomic theory, carried out important investigations of the behavior of gases. All of his contributions to science were made in spite of the fact that he was color-blind.

Dalton's Atomic Theory	Modern Modifications
1. All matter is composed of extremely small particles called atoms.	1. Dalton assumed atoms to be indivisible. This isn't quite true.
2. All atoms of a given element are alike, but atoms of a given element differ from the atoms of any other element.	2. Dalton assumed that all the atoms of a given element were identical in all respects, including mass. We now know this to be incorrect.
3. Compounds are formed when atoms of different elements combine in fixed proportions.	3. Unmodified. The numbers of each kind of atom in simple compounds usually form a simple ratio. For example, the ratio of carbon atoms to oxygen atoms is 1:1 in carbon monoxide and 1:2 in carbon dioxide.
4. A chemical reaction involves a *rearrangement* of atoms. No atoms are created, destroyed, or broken apart in a chemical reaction.	4. Unmodified for *chemical* reactions. Atoms are broken apart in *nuclear* reactions.

3. Why is it often difficult to destroy hazardous wastes? Hazardous wastes that are compounds or mixtures can be converted to other compounds or mixtures—but the elements from those compounds or mixtures are still present and may be hazardous as well. For example, insecticide containing arsenic oxide can be broken down into the elements arsenic and oxygen—but the element arsenic is poisonous and can't be broken down into something else.

Explanations Using Atomic Theory

Dalton's theory clearly explains the difference between elements and compounds. *Elements* are composed of only one kind of atom. For example, a sample of the element phosphorus contains only phosphorus atoms. *Compounds* are made up of two or more kinds of atoms chemically combined in definite proportions.

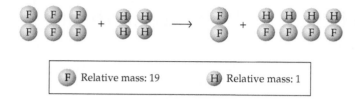

| **F** Relative mass: 19 | **H** Relative mass: 1 |

▶ **Figure 8** The law of definite proportions and the law of conservation of mass interpreted in terms of Dalton's atomic theory.

Q: *If 20 molecules of fluorine and 28 molecules of hydrogen react, how many molecules of HF can form? Which element is left over? How many molecules of the leftover element are there?*

Dalton set up a table of relative atomic masses based on hydrogen having a mass of 1. Many of Dalton's atomic masses were inaccurate, as we might expect because of the equipment available at that time. The masses we use today are relative atomic masses, usually called simply *atomic masses*. Historically, these relative masses were determined by comparison with a standard mass, a technique called *weighing*. For this historical reason, these relative masses are often called *atomic weights*. You will find a table of atomic masses on the inside front cover of this text. We will use these modern values in some examples showing how Dalton's atomic theory explains the various laws.

To explain the law of definite proportions, Dalton's reasoning went something like this: Why should 1.0 g of hydrogen always combine with 19 g of fluorine? Why shouldn't 1.0 g of hydrogen also combine with 18 g, or 20 g, or any other mass of fluorine? If an atom of fluorine has a mass 19 times that of a hydrogen atom, the compound formed by the union of one atom of each element would have to consist of 1 part by mass of hydrogen and 19 parts by mass of fluorine. Matter must be atomic for the law of definite proportions to be valid (Figure 8).

Atomic theory also explains the law of conservation of mass. When fluorine atoms combine with hydrogen atoms to form hydrogen fluoride, the atoms are merely rearranged. Matter is neither lost nor gained; the mass does not change.

Finally, atomic theory explains the law of multiple proportions. For example, 1.00 g of carbon combines with 1.33 g of oxygen to form carbon monoxide or with 2.66 g of oxygen to form carbon dioxide. Carbon dioxide has twice the mass of oxygen per gram of carbon as carbon monoxide does. This is because one atom of carbon combines with *one* atom of oxygen to form carbon monoxide, whereas one atom of carbon combines with *two* atoms of oxygen to form carbon dioxide.

Using modern values, we assign an oxygen atom a relative mass of 16.0 and a carbon atom a relative mass of 12.0. One atom of carbon combined with one atom of oxygen (in carbon monoxide) means a mass ratio of 12.0 parts carbon to 16.0 parts oxygen, or 3.00 : 4.00. One atom of carbon combined with two atoms of oxygen (in carbon dioxide) gives a mass ratio of 12.0 parts carbon to $2 \times 16.0 = 32.0$ parts oxygen, or 3.00 : 8.00. Because all oxygen atoms have the same average mass, and all carbon atoms have the same average mass, the ratio of oxygen in carbon dioxide to oxygen in carbon monoxide is 8.00 to 4.00 or 2 : 1. The same law holds true for other compounds formed from the same two elements. Table 1 shows another example of the law of multiple proportions, involving nitrogen and oxygen.

Dalton also invented a set of symbols (Figure 9) to represent the different kinds of atoms. These symbols have since been replaced by modern symbols of one or two letters (inside front cover).

▲ **It DOES Matter!**

A molecule with one carbon (C) atom and two oxygen (O) atoms is carbon dioxide (CO_2), a gas that you exhale and that provides the "fizz" in soft drinks. Cooled to about −80 °C, it becomes dry ice (shown above), used to keep items frozen during shipping. But a molecule with one less O atom is deadly carbon monoxide, CO. Just 0.2% CO in the air is enough to kill. Unfortunately, most fuels produce a little CO when they burn, which is why a car engine should never be left running in a closed garage.

Isotopes: Atoms of an Element with Different Masses

As we have noted, Dalton's second assumption, that all atoms of an element are alike, has been modified. Atoms of an element can have different masses, and such atoms are called *isotopes*. For example, most carbon atoms have a relative atomic

Table 1	The Law of Multiple Proportions		
Compound	Representation[a]	Mass of N per 1.000 g of O	Ratio of the Masses of N[b]
Nitrous oxide	(image)	1.750 g	$(1.750 \div 0.4375) = 4.000$
Nitric oxide	(image)	0.8750 g	$(0.8750 \div 0.4375) = 2.000$
Nitrogen dioxide	(image)	0.4375 g	$(0.4375 \div 0.4375) = 1.000$

[a] ⬤ = nitrogen atom and ⬤ = oxygen atom

[b] We obtain the ratio of the masses of N that combine with a given mass of O by dividing each quantity in the third column by the smallest (0.4375 g).

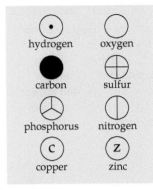

▲ **Figure 9** Some of Dalton's symbols for the elements.

Q: *Using Dalton's symbols, draw diagrams for sulfur dioxide and sulfur trioxide. (Place the sulfur atom in the center and arrange the oxygen atoms around it.) What law do these two compounds illustrate?*

mass of 12 (carbon-12), but 1.1% of carbon atoms have a relative atomic mass of 13 (carbon-13).

Problem Solving: Mass and Atom Ratios

We can use proportions, such as those determined by Dalton, to calculate the amount of a substance needed to combine with (or form) a given quantity of another substance. To learn how to do this, let's look at some examples.

CONCEPTUAL Example 1 Mass Ratios

Hydrogen gas for fuel cells can be made by decomposing *methane* (CH_4), the main component of natural gas. The decomposition gives carbon (C) and hydrogen (H) in a ratio of 3.00 parts by mass of carbon to 1.00 part by mass of hydrogen. How much hydrogen can be made from 90.0 g of methane?

Solution
We can express the ratio of parts by mass in any units we choose—pounds, grams, kilograms—as long as it is the same for both elements. Using grams as the units, we see that 3.00 g of C and 1.00 g of H would be produced if 4.00 g of CH_4 were decomposed. To convert g CH_4 to g H, we need a conversion factor that includes 1.00 g H and 4.00 g CH_4.

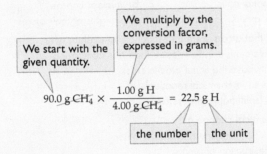

We start with the given quantity.

We multiply by the conversion factor, expressed in grams.

$$90.0 \text{ g } CH_4 \times \frac{1.00 \text{ g H}}{4.00 \text{ g } CH_4} = 22.5 \text{ g H}$$

the number | the unit

■ EXERCISE 1A
The gas ammonia can be decomposed to give 3.00 parts by mass of hydrogen and 14.0 parts by mass of nitrogen. What mass of nitrogen is obtained if 10.2 g of ammonia is decomposed?

■ EXERCISE 1B
Nitrous oxide, sometimes called "laughing gas," can be decomposed to give 7.00 parts by mass of nitrogen and 4.00 parts by mass of oxygen. What mass of nitrogen is obtained if enough nitrous oxide is decomposed to yield 36.0 g of oxygen?

4. Is light made of atoms?

Light is not matter and is not made of atoms. Light is a form of *energy*. Energy—including chemical energy, electrical energy, and nuclear energy—is defined as the ability to do work.

CONCEPTUAL Example 2 — Atom Ratios

Hydrogen sulfide gas can be decomposed to give sulfur and hydrogen in a mass ratio of 16.0:1.00. If the relative mass of sulfur is 32.0 when the mass of hydrogen is taken to be 1.00, how many hydrogen atoms are combined with each sulfur atom in the gas?

Solution

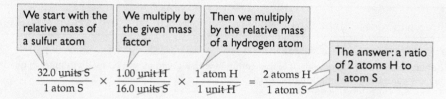

We start with the relative mass of a sulfur atom

We multiply by the given mass factor

Then we multiply by the relative mass of a hydrogen atom

The answer: a ratio of 2 atoms H to 1 atom S

$$\frac{32.0 \text{ units S}}{1 \text{ atom S}} \times \frac{1.00 \text{ unit H}}{16.0 \text{ units S}} \times \frac{1 \text{ atom H}}{1 \text{ unit H}} = \frac{2 \text{ atoms H}}{1 \text{ atom S}}$$

■ EXERCISE 2

Phosphine gas can be decomposed to give phosphorus and hydrogen in a mass ratio of 10.3:1.00. If the relative mass of phosphorus is 31.0 when the mass of hydrogen is taken to be 1.00, how many hydrogen atoms are combined with each phosphorus atom in the gas?

Despite some inaccuracies, Dalton's atomic theory was a great success. Why? Because it served—and still serves—to explain a large amount of experimental data. It also successfully predicted how matter would behave under a wide variety of circumstances. Dalton arrived at his atomic theory by basing his reasoning on experimental findings, and with modest modification, the theory has stood the test of time and of modern, highly sophisticated instrumentation. Formulation of so successful a theory was quite a triumph for a Quaker schoolteacher in 1803.

Self-Assessment Questions

1. Two compounds, ethylene and acetylene, both contain only carbon and hydrogen. A sample of acetylene contains 92.26 g of C and 7.74 g H. An ethylene sample contains 46.13 g of C and 7.74 g H. If the formula for acetylene is C_2H_2, the formula for ethylene is
   a. CH
   b. C_2H
   c. CH_3
   d. C_2H_4

2. According to Dalton, elements are distinguished from each other by
   a. density in the solid state
   b. nuclear charge
   c. shapes of their atoms
   d. weights of their atoms

3. Dalton postulated that atoms were indestructible to explain why
   a. the same two elements can form more than one compound
   b. no two elements have the same atomic mass
   c. mass is conserved in chemical reactions
   d. nuclear fission (splitting) is impossible

4. Dalton viewed chemical change as
   a. a change of atoms from one type into another
   b. creation and destruction of atoms
   c. a rearrangement of atoms
   d. a transfer of electrons

5. How many types of atoms are present in a given compound?
   a. at least two
   b. hundreds
   c. three or more
   d. depends on the mass of the compound

6. Hydrogen and carbon combine in a 4.0:12.0 mass ratio to form methane. If every molecule of methane contains 4 H atoms and 1 C atom, an atom of carbon must have a mass that is
   a. $\frac{4}{12}$ times the mass of a hydrogen atom
   b. 4 times the mass of a hydrogen atom
   c. $\frac{12}{3}$ times the mass of a hydrogen atom
   d. 12 times the mass of a hydrogen atom

Questions 7–9 refer to the following figures:

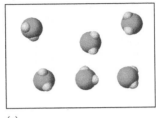
(a)

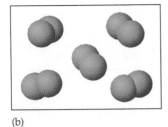
(b)

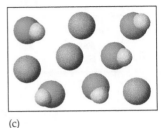
(c)

7. Which figure represents an element?

8. Which figure represents a compound?

9. Which figure represents a mixture?

Answers: 1, d; 2, d; 3, c; 4, c; 5, a; 6, d; 7, b; 8, a; 9, c

4 Mendeleev and the Periodic Table

Learning Objective ❯ Describe how the elements are arranged in the periodic table and why the arrangement is important.

During the eighteenth and nineteenth centuries, new elements were discovered with surprising frequency. By 1830 there were 55 known elements, all with different properties that demonstrated no apparent order. Dalton had set up a table of relative atomic masses in his 1808 book *A New System of Chemical Philosophy*. Dalton's rough values were improved in subsequent years, notably by Berzelius, who, in 1828, published a table of atomic weights containing 54 elements. Most of Berzelius's values agree well with modern values.

Relative Atomic Masses

Although it was impossible to determine actual masses of atoms in the nineteenth century, chemists were able to determine relative atomic masses by measuring the amounts of various elements that combined with a given mass of another element. Dalton's atomic masses were based on an atomic mass of 1 for hydrogen. As more accurate atomic masses were determined, this standard was replaced by one in which the atomic mass of naturally occurring oxygen was assigned a value of 16.0000. Because the isotopic composition of oxygen varies a bit depending on its source, the oxygen standard was replaced in 1961 by a more logical one based on a single isotope of carbon, carbon-12. Adoption of this new standard caused little change in atomic masses. These relative atomic masses are usually expressed in **atomic mass units (amu)**, commonly referred to today simply as *units (u)*.

In December 2010, the atomic masses for eleven elements were adjusted slightly. Although their atomic masses had not actually changed, the isotopic composition of these elements varies slightly from location to location. For example, boron's atomic mass is now listed in some sources as 10.806–10.821 u. Most periodic tables still list a single value, however, which is accurate enough for most purposes.

Mendeleev's Periodic Table

Various attempts were made to arrange the elements in some sort of systematic fashion. The most successful arrangement—one that soon became widely accepted by chemists—was published in 1869 by Dmitri Ivanovich Mendeleev (1834–1907), a Russian chemist. Mendeleev's **periodic table** arranged the 63 elements known at the time primarily in order of increasing atomic mass. However, his first consideration in this table was an element's *properties*. He placed silver, gold, and several other

▲ Dmitri Mendeleev, the Russian chemist who arranged the 63 known elements into a periodic table similar to the one we use today, was considered one of the great teachers of his time. Unable to find a suitable chemistry textbook, he wrote his own, *The Principles of Chemistry*. Mendeleev also studied the nature and origin of petroleum and made many other contributions to science. Element 101 is named mendelevium (Md) in his honor.

13

Tabelle II.

Reihen	Gruppe I. — R^2O	Gruppe II. — RO	Gruppe III. — R^2O^3	Gruppe IV. RH^4 RO^2	Gruppe V. RH^3 R^2O^5	Gruppe VI. RH^2 RO^3	Gruppe VII. RH R^2O^7	Gruppe VIII. — RO^4
1	H = 1							
2	Li = 7	Be = 9,4	B = 11	C = 12	N = 14	O = 16	F = 19	
3	Na = 23	Mg = 24	Al = 27,3	Si = 28	P = 31	S = 32	Cl = 35,5	
4	K = 39	Ca = 40	— = 44	Ti = 48	V = 51	Cr = 52	Mn = 55	Fe = 56, Co = 59, Ni = 59, Cu = 63.
5	(Cu = 63)	Zn = 65	— = 68	— = 72	As = 75	Se = 78	Br = 80	
6	Rb = 85	Sr = 87	?Yt = 88	Zr = 90	Nb = 94	Mo = 96	— = 100	Ru = 104, Rh = 104, Pd = 106, Ag = 108.
7	(Ag = 108)	Cd = 112	In = 113	Sn = 118	Sb = 122	Te = 125	J = 127	
8	Cs = 133	Ba = 137	?Di = 138	?Ce = 140	—	—	—	— — — —
9	(—)	—	—	—	—	—		
10	—	—	?Er = 178	?La = 180	Ta = 182	W = 184	—	Os = 195, Ir = 197, Pt = 198, Au = 199.
11	(Au = 199)	Hg = 200	Ti = 204	Pb = 207	Bi = 208	—	—	
12	—	—	—	Th = 231	—	U = 240	—	— — — —

der chemischen Elemente.

▲ **Figure 10** Mendeleev's periodic table. In this 1898 version, he wrongly "corrected" the atomic weight of tellurium to be less than that of iodine.

5. Why is the table of elements called the "periodic table"?

Periodic indicates that something occurs regularly. The physical and chemical properties of the elements are periodic. That is, many of those properties are similar for elements in a given column of the table.

metals slightly out of order. This allowed sulfur, selenium, and tellurium, which have similar chemical properties, to appear in the same column. This rearrangement also put iodine in the same column as chlorine and bromine, which it resembles chemically.

To place elements in groups with similar properties, Mendeleev also had to leave gaps in his table. Instead of considering these blank spaces as defects, he boldly predicted the existence of elements yet undiscovered. Further, he even predicted the properties of some of the missing elements. For example, three of the missing elements were soon discovered and named scandium, gallium, and germanium. As can be seen in Table 2, Mendeleev's predictions for germanium were amazingly successful. This remarkable predictive value led to wide acceptance of Mendeleev's table.

The modern periodic table (inside front cover) contains 118 elements, some of which have reportedly been observed or synthesized but have not yet been verified or named. Each element is represented by a box in the periodic table, as shown in Figure 11.

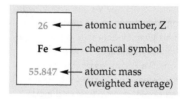

26 ← atomic number, Z
Fe ← chemical symbol
55.847 ← atomic mass (weighted average)

▲ **Figure 11** Representation of an element on the modern periodic table.

Table 2 | **Properties of Germanium: Predicted and Observed**

Property	Predicted by Mendeleev for Eka-Silikon (1871)	Observed by Winkler for Germanium (1886)
Atomic mass	72	72.6
Density (g/cm^3)	5.5	5.47
Color	Dirty gray	Grayish white
Density of oxide (g/cm^3)	EsO_2: 4.7	GeO_2: 4.703
Boiling point of chloride	$EsCl_4$: below 100 °C	$GeCl_4$: 86 °C

CONCEPTUAL Example 3 | Predicting Periodic Properties

In 1829, Johann Dobereiner, a German chemist, published his observations that there were several groups of three elements that were quite similar. In each case, the middle element seemed to be halfway between the other two in atomic mass, reactivity, and other properties. One such group, which he called *alkali formers*, was lithium, sodium, and potassium. Show that the relative atomic mass of the middle element in this triad is close to the average of the relative atomic masses of the other two elements.

Solution

The atomic mass of lithium (Li) is 6.941 u and that of potassium (K) is 39.098 u. The average of the two is (6.941 u + 39.098 u) ÷ 2 = 22.795 u, quite close to the modern value for sodium (Na) of 22.989 u.

■ EXERCISE 3

Another of Dobereiner's triads was the *salt formers* chlorine, bromine, and iodine. Show that the relative atomic mass of the middle element in this triad is close to the average of the relative atomic masses of the other two elements.

Self-Assessment Questions

1. Which of the following is *not* true of Mendeleev's periodic table?
   a. It includes new elements that he had just discovered.
   b. The elements are arranged generally in order of increasing atomic mass.
   c. He left gaps for predicted new elements.
   d. He placed some heavier elements before lighter ones.

2. Relative masses in the modern periodic table are based on the value for
   a. the carbon-12 isotope
   b. the hydrogen atom
   c. naturally occurring oxygen
   d. the oxygen-16 isotope

3. The number of elements known today is approximately
   a. 12
   b. 100
   c. 1000
   d. 30 million

Answers: 1, a; 2, a; 3, b

▲ An image of atoms of manganese obtained using STM.

Drs. Ali Yazdani & Daniel J. Hornbaker/Photo Researchers, Inc.

5 Atoms and Molecules: Real and Relevant

Learning Objective › Distinguish atoms from molecules.

Are atoms real? Certainly they are real as a concept, a highly useful concept. And scientists today can observe computer-enhanced images of individual atoms. These portraits provide powerful (though still indirect) evidence that atoms exist.

Are atoms relevant? Much of modern science and technology—including the production of new materials and the technology of pollution control—is based on the concept of atoms. We have seen that atoms are conserved in chemical reactions. Thus, material things—things made of atoms—can be recycled, for the atoms are not destroyed no matter how we use them. The one way we might "lose" a material from a practical standpoint is to spread its atoms so thinly that it would take too much time and energy to put them back together again. The essay on recycling describes a real-world example of such loss.

Now back to Leucippus and Democritus and their musings on that Greek beach. We now know that if we keep dividing drops of water, we will ultimately obtain a small particle—called a *molecule*—that is still water. A **molecule** is a group of atoms chemically bonded, or connected, to one another. Molecules are represented by chemical formulas. The symbol H represents an *atom* of hydrogen. The formula

6. What's the difference between atoms and molecules? A molecule is made of atoms that are combined in fixed proportions. A carbon atom is the smallest particle of the element carbon, and a carbon dioxide molecule is the smallest particle of the compound carbon dioxide. As you have probably figured out, molecules can be broken down into their atoms.

Recycling

Because it is an element, iron cannot be created or destroyed, but that does not mean it always exists in its elemental state. Let's consider two different pathways for the recycling of iron.

1. Hematite, an iron ore, is obtained from a mine and converted into pig iron, which is used to make steel cans. Once discarded, the cans rust. Iron ions slowly leach from the rust into groundwater and eventually wind up in the ocean. These dissolved ions can be absorbed by and incorporated into marine plants. Marine creatures that eat the plants will in turn absorb and incorporate iron ions. The original iron atoms are now widely separated in space. Some of them might even become part of the hemoglobin in your blood. The iron has been recycled, but it will never again resemble the original pig iron.

(a) Harry Taylor/Dorling Kindersley

(b) Mark Wragg/iStockphoto

(c) Sieto/iStockphoto

(d) Tammy Peluso/iStockphoto

2. Iron ore is taken from a mine and converted to pig iron and then into steel. The steel is used in making an automobile, which is driven for a decade and then sent to the junkyard. There it is compacted and sent to a recycling plant, where the steel is recovered and ultimately used again in a new automobile. Once the iron was removed from its ore, it was conserved in its elemental metallic form. In this form of recycling, the iron continues to be useful for a long time.

 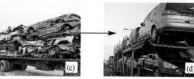

(a) Harry Taylor/Dorling Kindersley

(b) Michael Shake/Shutterstock

(c) Joe Potato Photo/iStockphoto

(d) Lya Cattel/iStockphoto

H_2 represents a *molecule* of hydrogen, which is composed of two hydrogen atoms. The formula H_2O represents a molecule of water, which is composed of two hydrogen atoms and one oxygen atom. If we divide a water molecule, we will obtain *two atoms* of hydrogen and *one atom* of oxygen.

And if we divide those atoms ... but that is a story for another time.

Dalton regarded the atom as indivisible, as did his successors up until the discovery of radioactivity in 1895.

Self-Assessment Questions

1. We can recycle materials because atoms
   a. always combine in the same way
   b. are conserved
   c. are indivisible
   d. combine in multiple portions

2. A molecule is
   a. a collection of like atoms
   b. conserved in chemical reactions
   c. a group of atoms chemically bonded to one another
   d. indivisible

Answers: 1, b; 2, c

Lallie C. McKenzie, *Chem11 LLC*

It's Elemental

In this chapter, you learned that everything is made up of atoms and that atoms are the smallest particles of an element. Although the universe is composed of an uncountable number of compounds and mixtures, the basic building blocks of these are elements. The periodic table (inside front cover) organizes the elements by relative mass and, more importantly, by their predictable chemical properties.

What do elements have to do with green chemistry? When chemists design products and processes, they take advantage of the entire periodic table, including elements used rarely or not at all in nature or in our bodies. It is important to think about possible impacts of the chosen elements on human health and on the environment. Two important factors to evaluate are inherent hazard and natural abundance. Hazard can be different for the element itself or when it is in a compound, so the element's form can determine whether it causes harm. For example, sodium is very reactive with water, but sodium chloride is a compound that we eat. Also, as you learned from the law of conservation of mass (Section 2), elements cannot be created or destroyed. Therefore, the amounts of these materials on the planet are limited and may be scarce.

Green Chemistry Principles 3, 7, and 10 apply to products and processes that involve hazardous and rare elements. Understanding the impacts of toxic elements and compounds on human health and the environment lets us reduce or eliminate their use by developing safer alternatives. Also, designing new technologies that rely on abundant elements can prevent depletion of resources. Finally, reclaiming materials after use is critical if they can cause harm or are scarce.

The use of lead and mercury, two particularly hazardous elements, has been reduced through green chemistry. These elements are known to harm many of the systems of the human body and can impact children's development. Although lead and mercury are important in many products, the urgent need to limit exposure to them has led to their replacement with safer alternatives. For example, lead in paints has been replaced with titanium dioxide, compounds with lower toxicity now substitute for lead stabilizers in plastics, and new lead-free chemicals are being used instead of traditional solder in electronics. In addition, recent developments have reduced the liquid mercury required in fluorescent lighting, and mercury-based thermometers and switches have been replaced with electronic or non-hazardous versions. Because coal-fired power plants emit mercury, advances in alternative energy sources also reduce our exposure to this element.

Many current technologies may be limited by their need for scarce elements. For example, the permanent magnets in computer hard drives, wind turbines, and hybrid cars are mainly made of neodymium and dysprosium. Green chemistry can promote new opportunities. Although almost all of the elements are found in the Earth's crust, eight account for more than 98% of the total. In fact, almost three-fourths of the crust is comprised of two elements, silicon and oxygen. Besides being scarce, some elements, such as rare earth metals like cerium, yttrium, neodymium, and lanthanum, are drawn from a single source and can be difficult to separate from other materials. Current supplies are much lower than needed to support projected growth.

Approaches based on earth-abundant elements (such as silicon, iron, and aluminum) would support technology and protect resources. As discussed in the essay on page 54, atoms of a material can be reclaimed directly through recycling processes or spread through the environment. If released, hazardous materials can impact health and the environment, so recycling of these elements should be a priority. Reclaimed raw materials reduce the demand for natural resources—notably, scarce elements. Green chemistry supports the design of materials where the individual elemental components can be recycled easily.

Green chemistry approaches are especially important when products and processes present health or environmental risks. Identifying and replacing hazardous and rare elements can lead to greener technologies and a sustainable future for everyone.

© Libby Welch/Alamy.

◀ New technologies have led to mercury-free efficient lightbulbs like this one. These products save energy and do not contain toxic elements used in traditional fluorescent lighting.

CRITICAL THINKING EXERCISES

Apply knowledge that you have gained in this chapter and one or more of the FLaReS principles to evaluate the following statements or claims.

1 In a science fiction movie, a woman proceeds through nine months of pregnancy in minutes. She takes in no nutrients during this time. She dies during labor and an emergency C-section is performed to save the child. The child lives for only a matter of hours, rapidly aging, and dies a withered old man. A classmate claims that the movie is based on a documented, secret alien encounter.

2 A health-food store has a large display of bracelets made of copper metal. Some people claim that wearing such a bracelet will protect the wearer from arthritis or rheumatoid diseases.

3 An old cookbook claims that cooking acidic food, such as spaghetti sauce, in an iron pot provides more nutrients than cooking the same food in an aluminum pot.

4 A company markets a device it calls a "water energizer." It claims the device can supply so much energy to drinking water that the mass of oxygen in the water is increased, thereby providing more oxygen to the body.

SUMMARY

Section 1—The concept of atoms was first suggested in ancient Greece by Leucippus and Democritus. However, this idea was rejected for almost 2000 years in favor of Aristotle's view that matter was continuous in nature.

Section 2—The law of conservation of mass resulted from careful experiments by Lavoisier and others, who weighed all the reactants and products for a number of chemical reactions and found that no change in mass occurred. Boyle said that a proposed element must be tested. If it could be broken down into simpler substances, it was not an element. The law of definite proportions (law of constant composition) was formulated by Proust, based on his experiments and on those of Berzelius. It states that a given compound always contains the same elements in exactly the same proportions by mass.

Section 3—In 1803, Dalton explained the laws of definite proportions and conservation of mass with his atomic theory, which had four main points: (1) Matter is made up of tiny particles called atoms; (2) atoms of the same element are alike; (3) compounds are formed when atoms of different elements combine in certain proportions; and (4) during chemical reactions, atoms are rearranged, not destroyed. Dalton also discovered the law of multiple proportions, which states that different elements might combine in two or more different sets of proportions, each set corresponding to a different compound. His atomic theory also explained this new law.

These laws can be used to perform calculations to find the amounts of elements that combine or are present in a compound or reaction. In more than two centuries atomic theory has undergone only minor modification.

Section 4—Berzelius published a table of atomic weights in 1828, and his values agree well with modern ones. In 1869, Mendeleev published his version of the periodic table, a systematic arrangement of the elements that allowed him to predict the existence and properties of undiscovered elements. In the modern periodic table, each element is listed, along with its symbol and the average mass of an atom of that element in atomic mass units, which are very tiny units of mass.

Section 5—Because atoms are conserved in chemical reactions, matter (which is made of atoms) can always be recycled. Atoms can be lost, in effect, if they are scattered in the environment. A molecule is a group of atoms chemically bonded together. Just as an atom is the smallest particle of an element, a modecule is the smallest particle of most compounds.

Green chemistry When chemists design products and processes, potential impacts on human health and the environment of the incorporated elements should be considered. Identifying and replacing toxic and rare elements can lead to greener technologies and enhance sustainability.

Learning Objectives

› Explain the ancient Greeks' ideas about the characteristics of matter. (1)	Problems 1–3
› Describe the significance of the laws of conservation of mass and definite proportions. (2)	Problems 6, 10, 15–28, 45, 48
› Calculate the amounts of elements from the composition of a compound. (2)	Problems 41–43, 46, 49–51
› Explain why the idea that matter is made of atoms is a theory. (3)	Problem 8
› Understand how atomic theory explains the law of conservation of mass. (3)	Problem 11, 35–40, 44, 47

> Describe how the elements are arranged in the periodic table and why the arrangement is important. (4)

Problem 50

> Distinguish atoms from molecules. (5)

Problem 12

> Identify elements that can be classified as hazardous or rare.

Problem 52

> Explain how green chemistry can change technologies that rely on hazardous or rare elements.

Problems 53, 54

REVIEW QUESTIONS

1. Distinguish between **(a)** the atomic view and the continuous view of matter and **(b)** the ancient Greek definition of an element and the modern one.

2. What was Democritus's contribution to atomic theory? Why did the idea that matter was continuous (rather than atomic) prevail for so long? What discoveries finally refuted the idea?

3. Consider the following *macroscopic* (visible to the unaided eye) objects. Which are best classified as *discrete* (like Democritus's description of matter) and which are *continuous* (like Aristotle's description)?
   a. people
   b. cloth
   c. calculators
   d. milk chocolate
   e. M&M's candies

4. Describe Lavoisier's contribution to the development of modern chemistry.

5. How did Boyle define an element?

6. State the law of definite proportions, and illustrate it using the compound zinc sulfide, ZnS.

7. State the law of multiple proportions. For a fixed mass of the first element in each of the following compounds, what is the relationship between (ratio of) the
   a. masses of oxygen in ClO_2 and in ClO?
   b. masses of fluorine in ClF_3 and ClF?
   c. masses of oxygen in P_4O_6 and P_4O_{10}?

8. Outline the main points of Dalton's atomic theory.

9. In the figure, the blue spheres represent phosphorus atoms, and the red ones represent oxygen atoms. The box labeled "Initial" represents a mixture. Which one of the other three boxes (A, B, or C) could *not* represent that mixture after a chemical reaction occurred? Explain briefly.

10. Fructose (fruit sugar) is always composed of 40.0% carbon, 53.3% oxygen, and 6.7% hydrogen regardless of the fruit that it comes from. What law does this illustrate?

11. Use Dalton's atomic theory to explain each of the following laws and give an example that illustrates each law.
    a. conservation of mass
    b. definite proportions
    c. multiple proportions

12. Lavoisier considered *alumina* an element. In 1825, the Danish chemist Hans Christian Oersted isolated aluminum metal by reacting aluminum chloride with potassium. Later experiments showed that alumina is formed by reacting aluminum metal with oxygen. What did these experiments prove?

13. What law does the following list of compounds illustrate? N_2O, NO, NO_2, N_2O_4

14. What did each of the following contribute to the development of modern chemistry?
    a. J. J. Berzelius
    b. Henry Cavendish
    c. Joseph Proust
    d. Dmitri Mendeleev

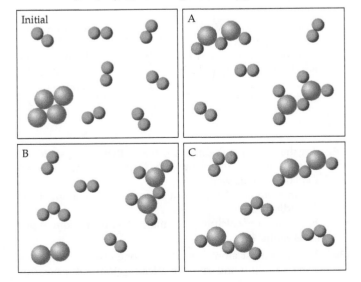

PROBLEMS

Conservation of Mass

15. If 45.0 g of vinegar is added to 5.0 g of baking soda in an open beaker, the total mass after reaction is less than 50.0 g. The vinegar bubbles and fizzes during the reaction. Has the law of conservation of mass been violated? Explain.

16. An iron nail dissolves in a solution of hydrochloric acid. The nail disappears. Have the iron atoms been destroyed? If so, how? If not, where are they?

17. Water is about 11.2% hydrogen and 88.8% oxygen by weight. If you fill a container with 11.2 g of hydrogen and 88.8 g of oxygen, does that vessel contain water? Explain.

18. Many reactions seem to violate the law of conservation of mass. For example, **(a)** when an iron object rusts, the rusty object has a greater mass than before, and **(b)** when a piece of charcoal burns, the remaining material (ash) has less mass than the charcoal. Explain these observations, and suggest an experiment that would demonstrate that mass is conserved in each case.

19. Acetylene, used for welding, contains 24.02 g of carbon for every 2.02 g of hydrogen. If you have 78.5 g of carbon that can be converted to acetylene, what mass of hydrogen will be needed for the conversion?

20. Nitrous oxide (N_2O, "laughing gas") contains 28.01 g of nitrogen in every 44.01 g of nitrous oxide. What mass of nitrous oxide can be formed from 48.7 g of nitrogen?

21. A student in a chemistry class calculates the mass of titanium(IV) oxide (which contains only titanium and oxygen) that can be formed from 37.7 g of titanium and 20.1 g of oxygen. Her calculated answer is 59.8 g of titanium(IV) oxide. Explain to the student why her answer is impossible.

22. A student heats 2.796 g of zinc powder with 2.414 g of sulfur. He reports that he obtains 4.169 g of zinc sulfide and recovers 1.041 g of unreacted sulfur. Show by calculation whether or not his results obey the law of conservation of mass.

23. When 1.00 g zinc and 0.80 g sulfur are allowed to react, all the zinc is used up, 1.50 g of zinc sulfide is formed, and some unreacted sulfur remains. What is the mass of *unreacted* sulfur (choose one)?
a. 0.20 g
b. 0.30 g
c. 0.50 g
d. impossible to determine from this information alone

24. A city has to come up with a plan to dispose of its solid wastes. The solid wastes consist of many different kinds of materials, and the materials are comprised of many different kinds of atoms. The options for disposal include burying the wastes in a landfill, incinerating them, and dumping them at sea. Which method, if any, will get rid of the atoms that make up the wastes? Which method, if any, will immediately change the chemical form of the wastes?

Definite Proportions

25. When 18.02 g of water is decomposed by electrolysis, 16.00 g of oxygen and 2.02 g of hydrogen are formed. According to the law of definite proportions, what masses, in grams, of **(a)** hydrogen and **(b)** oxygen will be formed by the electrolysis of 775 g of water?

26. Hydrogen from the decomposition of water has been promoted as the fuel of the future. What mass of water, in kilograms, would have to be electrolyzed to produce 125 kg of hydrogen? (See Problem 25.)

27. Given a plentiful supply of air, 3.0 parts carbon will react with 8.0 parts oxygen by mass to produce carbon dioxide. Use this mass ratio to calculate the mass of carbon required to produce 14 kg of carbon dioxide.

28. When 31 g of phosphorus reacts with oxygen, 71 g of an oxide of phosphorus is the product. What mass of phosphorus is needed to produce 39 g of this product?

Multiple Proportions

29. Carbon combines with oxygen in a mass ratio of 1.000:2.664 to form carbon dioxide (CO_2) and in a mass ratio of 1.000:1.332 to form carbon monoxide (CO). A third carbon-oxygen compound, called carbon suboxide, is 52.96% C by mass and 47.04% O by mass. Show that these compounds follow the law of multiple proportions.

30. A compound containing only oxygen and rubidium has 0.187 g of O per 1.00 g of Rb. The relative atomic masses are 16.0 for O and 85.5 for Rb. What is a possible O-to-Rb mass ratio for a different oxide of rubidium (choose one)?
a. 8.0:85.5   **b.** 16.0:85.5
c. 32.0:85.5   **d.** 16.0:171

31. A sample of an oxide of tin with the formula SnO consists of 0.742 g of tin and 0.100 g of oxygen. A sample of another oxide of tin consists of 0.555 g of tin and 0.150 g of oxygen. What is the formula of the second oxide?

32. Consider three oxides of nitrogen, X, Y, and Z. Oxide X has an oxygen-to-nitrogen mass ratio of 2.28:1.00, oxide Y has an oxygen-to-nitrogen mass ratio of 1.14:1.00, and oxide Z has an oxygen-to-nitrogen mass ratio of 0.57:1.00. What is the whole-number ratio of masses of oxygen in these compounds given a fixed mass of nitrogen?

33. Sulfur forms two compounds with fluorine, T and U. Compound T has 0.447 g of sulfur combined with 1.06 g of fluorine; compound U has 0.438 g of sulfur combined with 1.56 g of fluorine. Show that these data support the law of multiple proportions.

34. Two compounds, V and W, are composed only of hydrogen and carbon. Compound V is 80.0% carbon by mass and 20.0% hydrogen by mass. Compound W is 83.3% carbon by mass and 16.7% hydrogen by mass. What is the ratio of masses of hydrogen in these compounds given a fixed mass of carbon?

Dalton's Atomic Theory

35. Are the following findings, expressed to the nearest atomic mass unit, in agreement with Dalton's atomic theory? Explain your answers.
a. An atom of calcium has a mass of 40 u; an atom of vanadium, 50 u.
b. An atom of calcium has a mass of 40 u; an atom of potassium, 40 u.

36. To the nearest atomic mass unit, one calcium atom has a mass of 40 u and another calcium atom has a mass of

44 u. Do these findings support or contradict Dalton's atomic theory? Explain.

37. An atom of uranium splits into two smaller atoms when struck by a particle called a *neutron*. Do these findings support or contradict Dalton's atomic theory? Explain.

38. According to Dalton's atomic theory, when elements react, their atoms combine in (choose one)
   a. a simple whole-number ratio that is unique for each set of elements
   b. exactly a 1:1 ratio
   c. one or more simple whole-number ratios
   d. pairs
   e. random proportions

39. Hydrogen and oxygen combine in a mass ratio of about 1:8 to form water. If every water molecule consists of two atoms of hydrogen and one atom of oxygen, what fraction or multiple of the mass of a hydrogen atom is the mass of an oxygen atom?
   a. $\frac{1}{16}$ b. $\frac{1}{8}$ c. 8 times   d. 16 times

40. The elements fluorine and nitrogen combine in a mass ratio of 57:14 to form a compound. If every molecule of the compound consists of three atoms of fluorine and one atom of nitrogen, what fraction or multiple of the mass of a fluorine atom is the mass of a nitrogen atom?
   a. $\frac{19}{14}$ b. 3 times   c. $\frac{14}{19}$ d. 14 times

Chemical Compounds

41. A blue solid called *azulene* is thought to be a pure compound. Analyses of three samples of the material yield the following results.

	Mass of Sample	Mass of Carbon	Mass of Hydrogen
Sample 1	1.000 g	0.937 g	0.0629 g
Sample 2	0.244 g	0.229 g	0.0153 g
Sample 3	0.100 g	0.094 g	0.0063 g

Could the material be a pure compound?

42. A colorless liquid is thought to be a pure compound. Analyses of three samples of the material yield the following results.

	Mass of Sample	Mass of Carbon	Mass of Hydrogen
Sample 1	1.000 g	0.862 g	0.138 g
Sample 2	1.549 g	1.295 g	0.254 g
Sample 3	0.988 g	0.826 g	0.162 g

Could the material be a pure compound? Explain.

ADDITIONAL PROBLEMS

43. When 0.2250 g of magnesium is heated with 0.5331 g of nitrogen in a closed container, the magnesium is completely converted to 0.3114 g of magnesium nitride. What mass of unreacted nitrogen must remain?

44. Gasoline can be approximated by the formula C_8H_8. An environmental advocate points out that burning one gallon (about 7 lb) of gasoline produces about 19 lb of carbon dioxide, a greenhouse gas that raises the temperature of the atmosphere. Explain this seeming contradiction of the law of conservation of mass.

45. A compound of uranium and fluorine is used to generate uranium for nuclear power plants. The gas can be decomposed to yield 2.09 parts by mass of uranium for every 1 part by mass of fluorine. If the relative mass of a uranium atom is 238 and the relative mass of a fluorine atom is 19, calculate the number of fluorine atoms that are combined with one uranium atom.

46. Two experiments were performed in which sulfur was burned completely in pure oxygen gas, producing sulfur dioxide and leaving some unreacted oxygen. In the first experiment, burning 0.312 g of sulfur produced 0.623 g of sulfur dioxide. In the second experiment, 1.305 g of sulfur was burned. What mass of sulfur dioxide was produced?

47. In an experiment illustrated at right, about 15 mL of hydrochloric acid solution was placed in a flask and approximately 3 g of sodium carbonate was put into a balloon. The opening of the balloon was then carefully stretched over the top of the flask, taking care not to allow the sodium carbonate to fall into the acid in the flask. The flask was placed on an electronic balance, and the mass of the flask and its contents was found to be 38.61 g. The sodium carbonate was then slowly shaken into the acid. The balloon began to fill with gas. When the reaction was complete, the mass of the flask and its contents, including the gas in the balloon, was found to be 38.61 g. What law does this experiment illustrate? Explain.

Richard Megna/Fundamental Photographs

48. In one experiment, 3.06 g hydrogen was allowed to react with an excess of oxygen to form 27.35 g water. In a second experiment, electric current broke down a sample of water into 1.45 g hydrogen and 11.51 g oxygen. Are these results consistent with the law of definite proportions? Show why or why not.

49. Use Figure 4 to calculate the mass of mercuric oxide that would be needed to produce 100.0 g of mercury metal.

50. Gold chloride, $AuCl_3$, is formed when gold metal is dissolved in *aqua regia*, a highly corrosive mixture of acids. Determine the mass ratio of gold to chlorine in gold chloride:
   a. based on Mendeleev's values from his periodic table (Figure 10)
   b. based on values in the modern periodic table in the inside front cover of this text

51. See Table 1. Another compound of nitrogen and oxygen contains 0.5836 g of nitrogen per 1.000 g of oxygen. Calculate the ratio of mass of N in this compound to mass of N in nitrogen dioxide. What *whole-number* ratio does this value represent?

52. Identify whether the following elements are hazardous, rare, or neither.
   a. silicon
   b. neodymium
   c. mercury
   d. oxygen
   e. lead

53. Give two examples of how green chemistry has helped to reduce the use of lead in consumer products.

54. Why is it important to recycle mercury-based fluorescent lightbulbs instead of putting them in landfills?

COLLABORATIVE GROUP PROJECTS

Prepare a PowerPoint, poster, or other presentation (as directed by your instructor) to share with the class.

1. Prepare a brief biographical report on one of the following.
   a. Henry Cavendish   **b.** Joseph Proust
   c. John Newlands   **d.** Lothar Meyer
   e. Dmitri Mendeleev   **f.** John Dalton
   g. Antoine Lavoisier   **h.** Marie-Anne Pierrette Paulze

2. Prepare a brief report on early Greek contributions to and ideas in the field of science, focusing on the work of one of the following: Aristotle, Leucippus, Democritus, Thales, Anaximander, Anaximenes of Miletus, Heraclitus, Empedocles, or another Greek philosopher of the time before 300 B.C.E.

3. Prepare a brief report on the *phlogiston theory*. Describe what the theory was, how it explained changes in mass when something is burned, and why it was finally abandoned.

4. Write a brief essay on recycling of one of the following: metals, paper, plastics, glass, food wastes, or grass clippings. Contrast a recycling method that maintains the properties of an element with one that changes them.   1
   A. 2.19 g nitrogen   **B.** 63.0 g nitrogen

BRIEF ANSWERS TO SELECTED PROBLEMS

Answers are provided for *all in-chapter exercises*. Brief answers are given for *odd-numbered Review Questions*; more complete answers can be obtained by reviewing the text. Answers are provided for *all odd-numbered Problems and Additional Problems*.

Note: For numerical problems, your answer may differ slightly from ours because of rounding and the use of significant figures.

1 **A.** 2.19 g nitrogen   **B.** 63.0 g nitrogen
2 3 atoms hydrogen/1 atom phosphorus
3 average Cl + I is 81.2; actual Br is 79.9.
1. **a.** atomic: matter is made of discrete particles; continuous: matter is infinitely divisible.
   b. Greek: four elements, no atoms; modern: each element has its own kind of atom.
3. discrete: a, c, e; continuous: b, d
5. An element is a substance that could not be broken down into simpler substances.
7. Different elements can combine in two or more different sets of proportions, each set corresponding to a different compound.
   a. 2:1   **b.** 3:1   **c.** 3:5
9. C has 15 oxygen atoms; the initial mixture has only 14.
11. **a.** conservation of mass: no atoms are created or destroyed.
   b. definite proportions: only whole atoms combine.
   c. multiple proportions; 1 C atom can combine with 1 O atom to make CO, or 1 C atom can combine with 2 O atoms to make CO_2.
13. Law of multiple proportions
15. No. In the open vessel, a gas has escaped and is not part of the weight after reaction.
17. No. The elements have only been mixed; they have not reacted chemically.
19. 6.60 g

21. The mass of titanium(IV) oxide formed cannot be greater than the masses of titanium and oxygen together.
23. (b)
25. **a.** 86.9 g hydrogen.   **b.** 688 g oxygen
27. 3.8 kg carbon
29. C:O ratio for carbon suboxide is 1.000:0.888. Ratio of 1.332:0.888 = 3:2; 2.664:0.888 = 3:1.
31. SnO_2
33. The S:F ratios are (T) 1.00:2.37 and (U) 1.00:3.56. 3.56:2.37 = 1.50:1 or 3:2.
35. **a.** Yes; Dalton assumed that atoms of different elements had different masses.
   b. No; Dalton assumed that atoms of one element differ (in mass) from atoms of any other element.
37. Contradict. Dalton regarded atoms as indivisible.
39. (d)
41. Yes; the ratio of carbon to hydrogen is the same for the different samples.
43. 0.4467 g nitrogen
45. Six fluorine atoms
47. Conservation of mass
49. 108.0 g of mercury oxide
51. 1.334:1.000 or 4:3
53. (1) Lead compounds, once used in paints, have been replaced with titanium dioxide, a much safer material. (2) Metal salts with lower toxicity now substitute for the lead stabilizers in plastics.

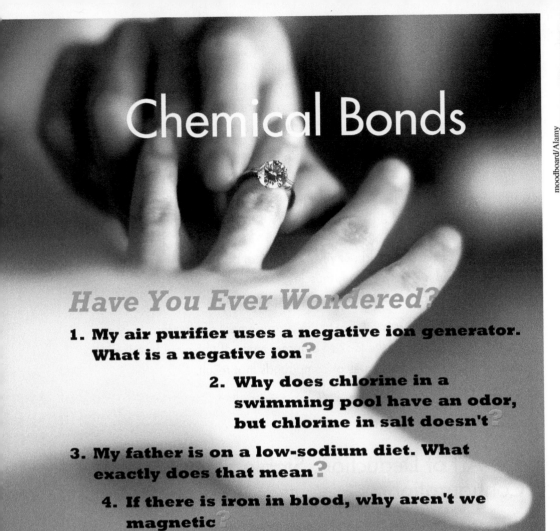

Chemical Bonds

Have You Ever Wondered?

1. My air purifier uses a negative ion generator. What is a negative ion?

2. Why does chlorine in a swimming pool have an odor, but chlorine in salt doesn't?

3. My father is on a low-sodium diet. What exactly does that mean?

4. If there is iron in blood, why aren't we magnetic?

Phase4Photography/Shutterstock

Learning Objectives

> Determine the number of electrons in an ion. (1)

> Write the Lewis symbol for an atom or ion. (2)

> Distinguish between an ion and an atom. (3)

> Describe the nature of the attraction that leads to formation of an ionic bond. (3)

> Write symbols for common ions, and determine their charges. (4)

> Describe the relationship between the octet rule and the charge on an ion. (4)

> Name and write formulas for binary ionic compounds. (5)

> Explain the difference between a covalent bond and an ionic bond. (6)

> Name and write formulas for covalent compounds. (6)

> Classify a covalent bond as polar or nonpolar. (7)

> Use electronegativities of elements to determine bond polarity. (7)

> Predict the number of bonds formed by common nonmetals (the HONC rules). (8)

> Recognize common polyatomic ions and be able to use them in naming and writing formulas for compounds. (9)

> Write Lewis formulas for simple molecules and polyatomic ions. (10)

> Identify free radicals. (10)

> Predict the shapes of simple molecules from their Lewis formulas. (11)

> Classify a simple molecule as polar or nonpolar from its shape and the polarity of its bonds. (12)

> Explain how shape and composition change the properties of molecules.

> Describe the concept of molecular recognition.

> Explain the green chemistry advantages of using production methods based on molecular recognition.

The Ties that Bind

The element carbon is commonly found as soft, black soot formed by incomplete combustion. By heating that soot under tremendous pressure, we can make the hardest material known—diamond. We have not changed the carbon in soot to a different element in this process ... so why is diamond so different from soot? The answer lies in the bonds that hold the carbon atoms together. We have learned a bit about the structure of the atom. Now we are ready to consider chemical bonds, the ties that bind atoms together.

Chemical bonds are the forces that hold atoms together in molecules and hold ions together in ionic crystals. The vast number and incredible

Atoms combine by forming chemical bonds. These bonds determine, to a great extent, the properties of the substance. Here we see carbon in the form of diamonds, which can form from carbon in the form of graphite (pencil lead) or soot. The only difference between the forms of carbon are the bonds between the carbon atoms. The arrangement and number of these bonds in diamond make it by far the hardest natural material in the world. In this chapter, we will look at the different kinds of bonding that can occur.

Fotocrisis/Shutterstock

From Chapter 4 of *Chemistry for Changing Times*, Thirteenth Edition. John W. Hill, Terry W. McCreary, Doris K. Kolb.

variety of chemical compounds—tens of millions are known—result from the fact that atoms can form bonds with many other types of atoms. In addition, chemical bonds determine the three-dimensional shapes of molecules. Some important consequences of chemical structure and bonding include

- Whether a substance is a solid, liquid, or gas at room temperature
- The strengths of materials (as well as adhesives that hold materials together) used for building bridges, houses, and many other structures
- Whether a liquid is light and volatile (like gasoline) or heavy and viscous (like corn syrup)
- The taste, odor, and drug activity of chemical compounds
- The structural integrity of skin, muscles, bones, and teeth
- The toxicity of certain molecules to living organisms

Chemical bonding is related to the arrangement of electrons in compounds. In this chapter, we look at different types of chemical bonds and some of the unusual properties of compounds that result.

1 The Art of Deduction: Stable Electron Configurations

Learning Objective ❯ Determine the number of electrons in an ion.

In our discussion of the atom and its structure, we followed the historical development of some of the more important atomic concepts. We could continue to look at chemistry in this manner, but that would require several volumes of print—and perhaps more of your time than you care to spend. We won't abandon the historical approach entirely but will emphasize another important aspect of scientific endeavor: deduction.

The art of deduction works something like this.

The outermost shell is filled when it contains eight electrons, two in an s orbital and six in a p orbital. The first shell is an exception: It holds only two electrons in the $1s$ orbital.

- **Fact:** Noble gases, such as helium, neon, and argon, are inert; they undergo few, if any, chemical reactions.
- **Theory:** The inertness of noble gases results from their electron configurations. Each (except helium) has an octet of electrons in its outermost shell.
- **Deduction:** Other elements that can alter their electron configurations to become like those of noble gases would become less reactive by doing so.

We can use an example to illustrate this deductive argument. Sodium has 11 electrons, one of which is in the third shell. Recall that electrons in the outermost shell are called **valence electrons**, while those in all the other shells are lumped together as **core electrons**. If the sodium atom got rid of its valence electron, its remaining core electrons would have the same electron configuration as an atom of the noble gas neon. Using main-shell configurations, we can represent this as

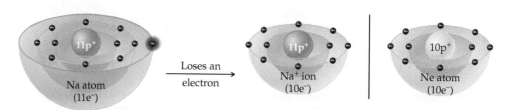

Na atom
(11e⁻)
Loses an electron →
Na⁺ ion
(10e⁻)
Ne atom
(10e⁻)

Similarly, if a chlorine atom gained an electron, it would have the same electron configuration as argon.

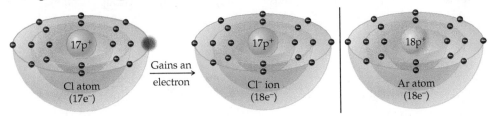

Cl atom (17e⁻) —Gains an electron→ Cl⁻ ion (18e⁻) | Ar atom (18e⁻)

The sodium atom, having lost an electron, becomes positively charged. It has 11 protons (11+) and only 10 electrons (10−). It is symbolized by Na^+ and is called a *sodium ion*. The chlorine atom, having gained an electron, becomes negatively charged. It has 17 protons (17+) and 18 electrons (18−). It is symbolized by Cl^- and is called a *chloride ion*. Note that a positive charge, as in Na^+, indicates that one electron has been lost. Similarly, a negative charge, as in Cl^-, indicates that one electron has been gained.

It is important to note that even though Cl^- and Ar are **isoelectronic** (have the same electron configuration), they are *different* chemical species. In the same way, a sodium atom does not *become* an atom of neon when it loses an electron; the sodium ion is simply isoelectronic with neon.

Self-Assessment Questions

1. Which group of elements in the periodic table is characterized by an especially stable electron arrangement?
   a. 2A   **b.** 2B   **c.** 8A   **d.** 8B

2. The structural difference between a sodium atom and a sodium ion is that the sodium ion has one
   a. less proton than the sodium atom
   b. less electron than the sodium atom
   c. more proton and one less electron than the sodium atom
   d. more proton than the sodium atom

3. Which of the following are isoelectronic?
   a. K^+ and Ar   **b.** Mg^{2+} and Ar   **c.** Ne and Cl^- **d.** Xe and Kr

4. The anion Cl^- is isoelectronic with the cation
   a. Ca^{2+} **b.** Li^+ **c.** Mg^{2+} **d.** Na^+

Answers: 1, c; 2, b; 3, a; 4, a

1. My air purifier uses a negative ion generator. What is a negative ion? A negative ion is an atom or a group of atoms with one or more extra electrons. In a negative ion generator, a high voltage produces negative ions.

2 Lewis (Electron-Dot) Symbols

Learning Objective ❯ Write the Lewis symbol for an atom or ion.

In forming ions, the cores of sodium atoms and chlorine atoms do not change. It is convenient therefore to let the element symbol represent the *core* of the atom (nucleus plus inner electrons). The valence electrons are then represented by dots. The equations of the preceding section then can be written as follows:

$$Na\cdot \rightarrow Na^+ + 1\,e^-$$

and

$$\cdot \ddot{Cl}\!: \;+\; 1\,e^- \longrightarrow :\ddot{Cl}\!:^-$$

In these representations, the element symbol represents the core, and dots stand for valence electrons. These electron-dot symbols are usually called **Lewis symbols**.

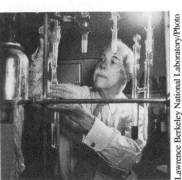

▲ Electron-dot symbols are called *Lewis symbols* after G. N. Lewis, the famous American chemist (1875–1946) who invented them. Lewis also made important contributions to our understanding of thermodynamics, acids and bases, and spectroscopy.

Lawrence Berkeley National Laboratory/Photo Researchers, Inc.

25

Table 1 | Lewis Symbols for Selected Main Group Elements

Group 1A	Group 2A	Group 3A	Group 4A	Group 5A	Group 6A	Group 7A	Noble Gases
H·							He:
Li·	·Be·	·Ḃ·	·Ċ·	:Ṅ·	:Ö·	:Ḟ·	:Ne:
Na·	·Mg·	·Äl·	·Si·	:Ṗ·	:S̈·	:C̈l·	:Är:
K·	·Ca·				:Se·	:B̈r·	:K̈r:
Rb·	·Sr·				:Te·	:Ï·	:Xe:
Cs·	·Ba·						

Lewis Symbols and the Periodic Table

It is especially easy to write Lewis symbols for most of the main group elements. The number of valence electrons for most of these elements is equal to the group number (Table 1). Because of their more complicated electron configurations, elements in the central part of the periodic table (the transition metals) cannot easily be represented by electron-dot symbols.

In writing a Lewis symbol, only the *number* of dots is important. The dots need not be drawn in any specific positions, except that there should be no more than two dots on any given side of the chemical symbol (right, left, top, or bottom).

Example 1 | Writing Lewis Symbols

Without referring to Table 1, write Lewis symbols for magnesium, oxygen, and phosphorus. You may use the periodic table.

Solution
Magnesium is in group 2A, oxygen is in group 6A, and phosphorus is in group 5A. The Lewis symbols, therefore, have two, six, and five dots, respectively. They are

$$·Mg· \qquad :Ö: \qquad :Ṗ·$$

■ EXERCISE 1
Without referring to Table 1, write Lewis symbols for each of the following elements. You may use the periodic table.

a. Ar   **b.** Ca   **c.** F   **d.** N   **e.** K   **f.** S

Self-Assessment Questions

1. How many dots surround Be in the Lewis symbol for beryllium?
   a. 2   **b.** 4   **c.** 5   **d.** 9

2. How many dots surround F in the Lewis symbol for fluorine?
   a. 1   **b.** 5   **c.** 7   **d.** 9

3. Which of the following Lewis symbols is *incorrect*?
   a. ·Ċ·   **b.** :C̈l·   **c.** Li: **d.** :Ṅ·

4. Which of the following Lewis symbols is *incorrect*?
   a. ·Äs·   **b.** :Ö·   **c.** Rb·   **d.** ·Si·

Answers: 1, a; 2, c; 3, c; 4, a

3 The Reaction of Sodium and Chlorine

Learning Objectives ❯ Distinguish between an ion and an atom. ❯ Describe the nature of the attraction that leads to formation of an ionic bond.

Sodium (Na) is a highly reactive metal. It is soft enough to be cut with a knife. When freshly cut, it is bright and silvery, but it dulls rapidly because it reacts with oxygen in the air. In fact, it reacts so readily in air that it is usually stored under oil or

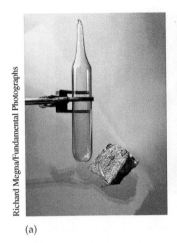  

(a) (b) (c)

Richard Megna/Fundamental Photographs

◀ **Figure 1** (a) Sodium, a soft, silvery metal, and chlorine, a greenish gas (b). The two react violently, to form sodium chloride (ordinary table salt), a white crystal-line solid (c).

Q: *What kinds of particles, ions or molecules, make up sodium chloride?*

kerosene. Sodium reacts violently with water, too, becoming so hot that it melts. A small piece forms a spherical bead after melting and races around on the surface of the water as it reacts.

Chlorine (Cl_2) is a greenish-yellow gas. It is familiar as a disinfectant for drinking water and swimming pools. (The actual substance added is often a compound that reacts with water to form chlorine.) Chlorine is extremely irritating to the eyes and nose. In fact, it was used as a poison gas in World War I.

If a piece of sodium is dropped into a flask containing chlorine gas, a violent reaction ensues, producing sodium chloride, beautiful white crystals that you might sprinkle on your food at the dinner table. These white crystals are ordinary table salt. Sodium chloride has very few properties in common with either sodium or chlorine (Figure 1).

The Reaction of Sodium and Chlorine: Theory

A sodium atom achieves a filled valence shell by losing one electron. A chlorine atom achieves a filled valence shell by adding one electron. What happens when sodium atoms come into contact with chlorine atoms? The obvious: A chlorine atom takes an electron from a sodium atom.

Chlorine gas is composed of Cl_2 molecules, not separate Cl atoms. Each atom of the chlorine molecule takes an electron from a sodium atom. Two sodium ions and two chloride ions are formed.

$$Cl_2 + 2\,Na \rightarrow 2\,Cl^- + 2\,Na^+$$

2. Why does chlorine in a swimming pool have an odor, but chlorine in salt doesn't? Chlorine used in swimming pools is often the element, Cl_2, while the chlorine in salt exists as chlor*ide* ions, Cl^-. An element is chemically quite different from its ions.

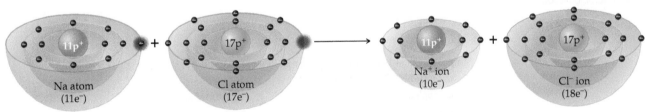

Na atom ($11e^-$) Cl atom ($17e^-$) Na⁺ ion ($10e^-$) Cl⁻ ion ($18e^-$)

With Lewis symbols, this reaction is written as

$$Na\cdot \; + \; :\!\overset{\cdot\cdot}{\underset{\cdot\cdot}{Cl}}\!\cdot \longrightarrow Na^+ + \; :\!\overset{\cdot\cdot}{\underset{\cdot\cdot}{Cl}}\!:^-$$

Ionic Bonds

The Na⁺ and Cl⁻ ions formed from sodium and chlorine atoms have opposite charges and are strongly attracted to one another. These ions arrange themselves in an orderly fashion. Each sodium ion attracts (and is attracted to) six chloride ions (above and below, front and back, left and right), as shown in Figure 2a. The arrangement is repeated many times in all directions (Figure 2b). The result is a **crystal** of sodium chloride. The orderly microscopic arrangement of the ions is reflected in the macroscopic shape, a cube, of a salt crystal (Figure 2c). Even the tiniest grain of salt has billions and billions of each type of ion. The forces holding the crystal together—the attractive forces between positive and negative ions—are called **ionic bonds**.

3. My father is on a low-sodium diet. What exactly does that mean? It means that he must restrict his intake of sodium *ions*. For many people, too many sodium ions in the body can increase blood pressure.

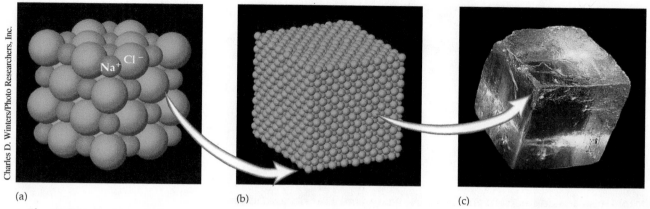

Charles D. Winters/Photo Researchers, Inc.

(a)   (b)   (c)

▲ **Figure 2** Molecular and macroscopic views of a sodium chloride crystal. (a) Each Na^+ ion (small purple spheres) is surrounded by six Cl^- ions (large green spheres), and each Cl^- ion by six Na^+ ions. (b) This arrangement repeats itself many, many times. (c) The highly ordered pattern of alternating Na^+ and Cl^- ions is observed in the macroscopic world as a crystal of sodium chloride.

Richard Megna/Fundamental Photographs

▲ **Figure 3** Forms of iron and calcium that are useful to the human body are the ions (usually Fe^{2+} and Ca^{2+}) in ionic compounds such as $FeSO_4$ and $CaCO_3$. The elemental forms (Fe and Ca) are chemically very different from the forms found in ionic compounds.

Atoms and Ions: Distinctively Different

Ions are emphatically different from the atoms from which they are made, much as a whole peach (an atom) and a peach pit (a positive ion) are different from one another. The names and symbols of an atom and its ion may look a lot alike, but the actual entities are very different (Figure 3). Unfortunately, the situation is confusing because people talk about needing iron to perk up "tired blood" and calcium for healthy teeth and bones. What they really need is iron(II) *ions* (Fe^{2+}) and calcium *ions* (Ca^{2+}). You wouldn't think of eating iron nails to get iron (although some enriched cereals do indeed have powdered iron added; the iron metal is readily converted to Fe^{2+} ions in the stomach). Nor would you eat highly reactive calcium metal.

Similarly, if you are warned to reduce your sodium intake, your doctor is not concerned that you are eating too much sodium metal—that would be exceedingly unpleasant—but that your intake of Na^+ *ions*—usually as sodium chloride—may be too high. Although the names are similar, the atom and the ion are quite different chemically. It is important to make careful distinctions and use precise terminology, as we shall do here.

Self-Assessment Questions

1. A potassium ion and an argon atom have the same
   a. electron configuration   b. net charge
   c. nuclear charge   d. properties

2. How many dots are shown on the Lewis symbol for chloride ion, and what is the ion's charge?
   a. five dots, no charge   b. six dots, + charge
   c. seven dots, − charge   d. eight dots, − charge

3. The bonding between K^+ ions and F^- ions in potassium fluoride is
   a. covalent   b. ionic   c. nonpolar   d. polar

Answers: 1, a; 2, d; 3, b

4 Using Lewis Symbols for Ionic Compounds

Learning Objectives ❯ Write symbols for common ions and determine their charges.
❯ Describe the relationship between the octet rule and the charge on an ion.

Potassium, a metal in the same family as sodium and therefore similar to sodium in properties, also reacts with chlorine. The reaction yields potassium chloride (KCl).

$$K\cdot + \cdot \ddot{\underset{\cdot\cdot}{Cl}}: \longrightarrow K^+ + :\ddot{\underset{\cdot\cdot}{Cl}}:^-$$

Potassium also reacts with bromine, a reddish-brown liquid in the same family as chlorine and therefore similar to chlorine in properties. The product, potassium bromide (KBr), is a stable, white, crystalline solid.

$$K\cdot \; + \; \cdot \ddot{\underset{..}{Br}}: \longrightarrow K^+ + :\ddot{\underset{..}{Br}}:^-$$

Example 2   Electron Transfer to Form Ions

Use Lewis symbols to show the transfer of electrons from sodium atoms to bromine atoms to form ions with noble gas configurations.

Solution
Sodium has one valence electron, and bromine has seven. Transfer of the single valence electron from sodium to bromine leaves each with a noble gas configuration.

$$Na\cdot \; + \; \cdot \ddot{\underset{..}{Br}}: \longrightarrow Na^+ + :\ddot{\underset{..}{Br}}:^-$$

■ EXERCISE 2A
Use Lewis symbols to show the transfer of electrons from lithium atoms to fluorine atoms to form ions with noble gas configurations.

■ EXERCISE 2B
Use Lewis symbols to show the transfer of electrons from rubidium atoms to iodine atoms to form ions with noble gas configurations.

Magnesium, a group 2A metal, is harder and less reactive than sodium. Magnesium reacts with oxygen, a group 6A element that is a colorless gas, to form a stable, white, crystalline solid called magnesium oxide (MgO).

$$\cdot Mg\cdot \; + \; \cdot \ddot{\underset{..}{O}}: \longrightarrow Mg^{2+} + :\ddot{\underset{..}{O}}:^{2-}$$

Magnesium must give up two electrons and oxygen must gain two electrons for each to have the same configuration as the noble gas neon.

An atom such as oxygen, which needs two electrons to achieve a noble gas configuration, may react with potassium atoms, which have only one electron each to give. In this case, two atoms of potassium are needed for each oxygen atom. The product is potassium oxide (K_2O).

$$\begin{matrix} K\cdot \\ \\ K\cdot \end{matrix} + \cdot \ddot{\underset{..}{O}}: \longrightarrow \begin{matrix} K^+ \\ \\ K^+ \end{matrix} + :\ddot{\underset{..}{O}}:^{2-}$$

Through this reaction, each potassium atom achieves the argon configuration. As before, oxygen ends up with the neon configuration.

Example 3   Electron Transfer to Form Ions

Use Lewis symbols to show the transfer of electrons from magnesium atoms to nitrogen atoms to form ions with noble gas configurations.

Solution

$$\begin{matrix} \cdot Mg\cdot \\ \cdot Mg\cdot \\ \cdot Mg\cdot \end{matrix} + \begin{matrix} \cdot\ddot{N}\cdot \\ \\ \cdot\ddot{N}\cdot \end{matrix} \longrightarrow \begin{matrix} Mg^{2+} \\ Mg^{2+} \\ Mg^{2+} \end{matrix} + \begin{matrix} :\ddot{N}:^{3-} \\ \\ :\ddot{N}:^{3-} \end{matrix}$$

When an Mg atom becomes an Mg^{2+} ion, its second shell becomes its outermost shell. The Mg^{2+} ion is isoelectronic with the Ne atom and has the same stable main-shell electron configuration: 2 8.

Each of the three magnesium atoms gives up two electrons (a total of six), and each of the two nitrogen atoms acquires three electrons (a total of six). Notice that the total positive and negative charges on the products are equal (6+ and 6−). Magnesium reacts with nitrogen to yield magnesium nitride (Mg_3N_2).

■ EXERCISE 3

Use Lewis symbols to show the transfer of electrons from aluminum atoms to oxygen atoms to form ions with noble gas configurations.

Generally speaking, metallic elements in groups 1A and 2A (those from the left side of the periodic table) react with nonmetallic elements in groups 6A and 7A (those from the right side) to form ionic compounds. These products are stable crystalline solids.

The Octet Rule

Each atom of a metal tends to give up the electrons in its outer shell, and each atom of a nonmetal tends to take on enough electrons to complete its valence shell. The resulting ions have noble gas configurations. A set of eight valence electrons—an *octet*—is characteristic of all noble gases except helium. When atoms react with each other, they often tend to attain this stable noble-gas electron configuration. Thus, they are said to follow the **octet rule**, or the "rule of eight." (In the case of helium, a maximum of two electrons can occupy its single electron shell, and so hydrogen follows the "rule of two.")

In following the octet rule, atoms of group 1A metals give up one electron to form 1+ ions, those of group 2A metals give up two electrons to form 2+ ions, and those of group 3A metals give up three electrons to form 3+ ions. Group 7A nonmetal atoms take on one electron to form 1− ions, and group 6A atoms tend to pick up two electrons to form 2− ions. Atoms of B group metals can give up various numbers of electrons to form positive ions with various charges. These periodic relationships are summarized in Figure 4.

Table 2 lists symbols and names for some ions formed when atoms gain or lose electrons. (The ion names are explained in the next section.) You can calculate the charge on the negative ions in the table by subtracting 8 from the group number. For example, the charge on the oxide ion (oxygen is in group 6A) is $6 - 8 = -2$. The nitride ion (nitrogen is in group 5A) has a charge of $5 - 8 = -3$.

Example 4	Determining Formulas by Electron Transfer

What is the formula of the compound formed by the reaction of sodium and sulfur?

Solution

Sodium is in group 1A; the sodium atom has one valence electron. Sulfur is in group 6A; the sulfur atom has six valence electrons.

$$Na\cdot \quad \cdot\ddot{\underset{\cdot\cdot}{S}}\cdot$$

Alexander Dvorak/Shutterstock

▲ It DOES Matter!

Loss of electrons is known as *oxidation*, and gain of electrons is called *reduction*. Oxidation by oxygen gas is both useful and destructive. Oxygen gas oxidizes fuels to produce energy, but it also oxidizes iron metal into familiar orange or red rust (Fe_2O_3), which causes billions of dollars of damage each year.

▶ **Figure 4** Periodic relationships of some simple ions. Many of the transition elements (B groups) can form different ions with different charges.

Q: *Can you write a formula for the simple ion formed from selenium (Se)? For the simple ion formed from indium (In)?*

1A	2A											3A	4A	5A	6A	7A	Noble gases
Li^+														N^{3-}	O^{2-}	F^-	
Na^+	Mg^{2+}	3B	4B	5B	6B	7B		8B		1B	2B	Al^{3+}		P^{3-}	S^{2-}	Cl^-	
K^+	Ca^{2+}						Fe^{2+} Fe^{3+}			Cu^+ Cu^{2+}	Zn^{2+}					Br^-	
Rb^+	Sr^{2+}									Ag^+						I^-	
Cs^+	Ba^{2+}																

Table 2	Symbols and Names for Some Simple (Monatomic) Ions		
Group	Element	Name of Ion	Symbol for Ion
1A	Hydrogen	Hydrogen ion	H^+
	Lithium	Lithium ion	Li^+
	Sodium	Sodium ion	Na^+
	Potassium	Potassium ion	K^+
2A	Magnesium	Magnesium ion	Mg^{2+}
	Calcium	Calcium ion	Ca^{2+}
3A	Aluminum	Aluminum ion	Al^{3+}
5A	Nitrogen	Nitride ion	N^{3-}
6A	Oxygen	Oxide ion	O^{2-}
	Sulfur	Sulfide ion	S^{2-}
7A	Fluorine	Fluoride ion	F^-
	Chlorine	Chloride ion	Cl^-
	Bromine	Bromide ion	Br^-
	Iodine	Iodide ion	I^-
1B	Copper	Copper(I) ion (cuprous ion)	Cu^+
		Copper(II) ion (cupric ion)	Cu^{2+}
	Silver	Silver ion	Ag^+
2B	Zinc	Zinc ion	Zn^{2+}
8B	Iron	Iron(II) ion (ferrous ion)	Fe^{2+}
		Iron(III) ion (ferric ion)	Fe^{3+}

4. If there is iron in blood, why aren't we magnetic? Iron metal is magnetic, but compounds—such as the hemoglobin in blood—that have iron usually have iron(II) ions or iron(III) ions. The ions differ chemically and physically from the metal and are not magnetic.

Sulfur needs two electrons to gain an argon configuration, but sodium has only one to give. The sulfur atom therefore must react with two sodium atoms.

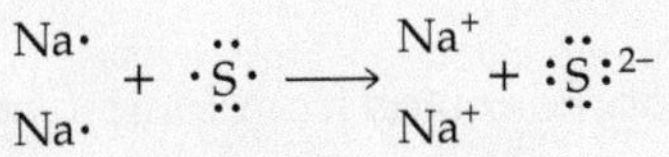

$$\begin{matrix} Na\cdot \\ Na\cdot \end{matrix} + \cdot\ddot{\underset{\cdot\cdot}{S}}\cdot \longrightarrow \begin{matrix} Na^+ \\ Na^+ \end{matrix} + :\ddot{\underset{\cdot\cdot}{S}}:^{2-}$$

The formula of the compound, called sodium sulfide, is Na_2S.

■ **EXERCISE 4A**
What are the formulas of the compounds formed by the reaction of **(a)** calcium with fluorine and **(b)** lithium with oxygen?

■ **EXERCISE 4B**
Use Figure 4 to predict the formulas of the two compounds that can be formed from iron (Fe) and chlorine.

Self-Assessment Questions

1. Which of the following pairs of elements would be most likely to form an ionic compound?
   a. Ca and Mg   **b.** Cd and Ca   **c.** K and S   **d.** Ne and Na

2. Sulfur forms a simple (monatomic) ion with a charge of
   a. 6−   **b.** 2−   **c.** 2+   **d.** 6+

3. Magnesium forms a simple (monatomic) ion with a charge of
   a. 2−   **b.** 2+   **c.** 4+   **d.** 8+

4. Mg and N react to form Mg_3N_2, an ionic compound. How many electrons are there in the valence shell of the N^{3-} ion?
   a. 2   **b.** 6   **c.** 8   **d.** 18

5. The formula of the ionic compound formed by lithium and oxygen is
   a. LiO **b.** Li$_2$O **c.** LiO$_2$ **d.** Li$_2$O$_3$

6. The formula of the ionic compound formed by magnesium and bromine is
   a. MgBr **b.** Mg$_2$Br **c.** MgBr$_2$ **d.** Mg$_2$Br$_3$

7. Only one of the following ions is likely to be formed in an ordinary chemical reaction; it is
   a. Ar^{3-} **b.** Br$^-$ **c.** K^{2+} **d.** S$^-$

Answers: 1, c; 2, b; 3, b; 4, c; 5, b; 6, c; 7, b

5 Formulas and Names of Binary Ionic Compounds

Learning Objective ❯ Name and write formulas for binary ionic compounds.

Names of simple positive ions (*cations*) are derived from those of their parent elements by the addition of the word *ion*. A sodium atom, on losing an electron, becomes a *sodium ion* (Na$^+$). A magnesium atom (Mg), on losing two electrons, becomes a *magnesium ion* (Mg^{2+}). When a metal forms more than one ion, the charges on the different ions are denoted by Roman numerals in parentheses. For example, Fe^{2+} is iron(II) ion and Fe^{3+} is iron(III) ion.

Names of simple negative ions (*anions*) are derived from those of their parent elements by changing the usual ending to *-ide* and adding the word *ion*. A chlor*ine* atom, on gaining an electron, becomes a chlor*ide ion* (Cl$^-$). A sulf*ur* atom gains two electrons, becoming a sulf*ide ion* (S^{2-}).

Simple ions of opposite charge can be combined to form **binary** (two-element) **ionic compounds**. To get the correct formula for a binary ionic compound, write each ion with its charge (positive ion to the left), then transpose the charge numbers (but not the plus and minus signs) and write them as subscripts. The process is best learned by practice, which is provided in the following examples and exercises and in the problems at the end of the chapter.

Example 5	Determining Formulas from Ionic Charges

Write the formulas for **(a)** calcium chloride and **(b)** aluminum oxide.

Solution

a. First, we write the symbols for the ions. (We write the charge on chloride ion explicitly as "1−" to illustrate the method. You may omit the "1" when you are comfortable with the process.)

$$Ca^{2+} \quad Cl^{1-}$$

We cross over the charge numbers (without the charges) as subscripts.

$$Ca^{2+} \qquad Cl^{1-}$$

Then we write the formula. The formula for calcium chloride is

$$Ca_1Cl_2 \quad \text{or} \quad \text{(dropping the "1") simply} \quad CaCl_2$$

b. We write the symbols for the ions.

$$Al^{3+} \quad O^{2-}$$

We cross over the charge numbers as subscripts.

$$Al^{3+} \qquad O^{2-}$$

We write the formula for aluminum oxide as

$$Al_2O_3$$

■ EXERCISE 5

Write the formulas for **(a)** potassium oxide, **(b)** calcium nitride, and **(c)** calcium sulfide.

The method just described, called the *crossover method*, works because it is based on the transfer of electrons and the conservation of charge. Two Al atoms lose three electrons each (a total of six electrons lost), and three O atoms gain two electrons each (a total of six electrons gained). The electrons lost must equal the electrons gained. Similarly, two Al^{3+} ions have six positive charges (three each), and three O^{2-} ions have six negative charges (two each). The net charge on Al_2O_3 is zero, just as it should be.

Now you are able to translate chemical words, such as aluminum oxide, into a chemical formula, Al_2O_3. You also can translate in the other direction, as shown in Example 6.

A Compound by Any Other Name ...

As you read labels on foodstuffs and pharmaceuticals, you will see some names that are beginning to sound familiar, and some that are confusing or mysterious. For example, why do we have two names for Fe^{2+}? Some names are historical: Iron, copper, gold, silver, and other elements have been known for thousands of years. In naming compounds of these elements, the ending *-ous* came to be used for the ion of smaller charge, and the ending *-ic* for the ion of larger charge. The modern system uses Roman numerals to indicate ionic charge. Although the new system is more logical and easier to apply, the old names persist, especially in everyday life and in some of the biomedical sciences.

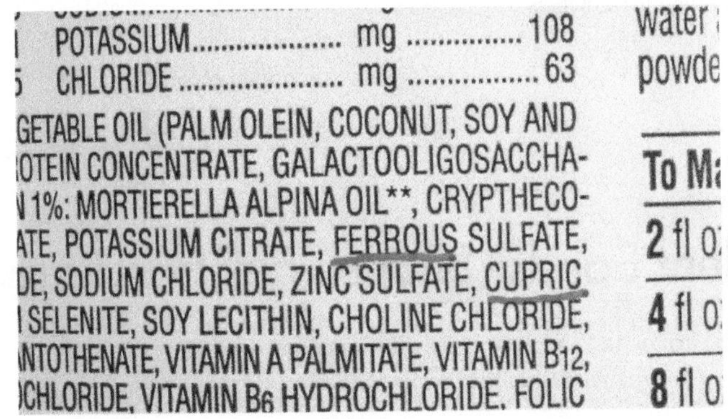

| POTASSIUM .... mg .... 108 | water |
| CHLORIDE .... mg .... 63 | powde |

GETABLE OIL (PALM OLEIN, COCONUT, SOY AND
IOTEIN CONCENTRATE, GALACTOOLIGOSACCHA-
N 1%: MORTIERELLA ALPINA OIL**, CRYPTHECO-
ATE, POTASSIUM CITRATE, FERROUS SULFATE,
DE, SODIUM CHLORIDE, ZINC SULFATE, CUPRIC
SELENITE, SOY LECITHIN, CHOLINE CHLORIDE,
NTOTHENATE, VITAMIN A PALMITATE, VITAMIN B_{12},
CHLORIDE, VITAMIN B_6 HYDROCHLORIDE. FOLIC

To M:

2 fl o:

4 fl o:

8 fl o

Pearson Education/Eric Schrader

▲ Labels for dietary supplements often use older, Latin-derived names.

Example 6 Naming Ionic Compounds

What are the names of **(a)** MgS and **(b)** $FeCl_3$?

Solution

a. From Table 2, we can determine that MgS is made up of Mg^{2+} (magnesium ion) and S^{2-} (sulfide ion). The name is simply magnesium sulfide.

b. From Table 2, we can determine that the ions in $FeCl_3$ are

$$Fe^{3+} \quad Cl^-$$

How do we know the iron ion in $FeCl_3$ is Fe^{3+} and not Fe^{2+}? Because there are three Cl^- ions, each with a 1− charge, the single Fe ion must have a 3+ charge since the compound, $FeCl_3$, is neutral. The names of these ions are iron(III) ion (or ferric ion) and chloride ion. Therefore, the compound is iron(III) chloride (or, by the older system, ferric chloride).

■ EXERCISE 6

What are the names of **(a)** CaF_2 and **(b)** $CuBr_2$?

Self-Assessment Questions

1. The formula for the binary ionic compound of barium and sulfur is
   a. BaS
   b. Ba_2S
   c. BaS_2
   d. Ba_2S_3

2. Which of the following formulas is incorrect?
   a. AlF_3
   b. K_2S
   c. MgF
   d. NaI

3. Which of the following formulas is incorrect?
   a. $AlCl_3$
   b. Al_3P_2
   c. CaS
   d. Cs_2S

4. The correct name for KCl is
   a. krypton chloride
   b. krypton chlorine
   c. potassium chloride
   d. potassium chlorine

5. The correct name for Al_2S_3 is
   a. aluminum sulfide
   b. aluminum trisulfide
   c. antimony sulfide
   d. antimony trisulfide

6. The correct name for LiI is
   a. indium lithide
   b. iodine lithide
   c. lithium indide
   d. lithium iodide

7. The correct name for $ZnCl_2$ is
   a. dichlorozirconium
   b. zinc chloride
   c. zinc dichloride
   d. zirconium chloride

Answers: 1, a; 2, c; 3, b; 4, c; 5, a; 6, d; 7, b

6 Covalent Bonds: Shared Electron Pairs

Learning Objectives ❯ Explain the difference between a covalent bond and an ionic bond. ❯ Name and write formulas for covalent compounds.

We might expect a hydrogen atom, with its one electron, to acquire another electron and achieve the configuration of the noble gas helium. In fact, hydrogen atoms do just that in the presence of atoms of a reactive metal such as lithium—that is, a metal that readily gives up an electron.

$$Li \cdot + H \cdot \longrightarrow Li^+ + H:^-$$

But what if there are no other kinds of atoms around, only hydrogen? One hydrogen atom can't gain an electron from another, for all hydrogen atoms have an equal attraction for electrons. Two hydrogen atoms can compromise, however, by *sharing a pair* of electrons.

$$H \cdot + \cdot H \longrightarrow H:H$$

By sharing electrons, the two hydrogen atoms form a hydrogen molecule. The bond formed when atoms share electrons is called a **covalent bond**. If one pair of electrons is shared, the bond is a **single bond**.

H:H

└─ covalent bond (shared pair of electrons)

Let's consider chlorine next. A chlorine atom readily takes an extra electron from anything willing to give one up. But again, what if the only things around are other chlorine atoms? Chlorine atoms can also attain a more stable arrangement by sharing a pair of electrons.

:Cl· + ·Cl: ⟶ :Cl:Cl:

The shared pair of electrons in the chlorine molecule is another example of a covalent bond; they are called a **bonding pair**. The electrons that stay on one atom and are not shared are called *nonbonding pairs*, or **lone pairs**.

:Cl:Cl:

For simplicity, the hydrogen molecule is often represented as H_2, and the chlorine molecule as Cl_2. In each case, the covalent bond between the atoms is understood. Sometimes the covalent bond is indicated by a dash: $H—H$ and $Cl—Cl$. Lone pairs of electrons often are not shown. Each chlorine atom in a chlorine molecule has eight electrons around it, an arrangement like that of the noble gas argon. Thus, the atoms involved in a covalent bond follow the octet rule by sharing electrons, just as those linked by an ionic bond follow it by giving up or accepting electrons.

Multiple Bonds

In some molecules, atoms must share more than one pair of electrons to follow the octet rule. In carbon dioxide (CO_2), for example, the carbon atom shares *two* pairs of electrons with each of the two oxygen atoms.

:Ö::C::Ö:

Note that each atom has an octet of electrons around it as a result of this sharing. We say that the atoms are joined by a **double bond**, a covalent linkage in which two atoms share two pairs of electrons. A double bond is indicated by a double dash between atoms ($O=C=O$).

Two atoms also can share three pairs of electrons. In the nitrogen (N_2) molecule, for example, each nitrogen atom shares three pairs of electrons with the other.

:N:::N:

The atoms are joined by a **triple bond**, a covalent linkage in which two atoms share three pairs of electrons ($N≡N$). Note that each of the nitrogen atoms has an octet of electrons around it.

Names of Covalent Compounds

Covalent, or *molecular*, compounds are those in which electrons are shared, not transferred. Such compounds generally have molecules that consist of two or more nonmetals. Many covalent compounds have common and widely used names. Examples are water (H_2O), ammonia (NH_3), and methane (CH_4).

For most other covalent compounds, the naming process is more systematic. The prefixes *mono-*, *di-*, *tri-*, and so on are used to indicate the number of atoms of each element in the molecule. A list of these prefixes for up to 10 atoms is given in Table 3. For example, the compound N_2O_4 is called *dinitrogen tetroxide*. (The ending vowel is often dropped from *tetra-* and other prefixes when they precede another vowel.) We often leave off the prefix *mono-* (NO is nitrogen oxide) but include it when we need to distinguish between two compounds of the same pair of elements (CO is carbon monoxide; CO_2 is carbon dioxide).

Covalent bonds are usually represented as dashes. The three kinds of covalent bonds are simply written as follows:
$H—Cl$ $O=C=O$ $N≡N$

Table 3	Prefixes That Indicate the Number of Atoms of an Element in a Covalent Compound
Prefix	**Number of Atoms**
Mono-	1
Di-	2
Tri-	3
Tetra-	4
Penta-	5
Hexa-	6
Hepta-	7
Octa-	8
Nona-	9
Deca-	10

Example 7   Naming Covalent Compounds

What are the names of **(a)** SCl_2 and **(b)** P_4S_3?

Solution

  a. With one sulfur atom and two chlorine atoms, SCl_2 is sulfur dichloride.

  b. With four phosphorus atoms and three sulfur atoms, P_4S_3 is tetraphosphorus trisulfide.

■ **EXERCISE 7**

What are the names of **(a)** BrF_3, **(b)** BrF_5, **(c)** N_2O, and **(d)** N_2O_5?

Example 8   Formulas of Covalent Compounds

Write the formula for tetraphosphorus hexoxide.

Solution

The prefix *tetra-* indicates four phosphorus atoms, and *hex-* specifies six oxygen atoms. The formula is P_4O_6.

■ **EXERCISE 8**

Write the formulas for **(a)** phosphorus trichloride, **(b)** dichlorine heptoxide, **(c)** nitrogen triiodide, and **(d)** disulfur dichloride.

You can have fun with chemical names. Some compounds have strange—even funny—common names. Curious? Curium(III) chloride ($CmCl_3$) is curous chloride. Nickel(II) curate ($NiCmO_3$) is nickelous curate. Titanium(IV) chloride ($TiCl_4$) is titanic chloride. Some ions of uranium, such as UO_2^{2-}, UO_3^{2-}, $U_2O_7^{2-}$, are uranates. The hydrides of group 4 elements include methane (CH_4), silane (SiH_4), and germane (GeH_4). Is GeH_4 relevant?

Self-Assessment Questions

1. A bond formed when two atoms share a pair of electrons is
   a. covalent   **b.** ionic   **c.** nonpolar   **d.** polar

2. The bond in Br_2 is
   a. double covalent   **b.** ionic
   c. single covalent   **d.** triple covalent

3. The bond in N_2 is
   a. double covalent   **b.** ionic
   c. single covalent   **d.** triple covalent

4. The formula for phosphorus trichloride is
   a. KCl_3 **b.** K_3Cl **c.** PCl_3 **d.** P_3Cl

5. The formula for disulfur difluoride is
   a. SF_2 **b.** S_2F_2 **c.** SFe_2 **d.** S_2Fl_2

6. The correct name for N_2S_4 is
   a. dinitrogen disulfide   **b.** dinitrogen tetrasulfide
   c. tetrasulfodinitrogen   **d.** tetrasulfur dinitride

7. The correct name for I_2O_5 is
   a. diiodine pentoxide   **b.** diiodopentoxide
   c. iridium pentoxide   **d.** pentaoxodiiodine

Answers: 1, a; 2, c; 3, d; 4, c; 5, b; 6, b; 7, a

7 Unequal Sharing: Polar Covalent Bonds

Learning Objectives ❯ Classify a covalent bond as polar or nonpolar. ❯ Use electronegativities of elements to determine bond polarity.

So far, we have seen that atoms combine in two different ways. Atoms that are quite different in electron configuration (from opposite sides of the periodic table) react by the complete transfer of one or more electrons from one atom to another to form an ionic bond. Some identical nonmetal atoms (such as two chlorine atoms or two hydrogen atoms) combine by sharing a pair of electrons to form a covalent bond. Now let's consider bond formation between atoms that are different, but not different enough to form ionic bonds.

Hydrogen Chloride

Hydrogen and chlorine react to form a colorless gas called *hydrogen chloride*. This reaction may be represented as

$$H\cdot + \cdot \overset{..}{\underset{..}{Cl}}: \longrightarrow H:\overset{..}{\underset{..}{Cl}}:$$

Ignoring the lone pairs of electrons and using a dash to represent the covalent bond, we can write the hydrogen chloride molecule as H—Cl. Both hydrogen and chlorine need an electron to achieve a noble gas configuration—a helium configuration for hydrogen and an argon configuration for chlorine. They achieve these configurations by sharing a pair of electrons to form a covalent bond.

Example 9   Covalent Bonds from Lewis Symbols

Use Lewis symbols to show the formation of a covalent bond **(a)** between two fluorine atoms and **(b)** between a fluorine atom and a hydrogen atom.

Solution

$$:\overset{..}{F}\cdot \; + \; \cdot \overset{..}{F}: \; \longrightarrow \; :\overset{..}{F}:\overset{..}{F}: \quad \text{—bonding pair}$$

$$H\cdot \; + \; \cdot \overset{..}{F}: \; \longrightarrow \; H:\overset{..}{F}: \quad \text{—bonding pair}$$

■ EXERCISE 9
Use Lewis symbols to show the formation of a covalent bond between **(a)** two bromine atoms, **(b)** a hydrogen atom and a bromine atom, and **(c)** an iodine atom and a chlorine atom.

You might reasonably ask why a hydrogen molecule and a chlorine molecule react at all. Have we not just learned that these molecules form because the result is a stable arrangement of electrons? Yes, indeed, that is the case. But there is stable, and there is *more* stable. The chlorine molecule represents a more stable arrangement than two separate chlorine atoms. However, given the opportunity, a chlorine atom selectively forms a bond with a hydrogen atom rather than with another chlorine atom.

For convenience and simplicity, the reaction of hydrogen (molecule) and chlorine (molecule) to form hydrogen chloride is often represented as

$$H_2 + Cl_2 \longrightarrow 2\,HCl$$

The bonds between the atoms and the lone pairs on the chlorine atoms are not shown explicitly, but remember that they are there.

Each molecule of hydrogen chloride consists of one atom of hydrogen and one atom of chlorine. These unlike atoms share a pair of electrons. *Share*, however, does not necessarily mean "share equally." Chlorine atoms have a greater attraction for a shared pair of electrons than hydrogen atoms do. Chlorine is said to be more *electronegative* than hydrogen.

Electronegativity

The **electronegativity** of an element is a measure of the attraction of an atom of that element *in a molecule* for a pair of shared electrons. The atoms to the right in the periodic table are, in general, more electronegative than those to the left. The ones on the right are precisely the atoms that, in forming ions, tend to gain electrons and form negative ions. The ones on the left—metals—tend to give up electrons and become positive ions. Within a column, electronegativity tends to be higher at the top and lower at the bottom of the column.

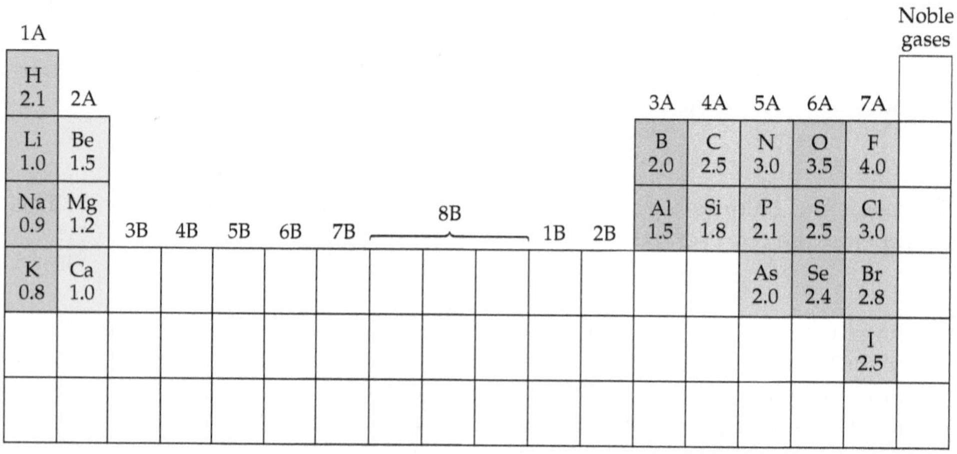

▶ **Figure 5** Pauling electronegativity values for several common elements.

Q: *Can you estimate a value for the electronegativity of germanium (Ge)? For the electronegativity of rubidium (Rb)?*

1A																	Noble gases
H 2.1	2A											3A	4A	5A	6A	7A	
Li 1.0	Be 1.5											B 2.0	C 2.5	N 3.0	O 3.5	F 4.0	
Na 0.9	Mg 1.2	3B	4B	5B	6B	7B		8B		1B	2B	Al 1.5	Si 1.8	P 2.1	S 2.5	Cl 3.0	
K 0.8	Ca 1.0													As 2.0	Se 2.4	Br 2.8	
																I 2.5	

The more electronegative an atom is, the greater its tendency to pull the electrons in the bond toward its end of the bond when it is involved in covalent bonding. The American chemist Linus Pauling (1901–1994) devised a scale of relative electronegativity values by assigning fluorine, the most electronegative element, a value of 4.0. Figure 5 displays the electronegativity values for some of the common elements that we will encounter in this text.

Chlorine (3.0) is more electronegative than hydrogen (2.1). In the hydrogen chloride molecule, the shared electrons are held more tightly by the chlorine atom. Thus, the chlorine end of the molecule is more negative than the hydrogen end. When the electrons in a covalent bond are not equally shared, the bond is said to be *polar*. The bond in a hydrogen chloride molecule is described as a **polar covalent bond**, whereas the bond in a hydrogen molecule or a chlorine molecule is a **nonpolar covalent bond**. A polar covalent bond is not an ionic bond. In an ionic bond, one atom completely loses an electron. In a polar covalent bond, the atom at the positive end of the bond (hydrogen in HCl) still has a fractional share in the bonding pair of electrons (Figure 6). To distinguish this kind of bond from an ionic bond or a nonpolar covalent bond, the following notation is used:

$$\overset{\delta+}{H}—\overset{\delta-}{Cl}$$

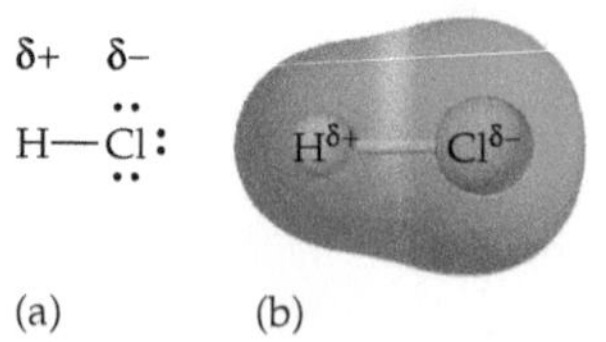

The line between the atoms represents the covalent bond, a pair of shared electrons. The δ+ and δ− (read "delta plus" and "delta minus") signify which end of the bond is partially positive and which is partially negative. (The word *partially* is used to distinguish these charges from the full charges on ions.)

We can use the electronegativity values for the two atoms joined by a bond to predict the type of bonding. When the electronegativity difference is zero or very small (<0.5), the bond is *nonpolar covalent*, with nearly equal sharing of the electrons. When the electronegativity difference is large (>2.0), complete electron transfer occurs and an *ionic* bond is formed, as in the case of sodium and chlorine. When the electronegativity difference is between 0.5 and 2.0, a *polar covalent* bond is formed.

$$\overset{\delta+}{H}—\overset{\delta-}{\underset{..}{\overset{..}{Cl}}}:$$

(a)   (b)

▲ **Figure 6** Representation of the polar hydrogen chloride molecule. (a) The electron-dot formula, with the symbols δ+ and δ− indicating the partial positive and partial negative charge, respectively. (b) An *electrostatic potential diagram* depicting the unequal distribution of electron density in the hydrogen chloride molecule.

▲ Chlorine hogs the electron blanket, leaving hydrogen partially, but positively, exposed.

Example 10   Using Electronegativities to Classify Bonds

Use data from Figure 5 to classify the bond between each of the following pairs of atoms as nonpolar covalent, polar covalent, or ionic:

a. H, H   **b.** O, H   **c.** C, H

Solution

a. Two H atoms have exactly the same electronegativity. The electronegativity difference is 0. The bond is nonpolar covalent.

b. The electronegativity difference is 3.5 − 2.1 = 1.4. The bond is polar covalent.

c. The electronegativity difference is 2.5 − 2.1 = 0.4. The bond is nonpolar covalent.

■ EXERCISE 10A

Use data from Figure 5 to classify the bond between each of the following pairs of atoms as nonpolar covalent, polar covalent, or ionic:

a. H, Br   **b.** Na, O   **c.** C, C

■ EXERCISE 10B

Use the periodic table to classify the following bonds as nonpolar covalent or polar covalent:

a. C—N   **b.** C—O   **c.** C=C

Self-Assessment Questions

1. When HCl is formed,
   a. a Cl atom gives one valence electron to an H atom
   b. an H atom gives one valence electron to a Cl atom
   c. a pair of valence electrons is shared, one each from the H atom and the Cl atom
   d. a pair of valence electrons is shared, none from the H atom and two from the Cl atom

2. Which of the following bonds is least polar?
   a. C—Br   **b.** C—Cl   **c.** C—F   **d.** H—H

3. Which of the following bonds is most polar?
   a. C—C   **b.** C—F   **c.** C—O   **d.** F—F

4. In a polar covalent bond, the atom with greater electronegativity bears a
   a. full negative charge   **b.** full positive charge
   c. partial negative charge   **d.** partial positive charge

5. For an ionic bond to exist between two atoms, their difference in electronegativity should be
   a. between 0 and 0.5   **b.** between 0.5 and 2.0
   c. greater than 2.0   **d.** zero

Answers: 1, c; 2, d; 3, b; 4, c; 5, c

8 Polyatomic Molecules: Water, Ammonia, and Methane

Learning Objective ❯ Predict the number of bonds formed by common nonmetals (the HONC rules).

To obtain an octet of electrons, an oxygen atom must share electrons with *two* hydrogen atoms, a nitrogen atom must share electrons with *three* hydrogen atoms, and a carbon atom must share electrons with *four* hydrogen atoms. In general, nonmetals tend to form a number of covalent bonds that is equal to eight minus the group number. Oxygen, which is in group 6A, forms $8 - 6 = 2$ covalent bonds in most molecules. Nitrogen, in group 5A, forms $8 - 5 = 3$ covalent bonds in most molecules. Carbon, in group 4A, forms $8 - 4 = 4$ covalent bonds in most molecules, including those of the great host of organic compounds. The following simple guidelines—sometimes called the HONC rules—will enable you to write formulas for many molecules.

- Hydrogen forms 1 bond.
- Oxygen forms 2 bonds.
- Nitrogen forms 3 bonds.
- Carbon forms 4 bonds.

Water

Water is one of the most familiar chemical substances. The electrolysis experiment of Nicholson and Carlisle and the fact that both hydrogen and oxygen are diatomic (two-atom) gases indicate that the molecular formula for water is H_2O. To attain an octet, oxygen shares two pairs of electrons. Because a hydrogen atom shares only one pair of electrons, however, an oxygen atom must bond with two hydrogen atoms, forming a *polyatomic* molecule—a molecule containing more than two atoms.

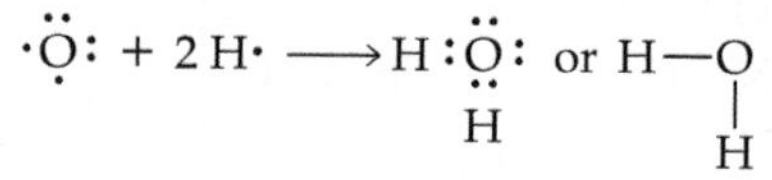

$$\cdot \ddot{O}\!: \;+\; 2\,H\!\cdot \;\longrightarrow\; H\!:\!\ddot{O}\!: \quad \text{or} \quad H\!-\!O$$

This arrangement completes the valence shell octet of the oxygen atom, giving it the neon configuration. It also completes the outer shell of each hydrogen atom, giving each of these atoms the helium configuration. Oxygen has a higher electronegativity than does hydrogen, so the H—O bonds formed are *polar covalent*.

Ammonia

A nitrogen atom has five electrons in its valence shell. It can attain the neon configuration by sharing three pairs of electrons with *three* hydrogen atoms. The result is the compound ammonia.

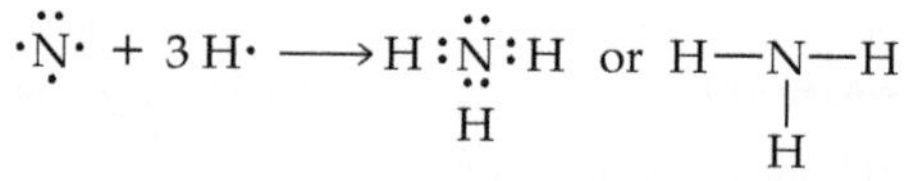

$$\cdot \ddot{N}\!\cdot \;+\; 3\,H\!\cdot \;\longrightarrow\; H\!:\!\ddot{N}\!:\!H \quad \text{or} \quad H\!-\!N\!-\!H$$

In ammonia, the bond arrangement is that of a tripod (see Figure 10) with a hydrogen atom at the end of each leg and the nitrogen atom with its unshared pair of electrons at the top. (We will see why it has this shape in Section 11.) The electronegativity of N is 3.0, and that of H is 2.1, so all three N—H bonds are *polar covalent*.

Methane

A carbon atom has four electrons in its valence shell. It can achieve the neon configuration by sharing pairs of electrons with four hydrogen atoms, forming the compound methane.

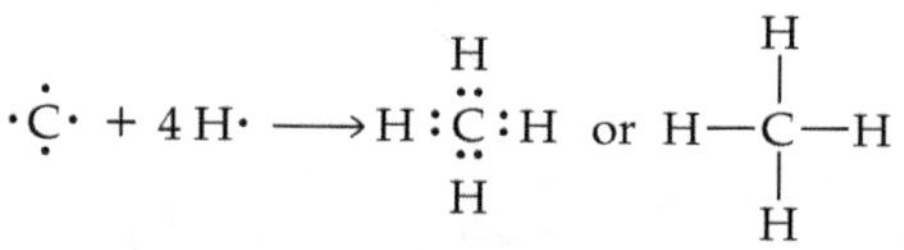

$$\cdot \dot{C}\!\cdot \;+\; 4\,H\!\cdot \;\longrightarrow\; H\!:\!\ddot{C}\!:\!H \quad \text{or} \quad H\!-\!C\!-\!H$$

The methane molecule, as shown above, appears to be planar but actually is not—as we shall see in Section 11. The electronegativity difference between H and C is so small that the C—H bonds are considered nonpolar.

Self-Assessment Questions

1. When two H atoms each share an electron with an O atom to form H_2O, the bonding is
   a. diatomic
   b. ionic
   c. nonpolar covalent
   d. polar covalent

2. How many electrons are in the valence shell of the N atom in an ammonia molecule?
   a. 2
   b. 5
   c. 6
   d. 8

3. To gain an octet of electrons in forming methane, a carbon atom must share an electron with each of
   a. 2 H atoms
   b. 4 H atoms
   c. 6 H atoms
   d. 8 H atoms

Answers: 1, d; 2, d; 3, b

9 Polyatomic Ions

Learning Objective › Recognize common polyatomic ions and be able to use them in naming and writing formulas for ionic compounds.

Many compounds contain both ionic and covalent bonds. Sodium hydroxide, commonly known as lye, consists of sodium ions (Na^+) and hydroxide ions (OH^-). The hydroxide ion contains an oxygen atom covalently bonded to a hydrogen atom,

Table 4 Some Common Polyatomic Ions

Charge	Name	Formula
1+	Ammonium ion	NH_4^+
	Hydronium ion	H_3O^+
1−	Hydrogen carbonate (bicarbonate) ion	HCO_3^-
	Hydrogen sulfate (bisulfate) ion	HSO_4^-
	Acetate ion	$CH_3CO_2^-$ (or $C_2H_3O_2^-$)
	Nitrite ion	NO_2^-
	Nitrate ion	NO_3^-
	Cyanide ion	CN^-
	Hydroxide ion	OH^-
	Dihydrogen phosphate ion	$H_2PO_4^-$
	Permanganate ion	MnO_4^-
2−	Carbonate ion	CO_3^{2-}
	Sulfate ion	SO_4^{2-}
	Chromate ion	CrO_4^{2-}
	Hydrogen (monohydrogen) phosphate ion	HPO_4^{2-}
	Oxalate ion	$C_2O_4^{2-}$
	Dichromate ion	$Cr_2O_7^{2-}$
3−	Phosphate ion	PO_4^{3-}

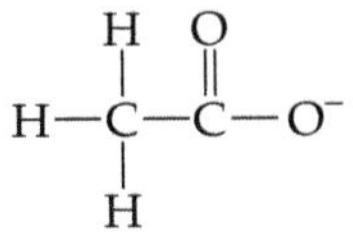

Acetate ion

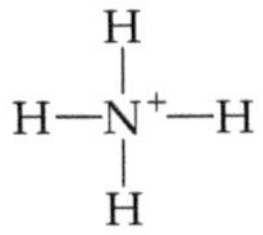

Ammonium ion

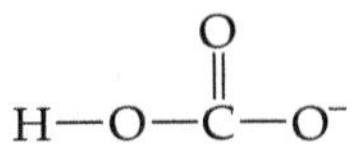

Hydrogen carbonate ion (bicarbonate ion)

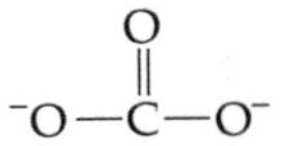

Carbonate ion 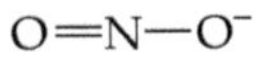   Nitrite ion

plus an "extra" electron. That extra electron gives hydroxide ion a negative charge and gives the O and the H atom each a filled shell.

$$e^- + \cdot\ddot{O}\cdot + \cdot H \longrightarrow :\ddot{O}:H^-$$

The formula for sodium hydroxide is NaOH. For each sodium ion, there is one hydroxide ion.

There are many groups of atoms that (like hydroxide ion) remain together through most chemical reactions. **Polyatomic ions** are charged particles containing two or more covalently bonded atoms. A list of common polyatomic ions is given in Table 4. You can use these ions, in combination with the simple ions in Table 2, to determine formulas for many ionic compounds.

Example 11 Formulas with Polyatomic Ions

What is the formula for ammonium sulfide?

Solution
Ammonium ion is found in Table 4. Sulfide ion is a sulfur atom (group 6A) with two additional electrons. The ions are

$$NH_4^+ \ S^{2-}$$

Crossing over gives

$$NH_4^{1+} \quad S^{2-}$$

The formula for ammonium sulfide is $(NH_4)_2S$. (Note the parentheses.)

■ **EXERCISE 11A**
What are the formulas for **(a)** calcium acetate, **(b)** potassium oxide, and **(c)** aluminum sulfate?

■ **EXERCISE 11B**
How many **(a)** sulfur atoms are in the formula for aluminum sulfate, how many and **(b)** how many carbon atoms are in the formula for calcium acetate?

Example 12   Naming Compounds with Polyatomic Ions

What are the names of **(a)** NaCN and **(b)** $Fe(OH)_2$?

Solution

As with compounds containing only monatomic ions, we name the cation and then the anion.

a. The cation is sodium ion, and the anion is cyanide ion (Table 4). The compound is sodium cyanide.

b. The cation is an iron ion, and the anion is hydroxide ion (Table 4). There are two hydroxide ions, each with a charge of $1-$, so the iron ion must be a $2+$ ion [iron(II)]. The compound is iron(II) hydroxide.

■ **EXERCISE 12A**

What are the names of **(a)** $CaCO_3$, **(b)** $Mg_3(PO_4)_2$, and **(c)** K_2CrO_4?

■ **EXERCISE 12B**

What are the names of **(a)** $(NH_4)_2SO_4$, **(b)** KH_2PO_4, and **(c)** $CuCr_2O_7$?

Self-Assessment Questions

1. Which of the following compounds incorporates a polyatomic ion?
   a. CO_2 **b.** $C_6H_{12}O_6$ **c.** K_2SO_3 **d.** $SrBr_2$

2. The formula for ammonium phosphate is
   a. NH_4PO_3 **b.** $NH_4(PO_4)_2$ **c.** $(NH_4)_2PO_4$ **d.** $(NH_4)_3PO_4$

3. The formula for sodium hydrogen carbonate is
   a. $NaHCO_3$ **b.** Na_2HCO_3 **c.** NaH_2CO_3 **d.** $NaHCO_4$

4. The formula for copper(I) hydrogen sulfate is
   a. $CuHSO_4$ **b.** Cu_2HSO_3 **c.** Cu_2HSO_4 **d.** $Cu(HSO_4)_2$

5. The formula for calcium nitrate is
   a. $CaNO_3$ **b.** Ca_2NO_3 **c.** $Ca(NO_3)_2$ **d.** $CaNO_4$

6. The correct name for NH_4HCO_3 is
   a. ammonium acetate   **b.** ammonium carbonate
   c. ammonium hydrogen carbonate   **d.** ammonium cyanide

Answers: 1, c; 2, d; 3, a; 4, a; 5, c; 6, c

10 Rules for Writing Lewis Formulas

Learning Objectives ❯ Write Lewis formulas for simple molecules and polyatomic ions. ❯ Identify free radicals.

As we have seen, electrons are transferred or shared in ways that leave most atoms with octets of electrons in their outermost shells. This section describes how to write **Lewis formulas** for molecules and polyatomic ions. To write a Lewis formula, we first put the atoms of the molecule or ion in their proper places, and then we place all the valence electrons so that each atom has a filled shell.

The *skeletal structure* of a molecule tells us the order in which the atoms are attached to one another. Drawing a skeletal structure takes some practice. However, if there is no experimental evidence, the following guidelines help us to devise likely skeletal structures:

■ Hydrogen atoms form only single bonds. They are always at the end of a sequence of atoms. Hydrogen is often bonded to carbon, nitrogen, or oxygen.

■ Oxygen tends to have two bonds, nitrogen usually has three bonds, and carbon has four bonds.

■ Polyatomic molecules and ions often consist of a central atom surrounded by atoms of higher electronegativity. (Hydrogen is an exception; it is always on the outside, even when bonded to a more electronegative element.) The central atom of a polyatomic molecule or ion is often the *least* electronegative atom.

After choosing a skeletal structure for a polyatomic molecule or ion, we can use the following steps to write the Lewis formula:

1. Determine the total number of valence electrons. This total is the sum of the valence electrons for all the atoms in the molecule or ion. You must also account for the charge(s) on a polyatomic ion. For a polyatomic anion, *add* to its total number of valence electrons the number of negative charges. For a polyatomic cation, *subtract* the number of positive charges.

   Examples:

   $$N_2O_4 \text{ has } (2 \times 5) + (4 \times 6) = 34 \text{ valence electrons.}$$

   $$NO_3^- \text{ has } [(1 \times 5) + (3 \times 6)] + 1 = 24 \text{ valence electrons.}$$

   $$NH_4^+ \text{ has } [(1 \times 5) + (4 \times 1)] - 1 = 8 \text{ valence electrons.}$$

2. Write a reasonable skeletal structure and connect bonded pairs of atoms by a dash (one shared electron pair).

3. Place electrons in pairs around outer atoms so that each (except hydrogen) has an octet.

4. Subtract the number of electrons assigned so far (both in bonds and as lone pairs) from the total calculated in step 1. Any electrons that remain are assigned in pairs to the central atom(s).

5. If a central atom has fewer than eight electrons after step 4, one or more multiple bonds are likely. Move one or more lone pairs from an outer atom to the space between the atoms to form a double or triple bond. A deficiency of two electrons suggests a double bond, and a shortage of four electrons indicates a triple bond or two double bonds to the central atom.

Example 13   Writing Lewis Formulas

Write Lewis formulas for **(a)** methanol (CH_3OH), **(b)** the BF_4^- ion, and **(c)** carbon dioxide (CO_2).

Solution

a. We start by following the preceding rules:

   1. The total number of valence electrons is $4 + (4 \times 1) + 6 = 14$.

   2. The skeletal structure must have all the H atoms on the outside. That means the C and O atoms must be bonded to each other. A reasonable skeletal structure is

$$
\begin{array}{c}
\text{H} \\
| \\
\text{H}-\text{C}-\text{O}-\text{H} \\
| \\
\text{H}
\end{array}
$$

   3. Now, we count five bonds with two electrons each, making a total of ten electrons. Thus, four of the 14 valence electrons are left to be assigned. They are placed (as two lone pairs) on the oxygen atom.

$$
\begin{array}{c}
\text{H} \\
| \\
\text{H}-\text{C}-\overset{\displaystyle ..}{\underset{\displaystyle ..}{\text{O}}}-\text{H} \\
| \\
\text{H}
\end{array}
$$

   (The remaining steps are not necessary. Both carbon and oxygen now have octets of electrons.)

b. Again, we start by applying the preceding rules:

1. There are $3 + (4 \times 7) + 1 = 32$ valence electrons.

2. The skeletal structure is

$$
\begin{array}{c}
\text{F} \\
| \\
\text{F} - \text{B} - \text{F} \\
| \\
\text{F}
\end{array}
$$

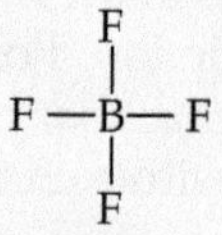

3. Placing three lone pairs on each fluorine atom gives

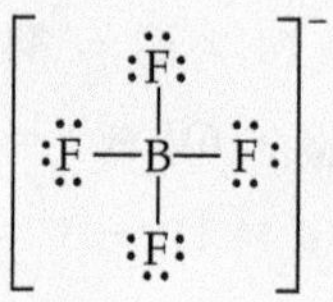

$$
\left[\begin{array}{c}
: \ddot{\text{F}} : \\
| \\
: \ddot{\text{F}} - \text{B} - \ddot{\text{F}} : \\
| \\
: \ddot{\text{F}} :
\end{array}\right]^{-}
$$

4. We have assigned 32 electrons. None remains to be assigned. Brackets and a negative sign are added to show that this is the structure for an anion, not a molecule. The charge is written outside the brackets to indicate the charge is on the ion as a whole, not necessarily on any particular atom.

c. Again, we start by applying the rules:

1. There are $4 + (2 \times 6) = 16$ valence electrons.

2. The skeletal structure is $O - C - O$.

3. We place three lone pairs on each oxygen atom.

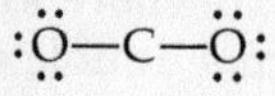

$$: \ddot{\text{O}} - \text{C} - \ddot{\text{O}} :$$

4. We have assigned 16 electrons. None remains to be placed.

5. The central carbon atom has only four electrons. It needs to have two double bonds in order to achieve an octet. We move a lone pair from each oxygen atom to the space between the atoms to form a double bond on each side of the carbon atom.

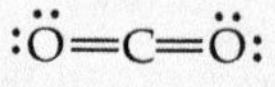

$$: \ddot{\text{O}} = \text{C} = \ddot{\text{O}} :$$

■ EXERCISE 13A

Write Lewis formulas for **(a)** oxygen difluoride, OF_2, and **(b)** methyl chloride, CH_3Cl.

■ EXERCISE 13B

Write Lewis formulas for **(a)** the azide ion, N_3^-, and **(b)** the nitryl fluoride molecule, NO_2F ($O - N - O - F$ skeleton).

The rules we have used here lead to the results for selected elements that are summarized in Table 5. Figure 7 relates the number of covalent bonds that a particular element forms to its position on the periodic table.

Odd-Electron Molecules: Free Radicals

There are some classes of molecules in which atoms do not conform to the octet rule. *Free radicals* are one such class. (See Problems 51 and 52 for two other types.) Molecules with odd numbers of valence electrons obviously cannot satisfy the octet rule. Examples of such molecules are nitrogen monoxide (NO, also called nitric oxide), with $5 + 6 = 11$ valence electrons; nitrogen dioxide (NO_2), with 17 valence electrons; and chlorine dioxide (ClO_2), which has 19 valence electrons.

An atom or molecule with unpaired electrons is called a **free radical**. Most free radicals are highly reactive and exist for only a very brief time before reacting with another species. Every atom or molecule with an odd number of electrons must have one unpaired electron. Filled shells and subshells contain all paired electrons, with two electrons in each orbital. Therefore, we need only consider valence electrons to determine whether an atom or molecule is a free radical. Lewis

Table 5 Number of Bonds Formed by Selected Elements

Lewis Symbol	Bond Picture	Number of Bonds	Representative Molecules	Ball-and-Stick Models
H·	H—	1	H—H H—Cl	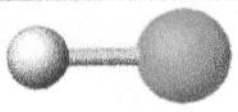 HCl
He:		0	He	 He
·C̈·	 —C̈—	4	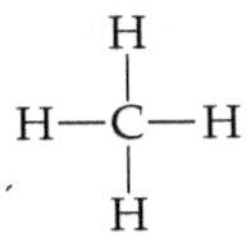 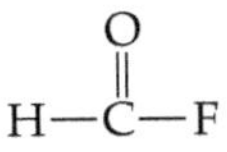 H—C̈—H (with H above and below) H—C̈—F (with O double bonded above)	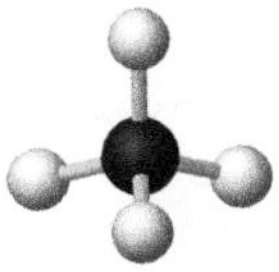 CH₄
·N̈·	—N—	3	H—N—H (with H below) H—C̈—H (with N—O—H double bonded above)	NH₃
·Ö:	—O—	2	H—O (with H below) H—C̈—H (with O double bonded above)	H₂O
·F̈:	—F	1	H—F F—F	 F₂
·C̈l:	—Cl	1	Cl—Cl 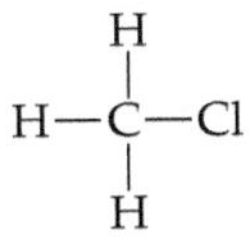 H—C̈—Cl (with H above and below)	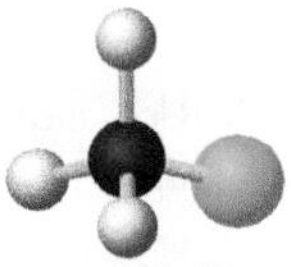 CH₃Cl

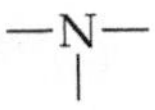

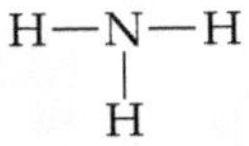

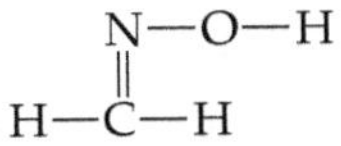

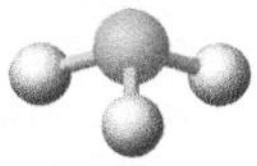

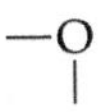

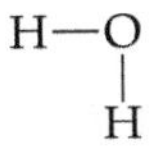

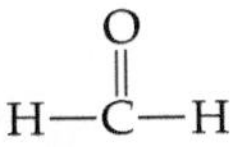

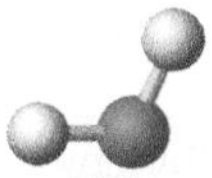

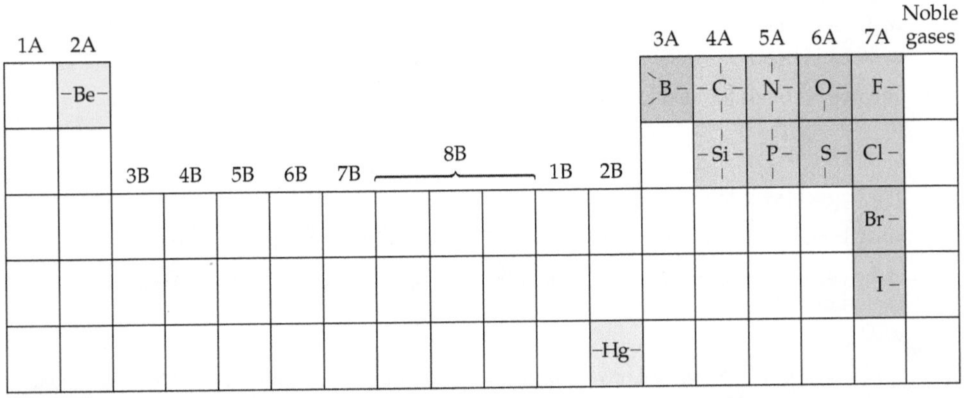

Figure 7 Covalent bonding of representative elements on the periodic table.

Q: *What is the relationship between an atom's position on the periodic table and the number of covalent bonds it tends to form? Why are the group 1A and most of the group 2A elements omitted from the table?*

formulas of NO, NO$_2$, and ClO$_2$ each have one atom with an unpaired electron. An atom having an unpaired electron cannot have an octet of electrons in its outer shell.

$$:\ddot{N}::\ddot{O}: \qquad :\ddot{O}:N::\ddot{O}: \qquad :\ddot{O}:\ddot{Cl}:\ddot{O}:$$

Nitrogen oxides are major components of smog. Chlorine atoms from the breakdown of chlorofluorocarbons in the stratosphere lead to depletion of the ozone layer. Some free radicals are quite stable, however, and have important functions in the body as well as in industrial processes (see the box on the next page).

Useful Applications of Free Radicals

The very reactive nature of free radicals does not preclude their importance and use in a variety of natural and industrial applications.

- Nitric oxide (NO) has been shown to be a signaling molecule in the human cardiovascular system. American scientists Robert F. Furchgott, Louis J. Ignarro, and Ferid Murad won the Nobel Prize in Physiology or Medicine in 1998 for that discovery. Interestingly, one of the physiological effects of sildenafil citrate (Viagra®) is the production of small quantities of NO in the bloodstream.

- Hydroxyl radicals (·OH) are produced in the body in the process of oxidation of foods and by radiation. The decomposition of hydrogen peroxide (HOOH) and other peroxides produces ·OH. These radicals inflict havoc on DNA and other essential substances and they have been implicated in the formation of cancerous cells due to their rapid reaction with DNA. Hydroxyl radicals are also play a role in air pollution.

- Many plastics, including polyethylene and polyvinyl chloride (PVC), are made using free radicals to initiate the reactions. Liquid polyester resin is used to repair automobiles and to construct small boats and surfboards. The resin is converted to hard plastic by the addition of a free-radical catalyst called *methyl ethyl ketone peroxide.*

- The free radical chlorine dioxide (ClO_2) is widely used to bleach paper and other products, including flour. Unbleached flour (left) is a pale cream color; bleached flour (right) is whiter and is considered more attractive to consumers.

Pearson Education/Eric Schrader

▲ Chlorine dioxide (ClO_2) is used to bleach flour. Unbleached flour (left) and bleached flour (right).

Self-Assessment Questions

1. How many lone pairs of electrons are there in the Lewis formula of CF_4?
   a. 4   b. 12   c. 14   d. 16

2. How many unshared electrons are there in the Lewis formula of H_2O_2?
   a. 3   b. 8   c. 14   d. 18

3. The Lewis formula for CCl_4 has
   a. 0 lone pairs   b. 1 double bond
   c. 4 ionic bonds   d. 24 unshared electrons

4. The correct Lewis formula for carbon dioxide is
   a. O—C—O   b. :O—C—O:
   c. :Ö—C—Ö: d. :Ö=C=Ö:

5. The correct Lewis formula for the Cl_2O molecule is
   a. :Cl̈—Cl̈—Ö: b. :Cl̈=O=Cl̈   c. :Ö—Cl̈—Ö: d. :Cl̈—Ö—Cl̈:

6. In the Lewis formula for CO_2, the number of lone pairs of electrons in the outer shell of the central atom is
   a. 0   b. 1   c. 2   d. 4

7. Which of the following must have a triple bond in order to complete an octet for each atom in its Lewis formula?
   a. F_2 b. HCN   c. HI   d. O_2

8. The Lewis formula for the SO_3^{2-} ion that follows the octet rule is

a. $\left[\ddot{\text{O}}-\text{S}-\ddot{\text{O}}:\ \text{with}\ :\ddot{\text{O}}:\right]^{2-}$ b. $\left[:\ddot{\text{O}}-\text{S}=\text{O}:\ \text{with}\ :\ddot{\text{O}}:\right]^{2-}$ c. $\left[:\ddot{\text{O}}=\text{S}=\text{O}:\ \text{with}\ :\ddot{\text{O}}:\right]^{2-}$ d. $\left[:\ddot{\text{O}}-\ddot{\text{S}}-\ddot{\text{O}}:\ \text{with}\ :\ddot{\text{O}}:\right]^{2-}$

Answers: 1, b; 2, b; 3, d; 4, d; 5, d; 6, a; 7, b; 8, d

11 Molecular Shapes: The VSEPR Theory

Learning Objective > Predict the shapes of simple molecules from their Lewis formulas.

We have represented molecules in two dimensions on paper, but molecules have three-dimensional shapes that are important in determining their properties. For example, the shapes of the molecules that make up gasoline determine its octane rating, and drug molecules must have the right atoms in the right places to be effective. We can use Lewis formulas as part of the process of predicting molecular shapes. Figure 8 shows the shapes that we consider in this book.

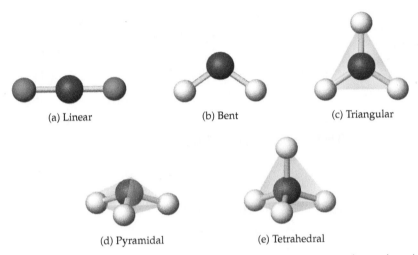

(a) Linear   (b) Bent   (c) Triangular

(d) Pyramidal   (e) Tetrahedral

▲ **Figure 8** Shapes of molecules. In a *linear* molecule (a), all the atoms are along a line; the bond angle is 180°. A *bent* molecule (b) has an angle less than 180°. Connecting the three outer atoms of a *triangular* molecule (c) with imaginary lines produces a triangle with an atom at the center. Imaginary lines connecting all four atoms of a *pyramidal* molecule (d) form a three-sided pyramid. Connecting the four outer atoms of a *tetrahedral* molecule (e) with imaginary lines produces a tetrahedron (a four-sided figure in which each side is a triangle) with an atom at the center.

We use the **valence shell electron pair repulsion (VSEPR) theory** to predict the arrangement of atoms about a central atom in a molecule. The basis of the VSEPR theory is that electron pairs arrange themselves about a central atom in a way that minimizes repulsions between these like-charged particles. This means that electron pairs (both lone pairs and shared pairs in bonds) will be as far apart as possible. In applying the VSEPR theory to predict molecular shapes, we will use the term *electron set* to refer to either a lone pair on a central atom or a bond— single, double, or triple—between the central atom and another atom. Table 6 presents the geometric shapes associated with the arrangement of two, three, or four electron sets about a central atom.

- When *two* electron sets are as far apart as possible, they are on opposite sides of the central atom at an angle of 180°.
- *Three* electron sets assume a triangular arrangement about the central atom, forming angles of separation of 120°.
- *Four* electron sets form a tetrahedral array around the central atom, giving a separation of about 109.5°.

We can determine the shapes of many molecules (and polyatomic ions) by following this simple procedure:

1. Draw a Lewis formula in which a shared electron pair (bonding pair) is indicated by a line. Use dots to show any unshared pairs (lone pairs) of electrons.

Table 6 Bonding and the Shapes of Molecules

Number of Bonded Atoms	Number of Lone Pairs	Number of Electron Sets	Molecular Shape	Examples of Molecules	Ball-and-Stick Models
2	0	2	Linear	$BeCl_2$ $HgCl_2$ CO_2 HCN	 $BeCl_2$
3	0	3	Triangular	BF_3 $AlBr_3$ CH_2O	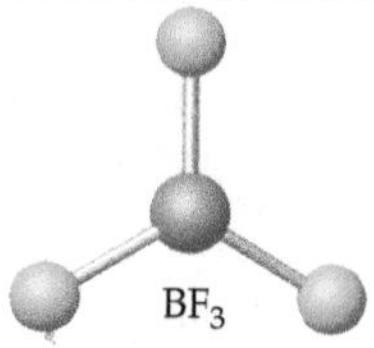 BF_3
4	0	4	Tetrahedral	CH_4 CBr_4 $SiCl_4$	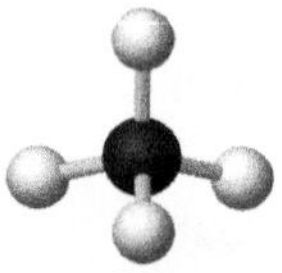 CH_4
3	1	4	Pyramidal	NH_3 PCl_3	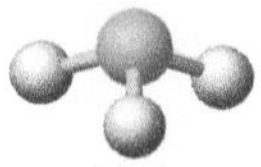 NH_3
2	2	4	Bent	H_2O H_2S SCl_2	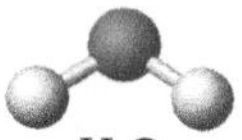 H_2O
2	1	3	Bent	SO_2 O_3	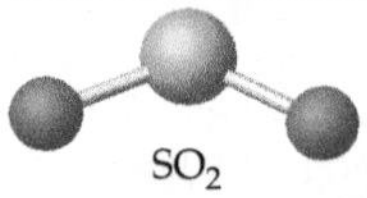 SO_2

2. To determine shape, count the number of electron sets around the *central* atom. Recall that a multiple bond counts only as one electron set. Examples are

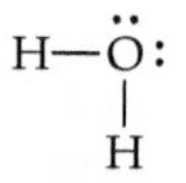

Four sets (2 atoms, 2 LPs)   Four sets (3 atoms, 1 LP)   Four sets (4 atoms)

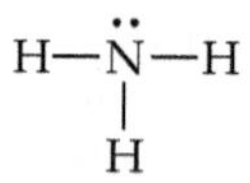

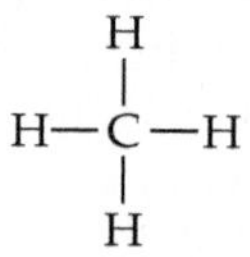

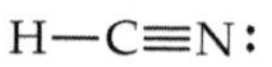

Two sets (2 atoms)   Two sets (2 atoms)   Three sets (3 atoms)   Three sets (2 atoms, 1 LP)

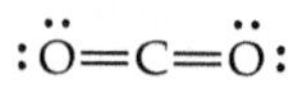

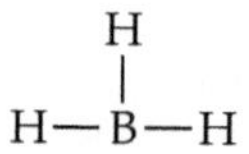

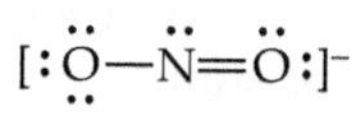

3. Using the number of electron sets determined in step 2, draw a shape *as if* all the sets were bonding pairs and place these electron sets as far apart as possible (Table 6).

4. If there are *no* lone pairs, the shape from step 3 is the shape of the molecule. If there *are* lone pairs, remove them, leaving the bonding pairs exactly as they were. (This may seem strange, but it stems from the fact that *all* the sets determine the geometry, but only the arrangement of bonded atoms is considered in the shape of the molecule.)

Example 14   Shapes of Molecules

What are the shapes of **(a)** the H_2CO molecule and **(b)** the SCl_2 molecule?

Solution

a. We follow the preceding rules, starting with the Lewis formula.

  1. The Lewis formula for H_2CO is

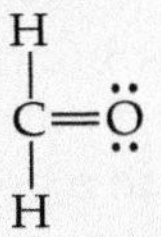

$$\begin{array}{c} H \\ | \\ C{=}\ddot{O} \\ | \\ H \end{array}$$

  2. There are three sets of electrons: two C—H single bonds and one C=O double bond.

  3. A triangular arrangement puts the three electron sets as far apart as possible.

$$\begin{array}{c} H \\ \diagdown \quad 120° \\ C{=}\ddot{O}: \\ \diagup \\ H \end{array}$$

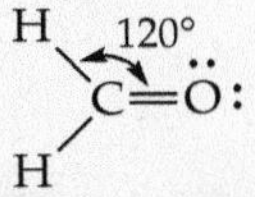

  4. All the electron sets are bonding pairs; the molecular shape is triangular, the same as the arrangement of the electron sets.

b. Again, we follow the rules, starting with the Lewis formula.

  1. The Lewis formula for SCl_2 is

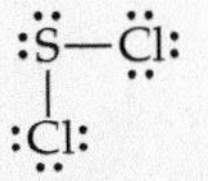

$$\begin{array}{c} :\ddot{S}{-}\ddot{\underset{..}{C}l}: \\ | \\ :\ddot{\underset{..}{C}l}: \end{array}$$

  2. There are four sets of electrons on the sulfur atom.

  3. A tetrahedral arrangement around the central atom puts the four sets of electrons as far apart as possible.

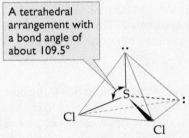

A tetrahedral arrangement with a bond angle of about 109.5°

  4. Two of the electron sets are bonding pairs and two are lone pairs. Ignore the lone pairs. The molecular shape is *bent*, with a bond angle of about 109.5°.

■ **EXERCISE 14A**
What are the shapes of **(a)** the PH_3 molecule and **(b)** the nitrate ion (NO_3^-)?

■ **EXERCISE 14B**
What are the shapes of **(a)** the carbonate ion (CO_3^{2-}) and **(b)** the hydrogen peroxide (H_2O_2) molecule?

Self-Assessment Questions

Match the formula in the left column with the molecular shape in the right column.

1. CS_2 **a.** bent

2. H_2S **b.** linear

3. PF_3 **c.** pyramidal

4. SiF_4 **d.** tetrahedral

Answers: 1, b; 2, a; 3, c; 4, d

12 Shapes and Properties: Polar and Nonpolar Molecules

Learning Objective > Classify a simple molecule as polar or nonpolar from its shape and the polarity of its bonds.

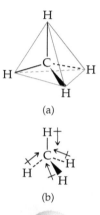

(a)

(b)

(c)

▲ **Figure 9** The methane molecule. In (a), black lines indicate covalent bonds; the red lines outline a tetrahedron; and all bond angles are 109.5°. The slightly polar C—H bonds cancel each other (b), resulting in a nonpolar, tetrahedral molecule (c).

Q: *How does the electrostatic potential diagram in (c) look different from the one in Figure 6?*

Section 7 discussed polar and nonpolar bonds. A diatomic molecule is nonpolar if its bond is nonpolar, as in H_2 or Cl_2, and polar if its bond is polar, as in HCl. Recall from Section 7 that the partial charges in a polar bond are indicated by $\delta+$ and $\delta-$. In the case of a **dipole**, a molecule with a positive end and a negative end, the polarity is commonly indicated with an arrow with a plus sign at the tail end (↔). The plus sign indicates the part of the molecule with a partial positive charge, and the head of the arrow signifies the end of the molecule with a partial negative charge.

$$H\text{—}H \quad \text{and} \quad Cl\text{—}Cl \qquad \overset{\delta+\ \ \delta-}{H\text{—}Cl} \quad \text{or} \quad \overset{\longleftrightarrow}{H\text{—}Cl}$$
$$\text{Nonpolar} \qquad\qquad\qquad \text{Polar}$$

For a molecule with three or more atoms, we must consider the polarity of the individual bonds as well as the overall geometry of the molecule to determine whether the molecule as a whole is polar. A **polar molecule** has separate centers of positive and negative charge, just as a magnet has north and south poles. Many properties of compounds—such as melting point, boiling point, and solubility—depend on the polarity of their molecules.

Methane: A Tetrahedral Molecule

There are four electron sets around the central carbon atom in methane, CH_4. Using the VSEPR theory, we would expect a tetrahedral arrangement and bond angles of 109.5° (Figure 9a). The actual bond angles are 109.5°, as predicted by the theory. All four electron sets are shared with hydrogen atoms and, therefore, occupy identical volumes. Each carbon-to-hydrogen bond is slightly polar (Figure 9b), but the methane molecule as a whole is symmetric. The slight bond polarities cancel out, leaving the methane molecule, as a whole, nonpolar (Figure 9c).

Ammonia: A Pyramidal Molecule

In ammonia, NH_3, the central nitrogen atom has three bonds and a lone pair around it. The N—H bonds of ammonia are more polar than the C—H bonds of methane. More important, the NH_3 molecule has a different geometry as a result of the lone pair on the nitrogen atom. The VSEPR theory predicts a tetrahedral arrangement of the four sets of electrons, giving bond angles of 109.5° (Figure 10a). However, the lone pair of electrons occupies a greater volume than a bonding pair, pushing the bonding pairs slightly closer together and resulting in actual bond angles of about 107°. The pyramidal geometry can be envisioned as a tripod with a hydrogen atom at the end of each leg and the nitrogen atom with its lone pair sitting at the top. Each nitrogen-to-hydrogen bond is somewhat polar (Figure 10b). The asymmetric structure makes the ammonia molecule polar, with a partial negative charge on the nitrogen atom and partial positive charges on the three hydrogen atoms (Figure 10c).

Water: A Bent Molecule

The O—H bonds in water are even more polar than the N—H bonds in ammonia because oxygen is more electronegative than nitrogen. (Recall that electronegativity increases from left to right in the periodic table.) Just because a molecule contains polar bonds, however, does not mean that the molecule as a whole is polar. If the atoms in the water molecule were in a straight line (that is, in a linear arrangement, as in CO_2), the two polar bonds would cancel one another and the molecule would be nonpolar.

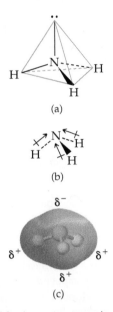

Figure 10 The ammonia molecule. In (a), black lines indicate covalent bonds. The red lines outline a tetrahedron. The polar N—H bonds do not cancel each other completely in (b), resulting in a polar, pyramidal molecule (c).

Q: *How does the electrostatic potential diagram in Figure 10 (c) resemble the one in Figure 6?*

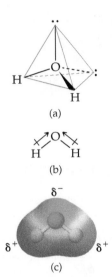

Figure 11 The water molecule. In (a), black lines indicate covalent bonds, and the red lines outline a tetrahedron. The polar O—H bonds do not cancel each other in (b), resulting in a polar, bent molecule (c).

In its physical and chemical properties, however, water acts like a polar molecule. Molecules such as water and ammonia, in which the polar bonds do not cancel out, act as dipoles. Such molecules have a positive end and a negative end.

We can understand the dipole in the water molecule by using the VSEPR theory. The two bonds and two lone pairs should form a tetrahedral arrangement of electron sets (Figure 11a). Ignoring the lone pairs, the molecular shape has the atoms in a bent arrangement, with a bond angle of about 104.5° (instead of 109.5°). As with ammonia, the actual angle is slightly smaller than the predicted angle because of the greater volume of space occupied by the two lone pairs compared to the bonding pairs. The larger space occupied by the lone pairs reduces the space in which the bonding pairs reside, pushing them closer together. The two polar O—H bonds do not cancel each other (Figure 11b), making the bent water molecule polar (Figure 11c).

Self-Assessment Questions

1. Which of the following molecules is polar?
   a. Br_2 **b.** CH_4 **c.** CO_2 **d.** NH_3

2. Which of the following molecules is polar?
   a. C_2H_2 (linear)   **b.** Cl_2 **c.** CCl_4 **d.** PF_3

3. Which of the following molecules is polar?
   a. CF_4 **b.** C_2H_4 (planar)   **c.** NF_3 **d.** O_2

4. Which of the following molecules has polar bonds but is not polar?
   a. CCl_4 **b.** Cl_2 **c.** NCl_3 **d.** OF_2

Answers: 1, d; 2, d; 3, c; 4, a

GREEN CHEMISTRY

John C. Warner, *Warner Babcock Institute for Green Chemistry*

Amy S. Cannon, *Beyond Benign*

Green Chemistry and Chemical Bonds

You learned in this chapter that atoms bond together to form compounds and these new compounds have properties that differ greatly from the component elements. In molecular compounds (molecules), atoms join by forming covalent bonds that cause the molecules to adopt specific geometric shapes (Sections 6, 7, 12). Each atom is held in a specific position relative to other atoms in the molecule. In ionic compounds, atoms are held together through ionic bonds (Section 3).

Molecular shape and composition of compounds control reactivity and interactions with other substances. As a chemist manipulates the geometry and composition of molecules, the properties can change drastically. A wonderful example of how shape impacts the design of molecules is seen in medicine. Within our bodies, biological molecules have particular shapes that are recognized by enzymes and other receptors, in the same way that a key matches a lock. The molecule and the receptor fit together to form complexes through *noncovalent forces* (intermolecular forces).

Medicinal chemists design new medicines and drug molecules so that they will resemble biological molecules and bind to enzymes or receptors in our body. But these molecule-receptor complexes must behave differently from the biological molecule. The binding triggers a response in our bodies and helps us to heal. Medicinal chemists use the shapes of molecules and forces between them to create new life-saving or life-changing medicines. Interaction between molecules caused by the geometric orientations of their atoms is called **molecular recognition**. The 1987 Nobel Prize in Chemistry was awarded to Donald J. Cram, Jean-Marie Lehn, and Charles J. Pedersen for pioneering work in this area. Scientists are now learning to use molecular recognition to control molecular properties and create not only new medicines but also new materials.

What does this have to do with green chemistry? The processes that chemists rely on to make materials often use large amounts of energy or highly reactive and toxic chemicals. New production methods that take advantage of molecular recognition typically use lower energy, solvent-free processes that do not require harsh conditions.

This way of making materials takes advantage of several of the twelve principles of green chemistry. Principles 3, 5, 6, and 8 focus on the choices we make as chemists as we design new molecules and materials. For example, using less hazardous chemicals to make new medicines means we can reduce the environmental impact of the manufacturing process for these compounds. Doing so ensures that they can change the lives of sick patients as well as provide safer workplaces for the workers making the new medicines.

Typical reactions carried out in laboratories use solvents that dissolve the molecules (solutes) and allow them to react to form new molecules. Many solvents can be hazardous to human health and the environment. Processes for making new noncovalent complexes that rely on molecular recognition often do not require solvents. This drastically reduces the environmental impact of these processes.

Many traditional processes require high temperatures, which translates to high energy use. Noncovalent complexes created through molecular recognition function in much the same way as molecules interact within our bodies at moderate temperatures. Therefore, these new approaches use very little energy, which benefits the environment and reduces the manufacturing cost. Also, many processes that generate new molecules and materials are quite complex. By understanding how molecules interact by shape and noncovalent forces, we can reduce the complexity in these processes and avoid the generation of waste and the reliance on hazardous materials.

By understanding molecular shape, the nature of chemical bonds, and how molecules interact with other molecules through noncovalent forces, chemists are able to design new medicines, molecules, and materials that benefit society and, at the same time, have minimal impact on the environment and human health. Green chemistry allows chemists to use these skills combined with new innovative techniques to design chemicals that do not harm our environment in the process.

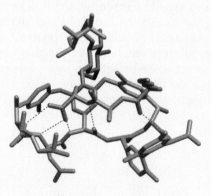

The antibiotic *vancomysin* carries out its function using molecular recognition. Vancomysin undergoes strong, selective hydrogen bonding with *peptides* (small protein chains) of bacteria, preventing formation of the cell wall.

A Chemical Vocabulary

Learning chemical symbolism is much like learning a foreign language. Once you have learned the basic "vocabulary," the rest is a lot easier. At first, the task is complicated because different chemical species or definitions sound a lot alike (sodium atoms versus sodium ions). Another complication is that we have several different ways to represent the *same* chemical species (Figure 12).

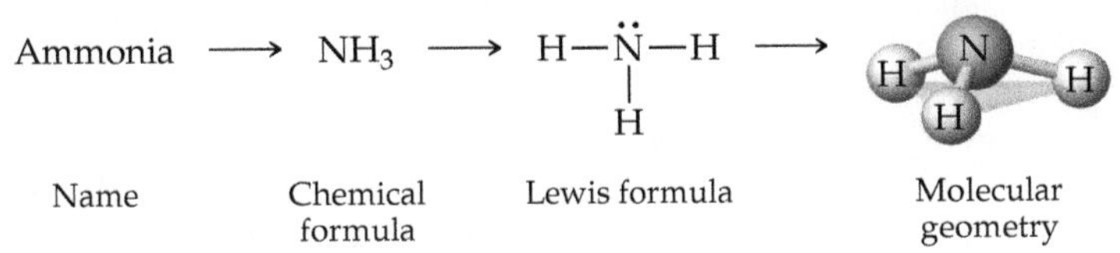

Ammonia $\longrightarrow$ NH_3 $\longrightarrow$ H—N̈—H $\longrightarrow$

Name   Chemical formula   Lewis formula   Molecular geometry

▲ **Figure 12** Several representations of the ammonia molecule.

This chapter covered chemical names and chemical formulas. Now you also know how to write Lewis symbols and formulas using dots to represent valence electrons and you can predict the shapes of thousands of different molecules with the VSEPR theory. You will add the mathematics of chemistry to your toolbox.

CRITICAL THINKING 🐿 EXERCISES

Apply knowledge that you have gained in this chapter and one or more of the FLaReS principles to evaluate the following statements or claims.

1 Some people believe that crystals have special powers. Crystal therapists claim that they can use quartz crystals to restore balance and harmony to a person's spiritual energy.

2 A "fuel-enhancer" device is being sold by an entrepreneur. The device contains a powerful magnet and is placed on the fuel line of an automobile. The inventor claims that the device "separates the positive and negative charges in the hydrocarbon fuel molecules, increasing their polarity and allowing them to react more readily with oxygen."

3 Sodium chloride (NaCl) is a metal–nonmetal compound held together by ionic bonds. A scientist has studied mercury(II) chloride ($HgCl_2$) and says that its atoms are held together by covalent bonds. The scientist says that since a solution of this substance in water does not conduct an electric current, it does not contain an appreciable amount of ions.

4 Another scientist, noting that the noble gas xenon does not contain any ions, states that xenon atoms must be held together by covalent bonds.

5 A web page claims, "Fifty years ago, the hydrogen bond angle in water was 108° and you rarely heard of anyone with cancer. Today, it's only 104° and, as a result, cancer is an epidemic!"

SUMMARY

Section 1—Outermost shell electrons are called valence electrons; those in all other shells are core electrons. The noble gases are inert because they (except He) have an octet of valence electrons. Atoms of other elements become more stable by gaining or losing electrons to attain an electron configuration that makes them isoelectronic with (having the same electron configuration as) a noble gas.

Section 2—The number of valence electrons for most main group elements is the same as the group number. Electron-dot symbols, or Lewis symbols, use dots singly or in pairs to represent valence electrons of an atom or ion.

Section 3—The element sodium reacts violently with elemental chlorine to give sodium chloride, or table salt. In this reaction, an electron is transferred from a sodium atom to a chlorine atom, forming ions.

The ions formed have opposite charges and are strongly attracted to one another; this attraction results in an ionic bond. The positive and negative ions arrange themselves in a regular array, forming a crystal of sodium chloride. The ions of an element have very different properties from the atoms of that element.

Section 4—Metal atoms tend to give up their valence electrons to become positively changed ions, and nonmetal atoms tend to accept (8 − group number) electrons to become negatively changed ions. In either case, the ions formed (except hydrogen ions and lithium ions) tend to have eight valence electrons. The formation of ions is thus said to follow the octet rule. The symbol for an ion is the element symbol with a superscript that indicates the number and type (+ or −) of charge. Some elements, especially the transition metals, can form ions of different charges. The formula of an ionic compound always has the same number of positive charges as negative charges.

Section 5—A binary ionic compound contains two different elements; it has a cation of a metal and an anion of a nonmetal. The formula of a binary ionic compound represents the numbers and types of ions in the compound. The formula is found by crossing over the charge numbers of the ions (without the plus and minus signs).

Binary ionic compounds are named by naming the cation first, and then putting an -ide ending on the stem of the anion name. Examples are calcium chloride, potassium oxide, aluminum nitride, and so on. Differently charged cations of a metal are named with Roman numerals to indicate the charge: Fe^{2+} is iron(II) ion and Fe^{3+} is iron(III) ion.

Section 6—Nonmetal atoms can bond by sharing one or more pairs of electrons, forming a covalent bond. A single bond is one pair of shared electrons; a double bond is two pairs; and a triple bond is three pairs. Shared pairs of electrons are called bonding pairs, and unshared pairs are called nonbonding pairs, or lone pairs. Most binary covalent compounds are named by naming the first element in the formula, followed by the stem of the second element with an -ide ending. Prefixes such as mono-, di-, tri-, and so on, are used to indicate the number of atoms of each element.

Section 7—Bonding pairs are shared equally when the two atoms are the same but may be unequally shared when the atoms are different. The electronegativity of an element is the attraction of an atom in a molecule for a bonding pair. Electronegativity generally increases toward the right and up on the periodic table, so fluorine is the most electronegative element. When electrons of a covalent bond are shared unequally, the more electronegative atom takes on a partial negative charge (δ−), the other atom takes on a partial positive charge (δ+), and the bond is said to be a polar covalent bond. The greater the difference in electronegativity, the more polar is the bond. A bonding pair shared equally is a nonpolar covalent bond.

Section 8—Carbon tends to form four covalent bonds, nitrogen three, and oxygen two; hydrogen can form only one bond. A water molecule has two bonding pairs (O—H bonds) and two lone pairs, an ammonia molecule has three bonding pairs (N—H bonds) and one lone pair, and a methane molecule has four bonding pairs (C—H bonds).

Section 9—A polyatomic ion is a charged particle containing two or more covalently bonded atoms. Compounds containing polyatomic ions are named, and their formulas written, in the same fashion as compounds containing monatomic ions, except that parentheses are placed around the formula for a polyatomic ion if there is more than one of it in the compound. Names of polyatomic ions often end in -ate or -ite.

Section 10—A Lewis formula shows the arrangement of atoms, bonds, and lone pairs in a molecule or polyatomic ion. To draw a Lewis formula, we (a) count the valence electrons; (b) draw a reasonable skeletal structure, showing the arrangement of atoms; (c) connect bonded atoms with a dash (one electron pair); (d) place electron pairs around outer atoms to give each an octet; and (e) place remaining electrons in pairs on the central atom. A multiple bond is included if there are not enough electrons to give each atom (except hydrogen) an octet. There are exceptions to the octet rule. Atoms and molecules with unpaired electrons are called free radicals. They are highly reactive and short-lived. Examples of free radicals are NO and ClO_2.

Section 11—The shape of a molecule can be predicted with the VSEPR theory, which assumes that sets of electrons (either lone pairs or electrons in a bond) around a central atom will get as far away from each other as possible. Two sets of electrons are 180° apart, three sets are about 120° apart, and four sets are about 109° apart. Once these angles have been established, we determine the shape of the molecule by examining only the bonded atoms. Simple molecules have shapes described as linear, bent, triangular, pyramidal, or tetrahedral.

Section 12—Like a polar bond, a polar molecule has separation between its centers of positive charge and negative charge. A molecule with nonpolar bonds is nonpolar. A molecule with polar bonds is nonpolar if its shape causes the polar bonds to cancel one another. If the polar bonds do not cancel, the molecule is polar or is said to be a dipole. The water molecule has polar O—H bonds and is bent, so it is polar.

Green chemistry Chemists manipulate the geometry and composition of molecules to change the properties of both molecules and materials. Typical methods for making these molecules and materials use highly reactive and toxic chemicals and high-energy processes. Greener approaches that take advantage of molecular recognition can instead use low energy, solvent-free processes that do not require harsh conditions.

Learning Objectives

› Determine the number of electrons in an ion. (1)	Problems 1–4
› Write the Lewis symbol for an atom or ion. (2)	Problems 7, 8
› Distinguish between an ion and an atom. (3)	Problems 1, 2, 59
› Describe the nature of the attraction that leads to formation of an ionic bond. (3)	Problems 41, 42
› Write symbols for common ions, and determine their charges. (4)	Problems 3, 11–16

> Describe the relationship between the octet rule and the charge on an ion. (4) Problem 4

> Name and write formulas for binary ionic compounds. (5) Problems 9, 10, 17–20, 55, 67

> Explain the difference between a covalent bond and an ionic bond. (6) Problems 23–28, 41, 42

> Name and write formulas for covalent compounds. (6) Problems 23–30

> Classify a covalent bond as polar or nonpolar. (7) Problems 35–42

> Use electronegativities of elements to determine bond polarity. (7) Problem 57

> Predict the number of bonds formed by common nonmetals (the HONC rules). (8) Problems 5, 6

> Recognize common polyatomic ions and be able to use them in naming and writing formulas for compounds. (9) Problems 21, 22, 65

> Write Lewis formulas for simple molecules and polyatomic ions. (10) Problems 31–34, 56, 66

> Identify free radicals. (10) Problems 49, 50

> Predict the shapes of simple molecules from their Lewis formulas. (11) Problems 43–44

> Classify a simple molecule as polar or nonpolar from its shape and the polarity of its bonds. (12) Problems 45–48

> Explain how shape and composition change the properties of molecules. Problem 68

> Describe the concept of molecular recognition. Problems 68, 69

> Explain the green chemistry advantages of using production methods based on molecular recognition. Problems 70, 71

REVIEW QUESTIONS

1. How does sodium metal differ from sodium ions (in sodium chloride, for example) in properties?

2. What are the structural differences among chlorine atoms, chlorine molecules, and chloride ions? How do their properties differ?

3. What are the charges on simple ions formed from atoms of the following?
   a. group 1A elements
   b. group 6A elements
   c. group 5A elements
   d. group 2A elements

4. In what group of the periodic table would elements that form ions with the following charges likely be found?
   a. 2−   b. 3+
   c. 1+   d. 2+

5. How many covalent bonds do each of the following usually form? You may refer to the periodic table.
   a. H   b. Cl
   c. S   d. F
   e. N   f. P

6. Of the elements H, O, N, and C, which one(s) can readily form triple bonds?

PROBLEMS

Lewis Symbols for Elements

7. Write Lewis symbols for each of the following elements. You may use the periodic table.
   a. calcium   b. sulfur
   c. silicon

8. Write Lewis symbols for each of the following elements. You may use the periodic table.
   a. phosphorus   b. fluorine
   c. boron

Lewis Formulas for Ionic Compounds

9. Write Lewis formulas for each of the following.
   a. sodium iodide   b. potassium sulfide
   c. calcium chloride   d. aluminum fluoride

10. Write Lewis formulas for each of the following.
    a. lithium bromide
    b. strontium sulfide
    c. sodium nitride
    d. aluminum oxide

Names and Symbols for Simple Ions

11. Without referring to Table 2, supply a symbol given the name or a name given the symbol for each of the following ions:
    a. magnesium ion   b. Na$^+$
    c. oxide ion   d. Cl$^-$
    e. zinc ion   f. Cu$^+$

12. Without referring to Table 2, supply a symbol given the name or a name given the symbol for each of the following ions:

    a. sulfide ion   **b.** K^+

    c. Br^- **d.** fluoride ion

    e. Ca^{2+} **f.** iron(III) ion

13. Use that information to name the following ions:

    a. Cr^{2+} **b.** Cr^{3+}

    c. Cr^{6+}

14. Use that information to name the following ions.

    a. Mo^{4+} **b.** Mo^{6+}

15. Write symbols for:

    a. vanadium(II) ion

    b. titanium(II) ion

    c. titanium(IV) ion

16. Write symbols for:

    a. manganese(II) ion

    b. manganese(III) ion

    c. manganese(VII) ion

Names and Formulas for Binary Ionic Compounds

17. Write a formula to match the name or a name to match the formula of the following binary ionic compounds:

    a. sodium iodide   **b.** KCl

    c. copper(I) oxide   **d.** MgF_2

    e. iron(II) bromide   **f.** $FeBr_3$

18. Write a formula to match the name or a name to match the formula of the following binary ionic compounds:

    a. LiF   **b.** calcium chloride

    c. MgS   **d.** silver iodide

    e. CuO   **f.** copper(I) sulfide

19. There are two common binary ionic compounds formed from chromium and oxygen. One of them contains chromium(III) ions; the other contains chromium(VI) ions. Write the formulas for the two compounds, and name them.

20. One of two binary ionic compounds is often added to toothpaste. One of these compounds contains sodium and fluorine; the other contains tin(II) ions and fluorine. Write the formulas for these two compounds, and name them.

Names and Formulas for Ionic Compounds with Polyatomic Ions

21. Supply a formula to match the name or a name to match the formula for the following:

    a. potassium hydroxide   **b.** $MgCO_3$

    c. iron(III) cyanide   **d.** iron(II) oxalate

    e. $CuSO_4$ **f.** $Na_2Cr_2O_7$

22. Supply a formula to match the name or a name to match the formula for the following:

    a. $AgNO_2$ **b.** lithium chromate

    c. $(NH_4)_2SO_3$

    d. magnesium hydrogen carbonate

    e. copper(I) phosphate

    f. $Al(MnO_4)_3$

Molecules: Covalent Bonds

23. Use Lewis symbols to show the sharing of electrons between a hydrogen atom and a fluorine atom.

24. Use Lewis symbols to show the sharing of electrons between two bromine atoms to form a bromine (Br_2) molecule. Label all electron pairs as bonding pairs (BPs) or lone pairs (LPs).

25. Use Lewis symbols to show the sharing of electrons between a phosphorus atom and hydrogen atoms to form a molecule in which phosphorus has an octet of electrons.

26. Use Lewis symbols to show the sharing of electrons between a silicon atom and hydrogen atoms to form a molecule in which silicon has an octet of electrons.

27. Use Lewis symbols to show the sharing of electrons between a carbon atom and chlorine atoms to form a molecule in which each atom has an octet of electrons.

28. Use Lewis symbols to show the sharing of electrons between a nitrogen atom and fluorine atoms to form a molecule in which each atom has an octet of electrons.

Names and Formulas for Covalent Compounds

29. Supply a formula for the name or a name for the formula for the following covalent compounds:

    a. dinitrogen tetroxide

    b. bromine trichloride

    c. OF_2

    d. nitrogen triiodide

    e. CBr_4

    f. N_2S_4

30. Supply a formula for the name or a name for the formula for the following covalent compounds:

    a. carbon disulfide   **b.** chlorine trifluoride

    c. PF_5 **d.** CI_4

    e. tricarbon dioxide   **f.** P_4S_3

Lewis Formulas for Molecules and Polyatomic Ions

31. Write Lewis formulas that follow the octet rule for the following covalent molecules:

    a. SiH_4 **b.** N_2F_4

    c. CH_5N **d.** H_2CO

    e. NOH_3 **f.** H_3PO_3

32. Write Lewis formulas that follow the octet rule for the following covalent molecules:

    a. NH_2Cl **b.** C_2H_4

    c. H_2SO_4 **d.** C_2N_2

    e. $COCl_2$ **f.** SCl_2

33. Write Lewis formulas that follow the octet rule for the following ions:

    a. ClO^- **b.** HPO_4^{2-}

    c. BrO_3^-

34. Write Lewis formulas that follow the octet rule for the following ions:

    a. CN^- **b.** ClO_2^-

    c. HSO_4^-

Electronegativity: Polar Covalent Bonds

35. Classify the following covalent bonds as polar or nonpolar.

    a. H—O   **b.** N—F

    c. Cl—B

36. Classify the following covalent bonds as polar or nonpolar.

    a. H—N   **b.** O—Be

    c. P—F

37. Use the symbol ↦ to indicate the direction of the dipole in each polar bond in Problem 35.

38. Use the symbol ↔ to indicate the direction of the dipole in each polar bond in Problem 36.

39. Use the symbols δ+ and δ− to indicate partial charges, if any, on the following bonds.
  a. Si—O
  b. F—F
  c. F—N

40. Use the symbols δ+ and δ− to indicate partial charges, if any, on the following bonds.
  a. O—H
  b. C—F
  c. C=C

Classifying Bonds

41. Classify the bonds in the following as ionic or covalent. For bonds that are covalent, indicate whether they are polar or nonpolar.
  a. K_2O
  b. BrCl
  c. MgF_2
  d. I_2

42. Classify the bonds in the following as ionic or covalent. For bonds that are covalent, indicate whether they are polar or nonpolar.
  a. Na_2O
  b. $CaCl_2$
  c. NBr_3
  d. CS_2

VSEPR Theory: The Shapes of Molecules

43. Use the VSEPR theory to predict the shape of each of the following molecules:
  a. silane (SiH_4)
  b. hydrogen selenide (H_2Se)
  c. phosphine (PH_3)
  d. silicon tetrafluoride (SiF_4)
  e. oxygen difluoride (OF_2)
  f. formaldehyde (H_2CO)

44. Use VSEPR theory to predict the shape of each of the following molecules:
  a. chloroform ($CHCl_3$)
  b. boron trichloride (BCl_3)
  c. carbon tetrafluoride (CF_4)
  d. sulfur difluoride (SF_2)
  e. nitrogen triiodide (NI_3)
  f. dichlorodifluoromethane (CCl_2F_2)

Polar and Nonpolar Molecules

45. The molecule BeF_2 is linear. Is it polar or nonpolar? Explain.

46. The molecule SF_2 is bent. Is it polar or nonpolar? Explain.

47. Look again at the molecules in Problem 43. For each one, are the bonds polar? What are the approximate bond angles? Is the molecule as a whole polar?

48. Look again at the molecules in Problem 44. For each one, are the bonds polar? What are the approximate bond angles? Is the molecule as a whole polar?

Molecules That Are Exceptions to the Octet Rule

49. Which of the following species (atoms or molecules) are free radicals?
  a. Br
  b. F_2
  c. CCl_3

50. Which of the following species (atoms or molecules) are free radicals?
  a. S
  b. NO_2
  c. N_2O_4

51. Free radicals are one class of molecules in which atoms do not conform to the octet rule. Another exception involves atoms with fewer than eight electrons, as seen in elements of group 3 and in beryllium. In some covalent molecules, these atoms can have six or four electrons, respectively. Write Lewis structures for the following covalent molecules:
  a. $AlBr_3$
  b. BeH_2
  c. BH_3

52. Exceptions to the octet rule include molecules that have atoms with more than eight valence electrons, most typically 10 or 12. Atoms heavier than Si can expand their valence shell, meaning that they can accommodate the "extra" electrons in unoccupied, higher-energy orbitals. Draw Lewis structures for the following molecules or ions:
  a. XeF_4
  b. I_3^-
  c. SF_4
  d. KrF_2

ADDITIONAL PROBLEMS

53. Why does neon tend not to form chemical bonds?

54. Draw an electrostatic potential diagram of the H_2S molecule. Use the symbols δ+ and δ− to indicate the polarity of the molecule.

55. The gas phosphine (PH_3) is used as a fumigant to protect stored grain and other durable produce from pests. Phosphine is generated where it is to be used by adding water to aluminum phosphide or magnesium phosphide. Give formulas for these two phosphides.

56. There are two different covalent molecules with the formula C_2H_6O. Write Lewis formulas for the two molecules.

57. Solutions of iodine chloride (ICl) are used as disinfectants. Is the compound ICl ionic, polar covalent, or nonpolar covalent?

58. Consider the hypothetical elements X, Y, and Z, which have the following Lewis symbols:

$$:\overset{\cdot\cdot}{\underset{\cdot\cdot}{X}}\cdot \qquad :\overset{\cdot\cdot}{Y}\cdot \qquad :\overset{\cdot\cdot}{Z}\cdot$$

  a. To which group in the periodic table would each element belong?
  b. Write the Lewis formula for the simplest compound each would form with hydrogen.
  c. Write Lewis formulas for the ions that would be formed when X reacted with sodium and when Y reacted with sodium.

59. Potassium is a soft, silvery metal that reacts violently with water and ignites spontaneously in air. Your doctor recommends that you take a potassium supplement. Would you take potassium metal? If not, what would you take?

60. What is wrong with the phrase "just a few molecules of potassium iodide"?

61. Use subshell notation to write an electron configuration for the most stable simple ion formed by each of the following elements.
  a. Ca   **b.** Rb
  c. S   **d.** I
  e. N   **f.** Se

62. Why is Na^+ smaller than Na? Why is Cl^- larger than Cl?

63. The halogens (F, Cl, Br, and I) tend to form only one single bond in binary molecules. Explain.

64. A science magazine for the general public contains this statement: "Some of these hydrocarbons are very light, like methane gas—just a single carbon molecule attached to three hydrogen molecules." Evaluate the statement, and correct any inaccuracies.

65. Sodium tungstate is Na_2WO_4. What is the formula for aluminum tungstate?

66. Scientists estimate that the atmosphere of Titan (a moon of Saturn) consists of about 98.4% nitrogen and 1.6% methane. They have also found traces of organic molecules with the molecular formulas C_2H_4, C_3H_4, C_4H_2, HCN, HC_3N, and C_2N_2. Write possible Lewis formulas for each of these molecules.

67. What is the formula for the compound formed by the imaginary ions Q^{2+} and ZX_4^{3-}?

68. Give two design criteria that chemists use to design new medicines.

69. What is the term for the science that explains how molecules interact through geometric orientation of atoms?

70. Give three ways that molecular recognition approaches can support greener methods for making molecules and materials.

71. How can an understanding of enzymes and biological receptors guide medicinal chemists?

 # COLLABORATIVE GROUP PROJECTS

Prepare a PowerPoint, poster, or other presentation (as directed by your instructor) for presentation to the class. Projects 1 and 2 are best done by a group of four students.

1. Make a form like the one below the column headings "Word" and "Definition" with "Name" and "Lewis Formula." Student 1 should write the name from the list below in the first column of the form and its Lewis formula in the second column. End by comparing the name in the last column with that in the first column. Discuss any differences in the two names. If the name in the last column differs from that in the first column, determine what went wrong in the process.
  a. bromide ion
  b. calcium fluoride
  c. phosphorus trifluoride
  d. carbon disulfide

2. Make a form like that below, using the column headings "Name" and "Structure." Then student 1 should write a name from the list below in the first column of the form and its structure in the second column. End by comparing the name in the last column with that in the first column. Discuss any differences in the two names. If the name in the last column differs from that in the first column, determine what went wrong in the process.
  a. ammonium nitrate   **b.** potassium phosphate
  c. lithium carbonate   **d.** copper(I) chloride

3. Starting with 20 balloons, blown up to about the same size and tied, tie two balloons together. Next, tie three balloons together. Repeat this with four, five, and six balloons. (*Suggestion*: Three sets of two balloons can be twisted together to form a six-balloon set, and so on.) Show how these balloon sets can be used to illustrate the VSEPR theory.

4. Prepare a brief biographical report on one of the following:
  a. Gilbert N. Lewis   **b.** Linus Pauling

5. There are several different definitions and scales for electronegativity. Search for information on these, and write a brief compare-and-contrast essay about two of them.

Text Entry	Student 1	Student 2	Student 3	Student 4
Word	Definition	Word	Definition	Word

BRIEF ANSWERS TO SELECTED PROBLEMS

Answers are provided for *all in-chapter exercises*. Brief answers are given for *odd-numbered Review Questions*; more complete answers can be obtained by reviewing the text. Answers are provided for *all odd-numbered Problems and Additional Problems*.

NOTE: For numerical problems, your answer may differ slightly from ours because of rounding and the use of significant figures.

1 **a.** :Är: **b.** ·Ca· **c.** :F̈· **d.** :N̈· **e.** K· **f.** :S̈·

2 **A.** Li· + :F̈· ⟶ Li⁺ + :F̈:⁻

   B. Rb· + :Ï· ⟶ Rb⁺ + :Ï:⁻

3 2 ·Al· + 3 :Ö· ⟶ 2 Al³⁺ + 3 :Ö:²⁻

4 **A. a.** CaF₂ **b.** Li₂O
   B. FeCl₂ and FeCl₃

5 **a.** K₂O **b.** Ca₃N₂ **c.** CaS

6 **a.** calcium fluoride **b.** copper(II) bromide

7 **a.** bromine trifluoride
   b. bromine pentafluoride
   c. dinitrogen monoxide
   d. dinitrogen pentoxide

8 **a.** PCl₃ **b.** Cl₂O₇
   c. NI₃ **d.** S₂Cl₂

9 **a.** :B̈r· + ·B̈r: ⟶ :B̈r:B̈r:

   b. H· + ·B̈r: ⟶ H:B̈r:

   c. :Ï· + ·C̈l: ⟶ :Ï:C̈l:

10 **A. a.** polar covalent **b.** ionic **c.** nonpolar covalent
   B. a. polar covalent **b.** polar covalent **c.** nonpolar covalent

11 **A. a.** Ca(C₂H₃O₂)₂ **b.** K₂O **c.** Al₂(SO₄)₃
   B. a. 3 **b.** 4

12 **A. a.** calcium carbonate **b.** magnesium phosphate
   c. potassium chromate
   B. a. ammonium sulfate
   b. potassium dihydrogen phosphate
   c. copper(II) dichromate

13 **A. a.** :F̈ — Ö — F̈: **b.** H—C̈—C̈l: (with H above and H below C)

   B. a. [:N̈=N=N̈:]⁻ **b.** :Ö=N̈—Ö—F̈:

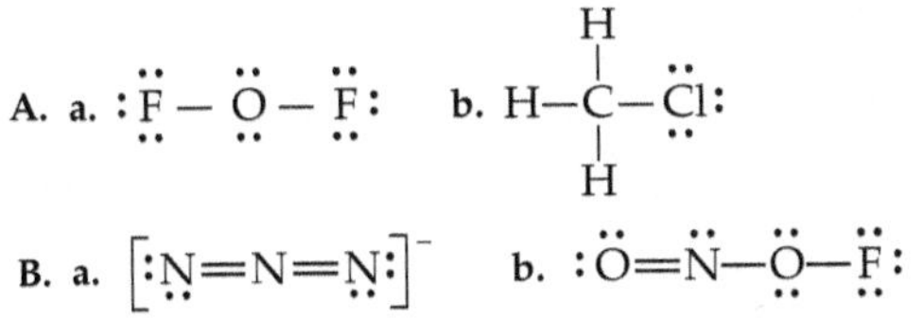

14 **A. a.** pyramidal **b.** triangular
   B. a. triangular **b.** bent (at both O)

1. Sodium metal is quite reactive; sodium ions (as in NaCl) are quite unreactive.

3. a. 1+ **b.** 2– **c.** 3– **d.** 2+

5. a. 1 **b.** 1 **c.** 2 **d.** 1
   e. 3 **f.** 3

7. a. ·Ca· **b.** :S̈: **c.** ·S̈i·

9. a. Na⁺ [:Ï:]⁻ **b.** 2 K⁺ [:S̈:²⁻]

   c. Ca²⁺ 2[:C̈l:]⁻ **d.** Al³⁺ 3[:F̈:]⁻

11. a. Mg²⁺ **b.** sodium ion **c.** O²⁻
   d. chloride ion **e.** Zn²⁺ **f.** copper(I) ion

13. a. chromium(II) ion **b.** chromium(III) ion
   c. chromium(VI) ion

15. a. V²⁺ **b.** Ti²⁺ **c.** Ti⁴⁺

17. a. NaI **b.** potassium chloride
   c. Cu₂O **d.** magnesium fluoride
   e. FeBr₂ **f.** iron(III) bromide

19. Cr₂O₃, chromium(III) oxide, and CrO₃, chromium(VI) oxide

21. a. KOH **b.** magnesium carbonate
   c. Fe(CN)₃ **d.** FeC₂O₄
   e. copper(II) sulfate **f.** sodium dichromate

23. H· + ·F̈: ⟶ H:F̈:

25. ·P̈· + 3 H· ⟶ H:P̈:H (with H below)

27. 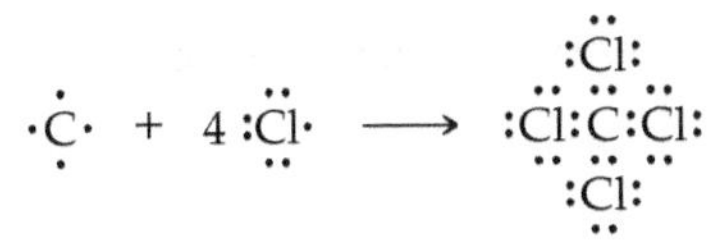 ·C̈· + 4 :C̈l· ⟶ :C̈l:C̈:C̈l: (with :Cl: above and :Cl: below)

29. a. N₂O₄ **b.** BrCl₃
   c. oxygen difluoride **d.** NI₃
   e. carbon tetrabromide **f.** dinitrogen tetrasulfide

31. 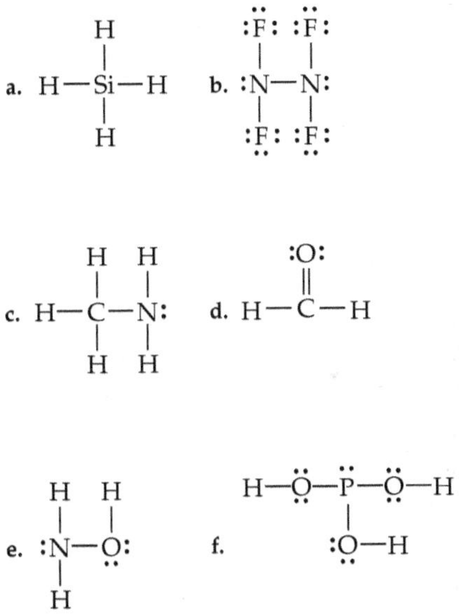 a. H—Si—H (with H above and H below) **b.** :F̈—N—N: with :F̈: below each N

   c. H—C—N: with H,H above and H,H below on C **d.** H—C—H with :O: double bonded above

   e. :N̈—Ö: with H,H above and H below **f.** H—Ö—P—Ö—H with :Ö—H below

33. 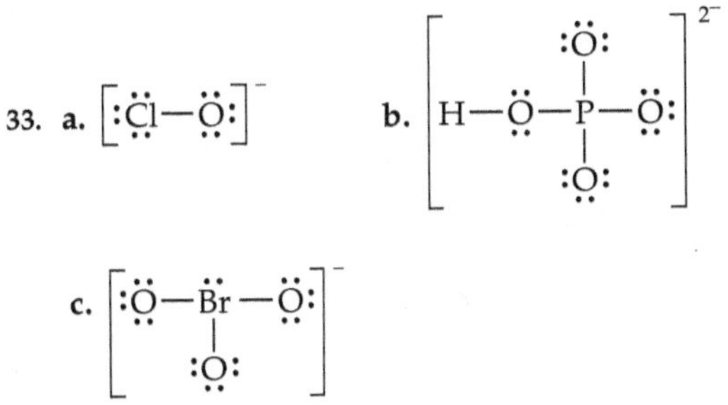 a. [:C̈l—Ö:]⁻ **b.** [H—Ö—P—Ö:]²⁻ with :O: above and :O: below

   c. [:Ö—B̈r—Ö:]⁻ with :O: below

35. a. polar **b.** polar **c.** polar

37. a. H⟶O **b.** N⟶F **c.** Cl⟵B

39. a. Si—O (δ+, δ–)
   b. is not polar
   c. F—N (δ–, δ+)

41. a. ionic **b.** nonpolar covalent
   c. ionic **d.** nonpolar covalent

43. **a.** tetrahedral   **b.** bent
    c. pyramidal   **d.** tetrahedral
    e. bent   **f.** triangular

45. Nonpolar; the two polar Be—F bonds cancel.

47. **a.** nonpolar bonds; 109.5°; nonpolar molecule
    b. nonpolar bonds; 109.5°; nonpolar molecule
    c. nonpolar bonds; 109.5°; nonpolar molecule
    d. polar bonds; 109.5°; nonpolar molecule
    e. polar bonds; 109.5°; polar molecule
    f. polar bonds; 120°; polar molecule

49. a, c

51. **a.**

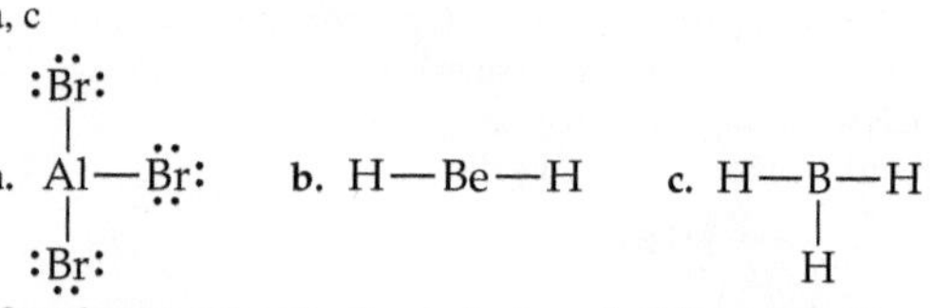

$$\overset{\displaystyle :\overset{..}{\underset{}{Br}}:}{\underset{\displaystyle :\overset{..}{\underset{..}{Br}}:}{Al - \overset{..}{\underset{..}{Br}}:}}$$

    b. H—Be—H

    c.

$$\underset{\displaystyle H}{H - \underset{|}{B} - H}$$

53. Neon has an octet of valence electrons (a full outer shell).

55. AlP; Mg_3P_2

57. Polar covalent

59. No; a potassium salt, to avoid having the mouth catch fire!

61. **a.** Ca^{2+}: $1s^2 2s^2 2p^6 3s^2 3p^6$
    b. Rb^+: $1s^2 2s^2 2p^6 3s^2 3p^6 3d^{10} 4s^2 4p^6$
    c. S^{2-}: $1s^2 2s^2 2p^6 3s^2 3p^6$

    d. I^-: $1s^2 2s^2 2p^6 3s^2 3p^6 3d^{10} 4s^2 4p^6 4d^{10} 5s^2 5p^6$
    e. N^{3-}: $1s^2 2s^2 2p^6$
    f. Se^{2-}: $1s^2 2s^2 2p^6 3s^2 3p^6 3d^{10} 4s^2 4p^6$

63. The halogens have seven valence electrons. Forming single bonds by sharing a bond with one other atom gives them an octet of electrons.

65. $Al_2(WO_4)_3$

67. $Q_3(ZX_4)_2$

69. Molecular recognition

71. Medicinal chemists design new drug molecules to resemble biological molecules that bind to enzymes which recognize the molecules by shapes and partial charges.

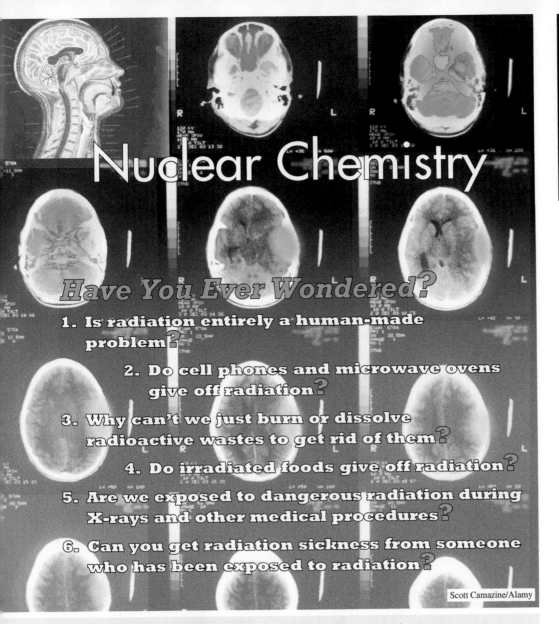

Nuclear Chemistry

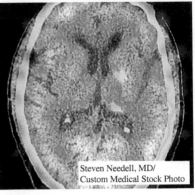

Steven Needell, MD/
Custom Medical Stock Photo

Have You Ever Wondered?

1. **Is radiation entirely a human-made problem?**

2. **Do cell phones and microwave ovens give off radiation?**

3. **Why can't we just burn or dissolve radioactive wastes to get rid of them?**

4. **Do irradiated foods give off radiation?**

5. **Are we exposed to dangerous radiation during X-rays and other medical procedures?**

6. **Can you get radiation sickness from someone who has been exposed to radiation?**

Scott Camazine/Alamy

Learning Objectives

> Identify the sources of the natural radiation to which we are exposed. (1)

> List the sources and dangers of ionizing radiation. (1)

> Balance nuclear equations. (2)

> Identify the products formed by various decay processes. (2)

> Solve simple half-life problems. (3)

> Use the concept of half-life to solve simple radioisotopic dating problems. (3)

> Write a nuclear equation for a transmutation, and identify the product element formed. (4)

> List some applications of radioisotopes. (5)

> Describe the nature of materials needed to block alpha, beta, and gamma radiation (6)

> Explain where nuclear energy comes from. (7)

> Describe the difference between fission and fusion. (7)

> Describe how uranium and plutonium bombs are made. (8)

> Identify the most hazardous fallout isotopes, and explain why they are particularly dangerous. (8)

> List some uses of nuclear energy. (9)

> Identify green chemistry principles that can help solve existing problems in nuclear chemistry.

> Explain how molecules used in nuclear waste processing can be designed to be safer, and give examples of such molecules.

The heart of matter

Many people associate the term *nuclear energy* with fearsome images of a mighty force: giant mushroom clouds from nuclear explosions that devastated cities, and nuclear power plant accidents at Three Mile Island, Pennsylvania, in 1979, Chernobyl, Ukraine, in 1986, and Fukushima, Japan, in 2011. But some amazing stories can also be told about life-giving applications of nuclear energy.

The discussion of atomic structure in has focused mainly on the electrons, because the electrons are the particles that determine an element's chemistry. In this chapter, we take a closer look at that tiny speck in the center of the atom—the atomic nucleus.

The photos show images from MRI (magnetic resonance imaging), PET (positron emission tomography), and x-rays for examining bones and internal organs. All of these diagnostic techniques use radiation or a radioactive isotope. With these techniques, we can examine tissues and diagnose diseases that were previously possible only by biopsy or exploratory surgery. The nuclear age has produced both serious problems and tremendous advantages, which will be examined in this chapter.

SergeyIT/Shutterstock

From Chapter 11 of *Chemistry for Changing Times*, Thirteenth Edition. John W. Hill, Terry W. McCreary, Doris K. Kolb.

An atom is incomprehensibly small, but the infinitesimal size of the atomic nucleus is almost beyond our imagination. The diameter of an atom is roughly 100,000 times greater than the diameter of its nucleus. If an atom could be magnified until it was as large as your classroom, the nucleus would be about as big as the period at the end of this sentence. Yet this tiny nucleus contains almost all the atom's mass. How dense the atomic nucleus must be! A cubic centimeter of water weighs 1 g, and a cubic centimeter of gold about 19 g. A cubic centimeter of pure atomic nuclei would weigh more than 100 million metric tons!

Even more amazing than the density of the nucleus is the enormous amount of energy contained within it. Some atomic nuclei undergo reactions that can fuel the most powerful bombs ever built or provide electricity for millions of people. Our sun is one huge nuclear power plant, supplying the energy that warms our planet and the light necessary for plant growth. The twinkling light from every star we see in the night sky is produced by powerful nuclear reactions. Radioactive isotopes are used in medicine to save lives every day, through diagnosis and treatment of diseases. Many applications of nuclear chemistry in science and industry have improved the human condition significantly. Nuclear reactions allow us to date archaeological and geological finds, to assess the quality of industrial materials, and to be alerted to deadly fires. In this chapter, you will learn about the destructive and the healing power of that infinitesimally small and wonderfully dense heart of every atom—the nucleus.

1 Natural Radioactivity

Learning Objectives ❯ Identify the sources of the natural radiation to which we are exposed. ❯ List the sources and dangers of ionizing radiation.

Most elements occur in nature in several isotopic forms, whose nuclei differ in their number of neutrons. Many of these nuclei are unstable and undergo **radioactive decay**. The nuclei that undergo such decay are called **radioisotopes**, and the process produces one or more types of radiation.

Background Radiation

Humans have always been exposed to radiation. Even as you read this sentence, you are being bombarded by *cosmic rays*, which originate from the sun and outer space. Other radiation reaches us from natural radioactive isotopes in air, water, soil, and rocks. We cannot escape radiation, because it is part of many natural processes, including those in our bodies. A naturally occurring radioactive isotope of potassium, ^{40}K, exists in all our cells and in many foods. The average person absorbs about 4000 particles of radiation each second from ^{40}K and another 1200 particles per second from ^{14}C. (This may sound like a lot, but recall how small atoms are and how many there are in even a tiny sample of matter.)

This ever-present natural radiation is called **background radiation**. Figure 1 shows that over three-fourths of the average radiation exposure comes from background radiation. Most of the remainder comes from medical irradiation such as X-rays. Other sources, such as fallout from testing of nuclear bombs, releases from nuclear industry power plants, and occupational exposure, account for only a minute fraction of the total average exposure.

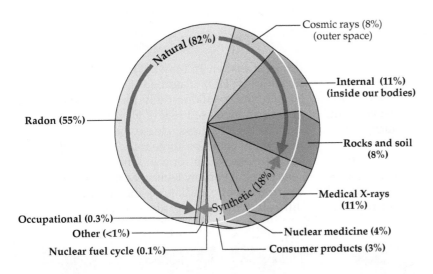

◀ Figure 1 Most of the radiation to which we are exposed comes from natural sources (blue shades). About 18% of this radiation comes from human activities (other colors).

Q: *What natural source of ionizing radiation contributes most to our exposure? What source provides the largest proportion of our exposure due to human activities?*

Harmful effects arise from the interaction of radiation with living tissue. Radiation with enough energy to knock electrons from atoms and molecules, converting them into ions (electrically charged atoms or groups of atoms), is called **ionizing radiation**. Nuclear radiation and X-rays are examples. Because radiation is invisible and because it has such great potential for harm, we are very much concerned with our exposure to it. However, it is worth noting that the total amount of background radiation the average person is exposed to is less than 0.5% of the amount that can cause symptoms of radiation sickness.

Radiation Damage to Cells

Radiation-caused chemical changes in living cells can be highly disruptive. Ionizing radiation can devastate living cells by interfering with their normal chemical processes. Molecules can be splintered into reactive fragments called *free radicals*, which can disrupt vital cellular processes. White blood cells, the body's first line of defense against bacterial infection, are particularly vulnerable. High levels of radiation also affect bone marrow, causing a drop in the production of red blood cells, which results in anemia. Radiation has also been shown to induce leukemia, a disease of the blood-forming organs.

Ionizing radiation also can cause changes in the molecules of heredity (DNA) in reproductive cells. Such changes can show up as mutations in the offspring of exposed parents. Little is known of the effects of such exposure on humans. However, many of the mutations that occurred during the evolution of present species may have been caused by background radiation.

Because of these potentially devastating effects on living things, knowledge of radiation, radioactive decay, and nuclear chemistry in general is crucial. Next, we will see how to write balanced nuclear equations and how to identify the various types of radiation that are emitted.

1. Is radiation entirely a human-made problem?

Figure 1 shows that the majority of the ionizing radiation to which we are exposed is from natural sources.

In 1993, a Ukrainian Academy of Science study group led by Vladimir Chernousenko investigated the aftereffects of the Chernobyl nuclear accident. Chernousenko claimed that 15,000 of those who helped clean up the accident site have died and that another 250,000 have become invalids. He also said that 200,000 children have experienced radiation-induced illnesses and that half of the children in Ukraine and Belarus have symptoms.

Self-Assessment Questions

1. What percentage of background radiation comes from natural sources?
   a. 5%   **b.** 18%   **c.** 45%   **d.** 82%

2. The largest artificial source of background radiation is
   a. accidents at nuclear power plants   **b.** consumer products
   c. fallout from tests of nuclear bombs   **d.** medical X-rays

3. The largest source of natural background radiation is
   a. cosmic rays   **b.** isotopes in the body
   c. radon   **d.** isotopes in rocks and soil

Answers: 1, d; 2, d; 3, c

Cell Phones and Microwaves and Power Lines, Oh My!

There are many types of radiation. *Ionizing* radiation that comes from decaying atomic nuclei is highly energetic and can damage tissue, as discussed above. *Electromagnetic* radiation has many forms—visible light, radio waves, television broadcast waves, microwaves, ultraviolet light, military ULF (ultra-low-frequency), and others. A few types of electromagnetic radiation— X-rays and gamma rays—have enough energy to ionize tissue, and ultraviolet light has been strongly implicated in *melanoma* (skin cancer). But what about microwaves and radio waves, which don't have nearly as much energy? Although very large amounts of microwaves can cause burns (by heating), there is no conclusive evidence that low levels of microwaves pose significant threat to human health. A 2006 study involving almost half a million Danish citizens failed to show a relationship between cell phone use and cancer, though some scientists consider this study inconclusive. However, higher levels of radio frequencies over long periods of time *may* be a

different matter. In May 2011, the World Health Organization (WHO) classified heavy cell phone use— 30 minutes of talking daily for ten years—as possible posing an increased risk of *glioma*, a type of brain cancer. The WHO's press release was very cautious, stating that "there could be some risk … therefore we need to keep a close watch for a link between cell phones and cancer risk." For low levels of exposure to non-ionizing electromagnetic radiation, the hazard appears to be difficult to measure, let alone assess.

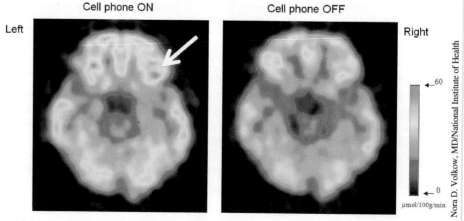

▲ A brain scan shows slight differences when a cell phone held to the ear is on (left) and off (right).

2. Do cell phones and microwave ovens give off radiation? Cell phones and microwave ovens *do* give off radiation, but it is not ionizing radiation and thus does not cause cell damage.

2 Nuclear Equations

Learning Objectives ❯ Balance nuclear equations. ❯ Identify the products formed by various decay processes.

Writing balanced equations for nuclear processes is relatively simple. Nuclear equations differ in two ways. First, while chemical equations must have the same elements on both sides of the arrow, nuclear equations rarely do. Second, while we balance atoms in ordinary chemical equations, we balance the *nucleons* (protons and neutrons) in nuclear equations. What this really means is that we must balance the atomic numbers (number of protons) and nucleon numbers (number of nucleons) of the starting materials and products. For this reason, we must always specify the *isotope* of each element appearing in a nuclear equation. We use nuclear symbols when writing nuclear equations because they make the equations easier to balance.

In one example of a nuclear reaction, radon-222 atoms break down spontaneously in a process called **alpha decay**, giving off alpha (α) particles, as shown in Figure 2(a). Because alpha particles are identical to helium nuclei, this reaction can be summarized by the equation

Mass number of starting material = 222   Mass numbers of products = 4 + 218 = 222

$$^{222}_{86}\text{Rn} \longrightarrow {}^{4}_{2}\text{He} + {}^{218}_{84}\text{Po}$$

Atomic number of starting material = 86   Atomic numbers of products = 2 + 84 = 86

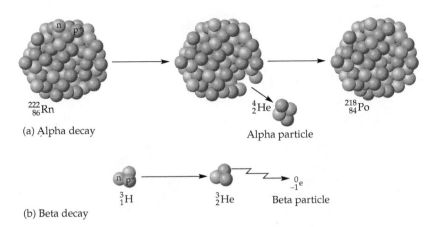

(a) Alpha decay

Alpha particle

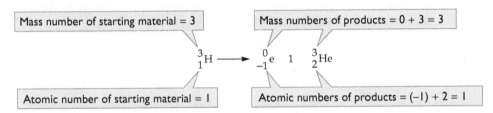

(b) Beta decay

Beta particle

◀ **Figure 2** Nuclear emission of (a) an alpha particle and (b) a beta particle.

Q: *What changes occur in a nucleus when it emits an alpha particle? A beta particle?*

We use the symbol ^4_2He (rather than α) for the alpha particle because it allows us to check the balancing of mass and atomic numbers more readily. The atomic number, $Z = 84$, identifies the element produced as polonium (Po). In nuclear chemistry, the mass number, A, equates with the number of nucleons in the starting material. The number of nucleons in the starting material must equal the total number of the nucleons in the products. The same is true for the atomic numbers.

The heaviest isotope of hydrogen, hydrogen-3, often called *tritium*, decomposes by a process called **beta decay** (Figure 2b). Because a beta (β) particle is identical to an electron, this process can be written as

| Mass number of starting material = 3 | | Mass numbers of products = 0 + 3 = 3 |

$$^3_1\text{H} \longrightarrow {^0_{-1}}\text{e} \ + \ {^3_2}\text{He}$$

| Atomic number of starting material = 1 | | Atomic numbers of products = (−1) + 2 = 1 |

The atomic number, $Z = 2$, identifies the product isotope as helium.

Beta decay is a little more complicated than indicated by the preceding reaction. In beta decay, a neutron within the nucleus is converted into a proton (which remains in the nucleus) and an electron (which is ejected).

$$^1_0\text{n} \longrightarrow {^1_1}\text{p} \ + \ {^0_{-1}}\text{e}$$

With beta decay, the atomic number increases, but the number of nucleons remains the same.

A third kind of radiation may be emitted in a nuclear reaction: gamma (γ) rays. **Gamma decay** is different from alpha and beta decay in that gamma radiation has no charge and no mass. Neither the nucleon number nor the atomic number of the emitting atom is changed; the nucleus simply become less energetic. Table 1 compares the properties of alpha, beta, and gamma radiation. Note that the penetrating power of gamma rays is extremely high. While a few millimeters of aluminum will stop most β particles, several centimeters of lead are needed to stop γ rays.

Table 1	Common Types of Radiation in Nuclear Reactions				
Radiation	Mass (u)	Charge	Identity	Velocity[a]	Penetrating Power
Alpha (α)	4	2+	He^{2+}	$0.1c$	Very low
Beta (β)	0.00055	1−	e^-	$<0.9c$	Moderate
Gamma (γ)	0	0	High-energy photon	c	Extremely high

[a]c is the speed of light.

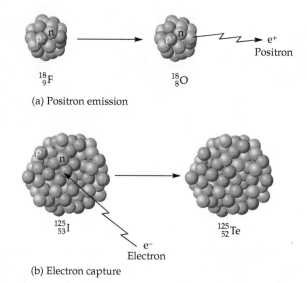

(a) Positron emission

(b) Electron capture

Two other types of radioactive decay are *positron emission* and *electron capture*. These two processes have the same effect on the atomic nucleus, but they occur by different pathways. Both result in a decrease of one in atomic number with no change in nucleon number (Figure 3).

The **positron** (β^+) is a particle equal in mass but opposite in charge to the electron. It is represented as $_{+1}^{0}e$. Fluorine-18 decays by positron emission.

$$^{18}_{9}F \longrightarrow {}^{0}_{+1}e + {}^{18}_{8}O$$

We can envision positron emission as the change of a proton in the nucleus into a neutron and a positron.

$$^{1}_{1}p \longrightarrow {}^{1}_{0}n + {}^{0}_{+1}e$$

After the positron is emitted, the original nucleus has one less proton and one more neutron than it had before. The nucleon number of the product nucleus is the same, but its atomic number has been reduced by one. The emitted positron quickly encounters an electron (there are many electrons in all kinds of matter), and both particles are changing into energy—in this case, two gamma rays.

$$^{0}_{+1}e + {}^{0}_{-1}e \longrightarrow 2{}^{0}_{0}\gamma$$

Electron capture (EC) is a process in which a nucleus absorbs an electron from an inner electron shell, usually the first or second. When an electron from a higher shell drops to the level vacated by the captured electron, an X-ray is released. Once inside the nucleus, the captured electron combines with a proton to form a neutron.

$$^{1}_{1}p + {}^{0}_{-1}e \longrightarrow {}^{1}_{0}n$$

Iodine-125, used in medicine to diagnose pancreatic function and intestinal fat absorption, decays by electron capture.

$$^{125}_{53}I + {}^{0}_{-1}e \longrightarrow {}^{125}_{52}Te$$

Note that, unlike alpha, beta, gamma, or positron emission, electron capture has the electron as a reactant (on the left side) and not a product. Conversion of a proton to a neutron (by the absorbed electron) yields a nucleus with the atomic number lowered by 1 but unchanged in atomic mass. Emission of a positron and absorption of an electron have the same effect on an atomic nucleus (lowering the atomic number by 1), except that positron emission is accompanied by gamma radiation and electron capture by X-radiation. Positron-emitting isotopes and those that undergo electron capture have important medical applications (Section 5).

The five types of radioactive decay are summarized in Table 2.

Table 2 Radioactive Decay and Nuclear Change

Type of Decay	Decay Particle	Particle Mass (u)	Particle Charge	Change in Nucleon Number	Change in Atomic Number
Alpha decay	α	4	2+	Decreases by 4	Decreases by 2
Beta decay	β	0	1−	No change	Increases by 1
Gamma radiation	γ	0	0	No change	No change
Positron emission	β^+	0	1+	No change	Decreases by 1
Electron capture (EC)	e^- absorbed	0	1−	No change	Decreases by 1

Example 1   Balancing Nuclear Equations

Write balanced nuclear equations for the following processes. In each case, identify the product element formed.

a. Plutonium-239 emits an alpha particle when it decays.

b. Protactinium-234 undergoes beta decay.

c. Carbon-11 emits a positron when it decays.

d. Carbon-11 undergoes electron capture.

Solution

a. We start by writing the symbol for plutonium-239 and a partial equation showing that one of the products is an alpha particle (helium nucleus).

$$^{239}_{94}\text{Pu} \longrightarrow {}^{4}_{2}\text{He} + ?$$

For this equation to balance, the other product must have $A = 239 - 4 = 235$ and $Z = 94 - 2 = 92$. The atomic number 92 identifies the element as uranium (U).

$$^{239}_{94}\text{Pu} \longrightarrow {}^{4}_{2}\text{He} + {}^{235}_{92}\text{U}$$

b. We write the symbol for protactinium-234 and a partial equation showing that one of the products is a beta particle (electron).

$$^{234}_{91}\text{Pa} \longrightarrow {}^{0}_{-1}\text{e} + ?$$

The other product must have a nucleon number of 234 and $Z = 92$ to balance the equation. The atomic number identifies this product as another isotope of uranium.

$$^{234}_{91}\text{Pa} \longrightarrow {}^{0}_{-1}\text{e} + {}^{234}_{92}\text{U}$$

c. We write the symbol for carbon-11 and a partial equation showing that one of the products is a positron.

$$^{11}_{6}\text{C} \longrightarrow {}^{0}_{+1}\text{e} + ?$$

To balance the equation, a particle with $A = 11 - 0 = 11$ and $Z = 6 - 1 = 5$ (boron) is required.

$$^{11}_{6}\text{C} \longrightarrow {}^{0}_{+1}\text{e} + {}^{11}_{5}\text{B}$$

d. We write the symbol for carbon-11 and a partial equation showing it capturing an electron.

$$^{11}_{6}\text{C} + {}^{0}_{-1}\text{e} \longrightarrow ?$$

To balance the equation, the product must have $A = 11 + 0 = 11$ and $Z = 6 + (-1) = 5$ (boron).

$$^{11}_{6}\text{C} + {}^{0}_{-1}\text{e} \longrightarrow {}^{11}_{5}\text{B}$$

As we noted previously, positron emission and electron capture result in identical changes in atomic number and, therefore, affect a given nucleus in the same way, as parts **(c)** and **(d)** illustrate for carbon-11. Also note that carbon-11 (and certain other nuclei) can undergo more than one type of radioactive decay.

■ EXERCISE 1

Write balanced nuclear equations for the following processes. In each case, identify the product element formed.

a. Uranium-235 decays by alpha emission.

b. Lead-210 undergoes beta decay.

c. Fluorine-18 decays by positron emission.

d. Oxygen-13 undergoes electron capture.

We noted earlier that nuclear *equations* differ in two ways from ordinary chemical equations. Nuclear *reactions* also exhibit many differences from chemical reactions. Some important ones are summarized in Table 3. Some nuclear reactions also involve processes other than the five simple ones we have discussed here. Regardless, all nuclear equations must be balanced according to nucleon (mass) numbers and atomic numbers. When an unknown particle has an atomic number that does not correspond to an atom, that particle may be a subatomic particle. A list of nuclear symbols for subatomic particles is given in Table 4.

Table 3	Some Differences Between Chemical Reactions and Nuclear Reactions
Chemical Reactions	**Nuclear Reactions**
Atoms retain their identity.	Atoms usually change their identity—from one element to another.
Reactions involve only electrons and usually only outermost electrons.	Reactions involve mainly protons and neutrons. It does not matter what the valence electrons do.
Reaction rates can be increased by raising the temperature.	Reaction rates are unaffected by changes in temperature.
The energy absorbed or given off in reactions is comparatively small.	Reactions sometimes involve enormous changes in energy.
Mass is conserved. The mass of products equals the mass of starting materials.	Huge changes in energy are accompanied by measurable changes in mass ($E = mc^2$).

Table 4	Symbols for Subatomic Particles	
Particle	**Symbol**	**Nuclear Symbol**
Proton	p	$_1^1p$ or $_1^1H$
Neutron	n	$_0^1n$
Electron	e^- or β	$_{-1}^0e$ or $_{-1}^0\beta$
Positron	e^+ or β^+	$_{+1}^0e$ or $_{+1}^0\beta$
Alpha particle	α	$_2^4He$ or $_2^4\alpha$
Beta particle	β or β^-	$_{-1}^0e$ or $_{-1}^0\beta$
Gamma ray	γ	$_0^0\gamma$

Self-Assessment Questions

Identify items 1–4 as one of the following.

a. alpha particle   b. beta particle   c. nucleon number   d. radioactivity

1. an electron
2. atomic mass of 4 u
3. emission of particles and energy from a nucleus
4. number of protons and neutrons in an atom

5. What are the mass and the charge, respectively, of gamma radiation?
   a. 0, – 1   **b.** 0, 0   **c.** 0, +1   **d.** 4, +2

6. What particle is needed to complete the following nuclear equation?

$$^{9}_{4}Be + ? \longrightarrow {}^{12}_{6}C + {}^{1}_{0}n$$

   a. alpha particle   **b.** beta particle   **c.** neutron   **d.** proton

Answers: 1, b; 2, a; 3, d; 4, c; 5, b; 6, a

3 Half-Life and Radioisotopic Dating

Learning Objectives ❯ Solve simple half-life problems. ❯ Use the concept of half-life to solve simple radioisotope dating problems.

Thus far, we have discussed radioactivity as applied to single atoms. In the laboratory, we generally deal with great numbers of atoms—numbers far larger than the number of all the people on Earth. If we could see the nucleus of an individual atom, we could tell whether or not it would undergo radioactive decay by noting its composition. Certain combinations of protons and neutrons are unstable. However, we could not determine *when* the atom would undergo a change. Radioactivity is a random process, generally independent of outside influences.

Half-Life

With large numbers of atoms, the process of radioactive decay becomes more predictable. We can measure the *half-life*, a property characteristic of each radioisotope. The **half-life** of a radioactive isotope is the time it takes for one-half of the original number of atoms to undergo radioactive decay.

Suppose, for example, we had 16.00 mg of the radioactive isotope iodine-131. The half-life of iodine-131 is 8.0 days. This means that in 8.0 days, half the iodine-131, or 8.00 mg, will have decayed, and there will be 8.00 mg left. In another 8.0 days, half of the remaining 8.00 mg will have decayed. After two half-lives, or 16.0 days, then, one-quarter of the original iodine-131, or 4.00 mg, will remain. Note that two half-lives, do not make a whole. The concept of half-life is illustrated by the graph in Figure 4. Half-lives of radio isotopes can differ enormously. The half-life of tellurium-128 is 8×10^{24} y, while that of beryllium-13 is 2.7×10^{-21} s.

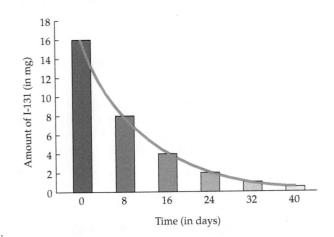

Time (in days)

◀ **Figure 4** The radioactive decay of iodine-131, which has a half-life of 8 days.

Q: *How much of a 32-mg sample of iodine-131 remains after five half-lives have passed?*

The rate of decay is inversely related to half-life. An isotope with a long half-life decays slowly; an isotope with a short half-life decays at a high rate. We measure the rate of decay, also referred to as the isotope's **activity**, in disintegrations per second, a unit called a **becquerel (Bq)**.

We cannot say when *all* the atoms of a radioisotope will have decayed. For most samples, we can assume that the activity is essentially gone after about ten half-lives (when the activity is $\frac{1}{2^{10}} = \frac{1}{1024}$ of the original value). That is, about a thousandth of the original activity remains.

3. Why can't we just burn or dissolve radioactive wastes to get rid of them? The half-life of a radioisotope is a nuclear property that isn't changed by chemical reactions. For example, if we burn radioactive carbon, we get radioactive carbon dioxide as the product. Dissolving radioactive plutonium in nitric acid produces radioactive plutonium nitrate. An isotope will be radioactive for a length of time determined by its half-life—and we can't change the half-life.

We can calculate the fraction of the original isotope that remains after a given number of half-lives from the relationship

$$\text{Fraction remaining} = \frac{1}{2^n}$$

where n is the number of half-lives.

Example 2   Half-Lives

A 4.00-mg sample of cobalt-60, half-life 5.271 y, is to be used for radiation treatment. How much cobalt-60 remains after 15.813 years (three half-lives)?

Solution
The fraction remaining after three half-lives is

$$\frac{1}{2^n} = \frac{1}{2^3} = \frac{1}{2 \times 2 \times 2} = \frac{1}{8}$$

The amount of cobalt-60 remaining is $\frac{1}{8} \times 4.00$ mg $= 0.50$ mg.

■ **EXERCISE 2A**
The half-life of phosphorus-32 is 14.3 days. What percentage of a sample of phosphorus-32 remains after four half-lives?

■ **EXERCISE 2B**
On April 4, 2011, a small fish caught about 50 mi south of the Fukushima nuclear complex had an activity of 4000 Bq of iodine-131 per kilogram. The half-life of iodine-131 is 8.0 d. What was the activity of the isotope **(a)** on April 28, 2011 (three half-lives later)? **(b)** On June 23, 2011 (ten half-lives later)?

CONCEPTUAL Example 3   Time and Radioactive Decay

We cannot determine how long it will take for *all* of a radioactive isotope to decay. For many isotopes, it is assumed that the activity is near zero after about ten half-lives. What mass of a 0.0260-mg sample of mercury-190, half-life 20 min, remains after ten half-lives?

Solution
The fraction remaining after ten half-lives is found in the usual manner.

$$\frac{1}{2^n} = \frac{1}{2^{10}} = \frac{1}{2 \times 2 \times 2 \times 2 \times 2 \times 2 \times 2 \times 2 \times 2 \times 2} = \frac{1}{1024}$$

The amount of mercury-190 remaining is $\frac{1}{1024} \times 0.0260$ mg $= 0.000025$ mg.

■ **EXERCISE 3**
The disposal of some radioactive materials is scheduled according to the rule stated in Conceptual Example 3. Would the rule work **(a)** for a 1.00-g sample of rubidium-87 with an initial decay rate of 3200 Bq? **(b)** For a 1.00-g sample of cobalt-60, which has an initial activity of 4.1×10^{13} Bq? Explain.

Radioisotopic Dating

The half-lives of certain radioisotopes can be used to estimate the ages of rocks and archaeological artifacts. Uranium-238 decays with a half-life of 4.5 billion years. The initial products of this decay are also radioactive, and they and subsequent products continue to decay until lead-206 is formed. By measuring the relative amounts of uranium-238 and lead-206, chemists can estimate the age of a rock. Some of the older rocks on Earth have been found to be 3.0–4.5 billion years old. Moon rocks

Why Are Isotopes Stable—or Unstable?

Most isotopes are radioactive, but some are stable. What factors tend to make an atomic nucleus stable? Stable isotopes tend to have:

1. *Even* numbers of either protons or neutrons or (especially) both. Of the 264 stable isotopes, 157 have *even* numbers of both protons and neutrons, and only four have odd numbers of both protons and neutrons. Elements with even Z have more stable isotopes than do those with odd Z.

2. So-called *magic numbers* of either protons or neutrons. (Magic numbers are 2, 8, 20, 50, 82, and 126.)

3. An atomic number of 83 or less. All isotopes with Z > 83 are radioactive.

4. Fewer, or the same number of, protons as neutrons in the nucleus, and a ratio of neutrons to protons close to 1 if the atomic number is 20 or below. As atomic number gets larger, the stable n/p ratio also increases, up to about 1.5. There is a zone of stability within which the n/p ratio should lie for an atom with a given atomic number.

and meteorites have been dated at a maximum age of about 4.5 billion years. Thus, the age of Earth (and the solar system itself) is generally estimated to be about 4.5 billion years.

The dating of artifacts derived from plants or animals usually involves radioactive carbon-14. Of the carbon on Earth, about 99% is carbon-12 and 1% is carbon-13, and both of these isotopes are stable. However, in the upper atmosphere, carbon-14 is formed by the bombardment of ordinary nitrogen by neutrons from cosmic rays.

$$^{14}_{7}N + ^{1}_{0}n \longrightarrow ^{14}_{6}C + ^{1}_{1}H$$

This process results in a tiny but steady concentration of carbon-14 in the CO_2 molecules of Earth's atmosphere. Plants use CO_2, and animals consume plants and other animals; thus, living things constantly incorporate this isotope into their cells. When organisms die, the incorporation of carbon-14 ceases, and the isotope begins to decay—with a half-life of 5730 years—back to nitrogen-14. We can measure the carbon-14 activity remaining in an artifact of plant or animal origin to determine its age, using the technique called **carbon-14 dating**. For instance, a sample that has half the carbon-14 activity of new plant material is 5730 years old; it has been dead for one half-life. Similarly, an artifact with a fourth of the carbon-14 activity of new plant material is 11,460 years old; it has been dead for two half-lives.

We have assumed that the formation of the carbon-14 isotope has been constant over the years, but this is not quite the case. For the last 7000 years or so, carbon-14 dates do correlate with those obtained from the annual growth rings of trees and with documents of known age. Calibration curves have been constructed from which accurate dates can be determined. Generally, carbon-14 is reasonably accurate for dating objects from about 100 to 50,000 years old. Newer objects may not yet have seen measurable decay of carbon-14. Objects older than 50,000 years have too little of the isotope left for accurate measurement.

Charcoal from the fires of ancient peoples, dated by determining the carbon-14 activity, is used to estimate the age of other artifacts found at the same archaeological sites. For example, carbon dating was used to confirm that ancient Hebrew writing found on a stone tablet unearthed in Israel dates from the ninth century B.C.E.

Tritium, the radioactive isotope of hydrogen, can also be used for dating materials. Its half-life of 12.26 years makes it useful for dating items up to about 100 years old. An interesting application of tritium dating is the dating of brandies. These alcoholic beverages are quite expensive when aged from 10 to 50 years. Tritium dating can be used to check the veracity of advertising claims about the ages of the most expensive kinds.

Many other isotopes are useful for estimating the ages of objects and materials. Several of the more important ones are listed in Table 5.

The Shroud of Turin

The Shroud of Turin is a very old piece of linen cloth, about 4 m long, bearing a faint human likeness. From about C.E. 1350 onward, it had been alleged to be part of the burial shroud of Jesus. However, carbon-14 dating studies in 1988 by three different laboratories indicated that the flax used to make the cloth was not grown until sometime between C.E. 1260 and 1390; therefore, the cloth could not possibly have existed at the time of Jesus. Unlike the Dead Sea Scrolls, which were shown by carbon-14 dating to be authentic records from a civilization that existed about 2000 years ago, the Shroud of Turin has been shown to be less than 800 years old. It is generally thought to be a work of art produced around that time.

Table 5	Several Isotopes Used in Radioactive Dating		
Isotope	**Half-Life (years)**	**Useful Range**	**Dating Applications**
Carbon-14	5730	100 to 50,000 years	Charcoal, organic material
Hydrogen-3 (tritium)	12.26	1 to 100 years	Aged wines and brandies
Lead-210	22	1 to 75 years	Skeletal remains
Potassium-40	1.25×10^9	10,000 years to the oldest Earth samples	Rocks, Earth's crust, the moon's crust
Rhenium-187	4.3×10^{10}	4×10^7 years to the oldest samples in the universe	Meteorites
Uranium-238	4.51×10^9	10^7 years to the oldest Earth samples	Rocks, the Earth's crust

Example 4 — Radioisotopic Dating

An old wooden implement shows carbon-14 activity that is one-eighth that of new wood. How old is the artifact? The half-life of carbon-14 is 5730 y.

Solution
Using the relationship

$$\text{Fraction remaining} = \frac{1}{2^n}$$

we see that one-eighth is $\frac{1}{2^n}$, where $n = 3$; that is, the fraction $\frac{1}{8}$ is $\frac{1}{2^3}$. The carbon-14 has gone through three half-lives. The wood is therefore about $3 \times 5730 = 17{,}190$ y old.

■ EXERCISE 4
Calculate the approximate age of each of the following. (a) Human remains have been preserved for centuries in the bogs of Northern Europe. How old is a bog body that has carbon-14 activity one-fourth that of living tissue? The half-life of carbon-14 is 5730 y. (b) How old is a bottle of brandy that has a tritium activity one-sixteenth that of new brandy? The half-life of tritium (hydrogen-3) is 12.26 years.

Self-Assessment Questions

1. A patient is given a 48-mg dose of technetium-99m (half-life 6.0 h) to treat a brain cancer. How much of it will remain in his body after 36 h?
   - **a.** 0.75 mg
   - **b.** 1.5 mg
   - **c.** 3.0 mg
   - **d.** 12 mg

2. What is the half-life of silver-112 if a 10.0-g sample decays to 2.5 g in 12.4 h?
   - **a.** 1.6 h
   - **b.** 3.1 h
   - **c.** 6.2 h
   - **d.** 12.4 h

3. Of a 64.0-g sample of strontium-90 (half-life 28.5 y) produced by a nuclear explosion, what mass in grams would remain unchanged after 285 y?
   - **a.** 0.000 g
   - **b.** 0.000625 g
   - **c.** 0.00625 g
   - **d.** 0.0625 g

4. Lead-210 (half-life 22.26 y) can be used to date skeletal remains. About how old is a bone that has an activity of 2.0 Bq if new bone has an activity of 16 Bq?
   a. 7.4 y   **b.** 44.5 y   **c.** 67 y   **d.** 89 y

5. About how old is a piece of wood from an aboriginal burial site that has a carbon-14 (half-life 5730 y) activity of 3.9 counts/min per gram of carbon? Assume that the carbon-14 activity of the wood was 15.6 counts per minute per gram of carbon at the time of the burial.
   a. 2865 y   **b.** 11,460 y   **c.** 17,190 y   **d.** 22,920 y

Answers: 1, a; 2, c; 3, d; 4, c; 5, b

Isotopic Signatures

For most chemical reactions, isotopes are unimportant. However, differences in isotopes can be quite important to some investigations. Isotopes' variance in mass affects their rates of reaction, with lighter isotopes generally moving a bit faster than heavier ones. This difference can lead to a measurable characteristic called an *isotopic signature* in an investigated material. For example, the ratio of carbon-13 to carbon-12 in materials formed by photosynthesis is less than that isotopic ratio in inorganic carbonates.

The ratio of oxygen-18 to oxygen-16 depends on the extent of evaporation that water has undergone because water molecules with oxygen-18 atoms are heavier and thus vaporize less readily than do water molecules with oxygen-16 atoms. This difference is less pronounced at higher temperatures. As oxygen is incorporated into the calcium carbonate shells of aquatic organisms, the isotopic ratio in the shells shifts. Fossilized shells thus provide a chronological record of the temperature of the water in which the organisms lived. The oxygen isotope ratio in the atmosphere varies with the season and with geographic location. This variation allows scientists to determine the location in which a material originated.

The ratio of nitrogen-14 to nitrogen-15 is different for herbivores and carnivores, because organisms higher in the food chain tend to concentrate the nitrogen-15 isotope in their tissues. Such variations enable scientists to determine much about the diet of people from ages past.

4 Artificial Transmutation

Learning Objective > Write a nuclear equation for a transmutation, and identify the product element formed.

During the Middle Ages, alchemists tried to turn base metals, such as lead, into gold. However, they were trying to do it chemically and were therefore doomed to failure because chemical reactions involve only atoms' outer electrons. **Transmutation** (changing one element into another) requires altering the *nucleus*.

Thus far, we have considered only natural forms of radioactivity. Nuclear reactions can also be brought about by bombardment of stable nuclei with alpha particles, neutrons, or other subatomic particles. These particles, given sufficient energy, can penetrate a stable nucleus and result in some kind of radioactive emission. Just as in natural radioactive processes, one element is changed into another. Because the change would not have occurred naturally, the process is called *artificial transmutation*.

In 1919, a few years after his famous gold-foil experiment, Ernest Rutherford reported on the bombardment of a variety of light elements with alpha particles. One such experiment, in which he bombarded nitrogen, resulted in the production of protons, as shown in this balanced nuclear equation.

$$^{14}_{7}\text{N} + {}^{4}_{2}\text{He} \longrightarrow {}^{17}_{8}\text{O} + {}^{1}_{1}\text{H}$$

(The hydrogen nucleus is simply a proton, which can be represented by the symbol $^{1}_{1}\text{H}$.) This provided the first empirical verification of the existence of protons in atomic nuclei, which Rutherford had first postulated in 1914.

Recall that Eugen Goldstein had produced protons in his gas-discharge tube experiments in 1886. The significance of Rutherford's experiment lay in the fact that he obtained protons from the *nucleus* of an atom other than hydrogen, thus establishing that protons are constituents of nuclei. Rutherford's experiment was the first induced nuclear reaction and the first example of artificial transmutation. In producing protons, he also changed nitrogen into oxygen.

Example 5 — Artificial Transmutation Equations

When potassium-39 is bombarded with neutrons, chlorine-36 is produced. What other particle is emitted?

$$^{39}_{19}\text{K} + ^{1}_{0}\text{n} \longrightarrow ^{36}_{17}\text{Cl} + ?$$

Solution

To determine the particle, we need a balanced nuclear equation. To balance the equation, the unknown particle must have $A = 4$ and $Z = 2$—it is an alpha particle.

$$^{39}_{19}\text{K} + ^{1}_{0}\text{n} \longrightarrow ^{36}_{17}\text{Cl} + ^{4}_{2}\text{He}$$

■ EXERCISE 5A

Technetium-97 is produced by bombarding molybdenum-96 with a deuteron (a hydrogen-2 nucleus). What other particle is emitted?

$$^{96}_{42}\text{Mo} + ^{2}_{1}\text{H} \longrightarrow ^{97}_{43}\text{Tc} + ?$$

■ EXERCISE 5B

A team of scientists wants to form uranium-235 by bombarding a nucleus of another element with an alpha particle. They expect a neutron to be produced along with the uranium-235 nucleus. What nucleus must be bombarded with the alpha particle?

▲ Ernest Rutherford (1871–1937) carried out the first nuclear bombardment experiment. Element 104 was named rutherfordium (Rf) in his honor.

Self-Assessment Questions

1. What isotope is formed in the following artificial transmutation?

   $$^{14}_{7}\text{N} + ^{1}_{0}\text{n} \longrightarrow ^{1}_{1}\text{H} + ?$$

   a. carbon-12   **b.** carbon-14   **c.** nitrogen-15   **d.** oxygen-15

2. What isotope is formed in the following artificial transmutation?

   $$^{9}_{4}\text{Be} + ^{1}_{1}\text{H} \longrightarrow ^{4}_{2}\text{He} + ?$$

   a. boron-9   **b.** boron-10   **c.** lithium-6   **d.** lithium-7

3. What isotope is formed in the following artificial transmutation?

   $$^{239}_{94}\text{Pu} + ^{4}_{2}\text{He} \longrightarrow ^{1}_{0}\text{n} + ?$$

   a. americium-242   **b.** berkelium-242   **c.** curium-242   **d.** curium-243

Answers: 1, b; 2, c; 3, c

5 Uses of Radioisotopes

Learning Objective ❯ List some applications of radioisotopes.

Most of the 3000 known radioisotopes are produced by artificial transmutation of stable isotopes. The value of both naturally occurring and artificial radioisotopes goes far beyond their contributions to our knowledge of chemistry.

Radioisotopes in Industry and Agriculture

Scientists in a wide variety of fields use radioisotopes as **tracers** in physical, chemical, and biological systems. Isotopes of a given element, whether radioactive or not, behave nearly identically in chemical and physical processes. Because radioactive isotopes are easily detected through their decay products, it is relatively easy to trace their movement, even through a complicated system. For example, tracing radioisotopes allows as to do the following:

- **Detect leaks in underground pipes.** Suppose there is a leak in a pipe that is buried beneath a concrete floor. We could locate the leak by digging up extensive areas of the floor, or we could add a small amount of radioactive material to liquid poured into the drain and trace the flow of the liquid with a Geiger counter (an instrument that detects radioactivity). Once we located the leak, only a small area of the floor would have to be dug up to repair it. A compound containing a short-lived isotope (for example, $^{131}_{53}I$, half-life 8.04 days) is usually employed for this purpose.

- **Measure thickness of sheet metal during production.** Radiation from a beta emitter is allowed to pass through sheet metal on the production line. The amount of radiation that passes through a sheet is related to its thickness.
- **Determine frictional wear in piston rings.** The ring is subjected to neutron bombardment, which converts some of the carbon in the steel to carbon-14. Wear in the piston ring is assessed by the rate at which the carbon-14 appears in the engine oil.
- **Determine the uptake of phosphorus and its distribution in plants.** This can be done by incorporating phosphorus-32, a β^- emitter with a half-life of 14.3 d, into phosphate fertilizers fed to plants.

Radioisotopes are also used to study the effectiveness of weed killers, compare the nutritional value of various feeds, determine optimal methods for insect control, and monitor the fate and persistence of pesticides in soil and groundwater.

One of the most successful applications of radioisotopes in agriculture involves inducing heritable genetic alterations known as *mutations*. Exposing seeds or other parts of plants to neutrons or gamma rays increases the likelihood of genetic mutations. At first glance, this technique may not seem very promising. However, genetic variability is vital, not only to improve varieties but also to protect species from extinction. Some hybrid plants, such as seedless watermelons and bananas, are sterile. The lack of genetic variability among these plants may place the entire population at risk.

Radioisotopes are also used to irradiate foodstuffs as a method of preservation (Figure 5). The radiation destroys microorganisms and enzymes that cause foods to spoil. Irradiated food shows little change in taste or appearance. Some people are concerned about possible harmful effects of chemical substances produced by the radiation, but there has been no good evidence of harm to laboratory animals fed irradiated food or any known adverse effects in humans living in countries where food irradiation has been used for years. No residual radiation remains in a food after irradiation because gamma rays do not have nearly enough energy to change nuclei.

Radioisotopes in Medicine

Nuclear medicine involves two distinct uses of radioisotopes: therapeutic and diagnostic. In a therapeutic application, an attempt is made to treat or cure disease with radiation. The diagnostic use of radioisotopes is aimed at obtaining information about the state of a patient's health.

William Paul Quick

▲ Scientists can trace the uptake of phosphorus by a green plant by adding a compound containing some phosphorus-32 to the applied fertilizer. When the plant is later placed on photographic film, radiation from the phosphorus isotopes exposes the film, much as light does. This type of exposure, called a *radiograph*, shows the distribution of phosphorus in the plant.

4. Do irradiated foods give off radiation? Irradiated foods have absorbed energy in the form of gamma rays. But the foods are *not* radioactive.

◀ **Figure 5** Exposure to gamma radiation delays the decay of strawberries. Those on the right were irradiated; the ones on the left were not.

Q: *Are the strawberries on the right radioactive?*

Richard Megna/Fundamental Photographs

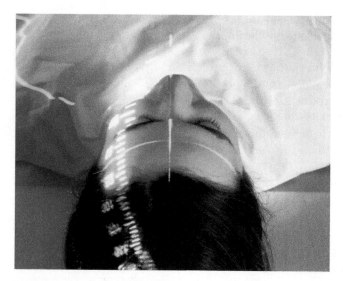

▲ It DOES Matter!

The difference between a radioactive isotope and the alpha, beta, gamma, or positron radiation that it produces is very important and often misunderstood. A radioisotope such as iodine-131 or radon-222, when absorbed by the human body, can cause great harm because the radiation continues to be released as the isotope decays. However, matter exposed to ionizing radiation simply absorbs that energy, causing a chemical change. A patient undergoing gamma-radiation treatment does *not* become radioactive.

5. Are we exposed to dangerous radiation during X-rays and other medical procedures? A number of medical procedures do use ionizing radiation or radioisotopes, but the amount of radiation is kept to a minimum. The hazard of the ionizing radiation is ordinarily much less than the risk due to a lack of diagnosis or treatment!

Table 6 lists some radioisotopes in common use in medicine. The list is necessarily incomplete, but it should give you an idea of their importance. The claim that nuclear medicine has saved many more lives than nuclear bombs have taken is not an idle one.

Cancer is not one disease but many. Some forms are particularly susceptible to radiation therapy. The aim of **radiation therapy** is to destroy cancerous cells before too much damage is done to healthy tissue. Radiation is most lethal to rapidly reproducing cells, and rapid reproduction is the characteristic of cancer cells that allows radiation therapy to be successful. Radiation is carefully aimed at cancerous tissue while minimizing the exposure of normal cells. If the cancer cells are killed by the destructive effects of the radiation, the malignancy is halted.

Patients undergoing radiation therapy often get sick from the treatment. Nausea and vomiting are the usual early symptoms of radiation sickness. Radiation therapy can also interfere with the replenishment of white blood cells and thus increase patients' susceptibility to infection.

Radioisotopes used for diagnostic purposes provide information about the functioning of some part of the body or about the type or extent of an illness. For example, radioactive iodine-131 is used to determine the size, shape, and activity of the thyroid gland, as well as to treat cancers in this gland and to control its hyperactivity. Small doses are used for diagnostic purposes, and large doses for treatment of thyroid cancer. After the patient drinks a solution of potassium iodide incorporating iodine-131, the iodide ions become concentrated in the thyroid. A detector showing the differential uptake of the isotope is used in diagnosis. The resulting

Table 6	Some Radioisotopes and Their Medical Applications		
Isotope	**Name**	**Half-Life[a]**	**Use**
^{11}C	Carbon-11	20.39 min	Brain scans
^{51}Cr	Chromium-51	27.8 d	Blood volume determination
^{57}Co	Cobalt-57	270 d	Measuring vitamin B_{12} uptake
^{60}Co	Cobalt-60	5.271 y	Radiation cancer therapy
^{153}Gd	Gadolinium-153	242 d	Determining bone density
^{67}Ga	Gallium-67	78.1 h	Scan for lung tumors
^{131}I	Iodine-131	8.040 d	Thyroid diagnoses and therapy
^{192}Ir	Iridium-192	74 d	Breast cancer therapy
^{59}Fe	Iron-59	44.496 d	Detection of anemia
^{32}P	Phosphorus-32	14.3 d	Detection of skin cancer or eye tumors
^{238}Pu	Plutonium-238	86 y	Provision of power in pacemakers
^{226}Ra	Radium-226	1600 y	Radiation therapy for cancer
^{75}Se	Selenium-75	120 d	Pancreas scans
^{24}Na	Sodium-24	14.659 h	Locating obstructions in blood flow
^{99m}Tc	Technetium-99m	6.0 h	Imaging of brain, liver, bone marrow, kidney, lung, or heart
^{201}Tl	Thallium-201	73 h	Detecting heart problems during treadmill stress test
^{3}H	Tritium	12.26 y	Determining total body water
^{133}Xe	Xenon-133	5.27 d	Lung imaging

[a] Abbreviations: y, years; d, days; h, hours; min, minutes.

photoscan can pinpoint the location of tumors or other abnormalities in the thyroid. In cancer treatment, radiation from therapeutic (large) doses of iodine-131 kills the thyroid cells in which the radioisotope has concentrated.

The radioisotope gadolinium-153 is used to determine bone mineralization. Its widespread use is an indication of the large number of people, mostly women, who suffer from osteoporosis (reduction in the quantity of bone) as they grow older. Gadolinium-153 gives off two types of radiation: gamma rays and X-rays. A scanning device compares these types of radiation after they pass through bone. Bone density is then determined from the difference in absorption of the rays.

Technetium-99m is used in a variety of diagnostic tests (Figure 6). The *m* stands for *metastable*, which means that this isotope gives up some energy when it changes to a more stable version of technetium-99 (which has the same atomic number and same atomic mass). The energy it gives up is in the form of a gamma ray.

(a)

(b)

Bristol Myers Squibb Medical Imaging MA

◄ **Figure 6** Gamma-ray imaging using technetium-99m. Directional slices through (a) a healthy human heart and (b) a diseased heart. The lighter regions of the images indicate regions receiving adequate blood flow.

$$^{99m}_{43}\text{Tc} \longrightarrow ^{99}_{43}\text{Tc} + \gamma$$

Note that the decay of technetium-99m produces no alpha or beta particles that could cause unnecessary damage to the body. Technetium-99m also has a short half-life (6.0 h), which means that the radioactivity does not linger very long in the body after the scan has been completed. With so short a half-life, use of the isotope must be carefully planned. In fact, technetium-99m is not what is purchased by medical labs. Technetium-99m is formed by the decay of molybdenum-99.

$$^{99}_{42}\text{Mo} \longrightarrow ^{99m}_{43}\text{Tc} + ^{0}_{-1}\text{e} + \gamma$$

A container of this molybdenum isotope is obtained, and the decay product, technetium-99m, is "milked" from the container as needed.

Using modern computer technology, *positron emission tomography (PET)* can measure dynamic processes occurring in the body, such as blood flow or the rate at which oxygen or glucose is being metabolized. For example, PET scans have shown that the brain of a schizophrenic metabolizes only about one-fifth as much glucose as a normal brain. These scans can also reveal metabolic changes that occur in the brain during tactile learning (learning by the sense of touch). PET scans can also pinpoint the area of brain damage that triggers severe epileptic seizures.

Compounds incorporating a positron-emitting isotope, such as carbon-11 or oxygen-15, are inhaled or injected before the scan. Before the emitted positron can travel very far in the body, it encounters an electron (numerous in any ordinary matter), and two gamma rays are produced, exiting from the body in exactly opposite directions.

$$^{11}_{6}\text{C} \longrightarrow ^{11}_{5}\text{B} + ^{0}_{+1}\text{e}$$

$$^{0}_{+1}\text{e} + ^{0}_{-1}\text{e} \longrightarrow 2\gamma$$

▶ **Figure 7** Modern computer technology used for medical diagnosis. (a) Patient undergoing positron emission tomography (PET), a technique that uses radioisotopes to scan internal organs. (b) Images created by PET scanning, showing parts of the brain involved in different functions.

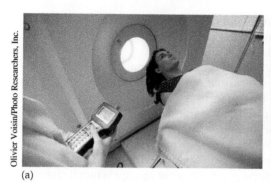

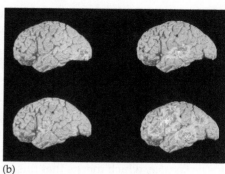

(a)

(b)

6. Can you get radiation sickness from someone who has been exposed to radiation? Alpha, beta and gamma rays, X-rays, and positrons that are absorbed by the body do cause cell damage, but by and large they are *not* energetic enough to create radioactive isotopes. One can no more "catch" radiation sickness from a person exposed to radiation than one can "catch" a sunburn.

Detectors, positioned on opposite sides of the patient, record the gamma rays. An image of an area in the body is formed using computerized calculations of the points at which annihilation of positrons and electrons occurs (Figure 7).

Example 6   **Positron Emission Equations**

One of the isotopes used to perform PET scans is oxygen-15, a positron emitter. What other isotope is formed when oxygen-15 decays?

Solution
First, we write the nuclear equation

$$^{15}_{8}O \longrightarrow {}^{0}_{+1}e + ?$$

The nucleon number, A, does not change, but the atomic number, Z, does: $8 - 1 = 7$. The product isotope is nitrogen-15.

$$^{15}_{8}O \longrightarrow {}^{0}_{+1}e + {}^{15}_{7}N$$

■ **EXERCISE 6**
Phosphorus-30 is a positron-emitting radioisotope suitable for doing PET scans. What other isotope is formed when phosphorus-30 decays?

Self-Assessment Questions

1. Iodine-131 is sometimes used for detecting leaks in underground pipes because
   a. it has a short half-life
   b. it is highly penetrating
   c. it is nontoxic
   d. its radiation is harmless

2. What is used to irradiate foodstuffs to extend shelf life?
   a. alpha particles   **b.** beta particles
   c. gamma rays   **d.** microwaves

For items 3–7, match each radioisotope with a major use.
3. cobalt-60   (a) bone density
4. gadolinium-153   (b) brain images
5. iodine-131   (c) heart problems
6. technetium-99m   (d) radiation therapy
7. thallium-201   (e) thyroid disorders

8. What form of radiation is detected in PET scans?
   a. beta   **b.** gamma   **c.** positron   **d.** X-rays

Answers: 1, a; 2, c; 3, d; 4, a; 5, e; 6, b; 7, c; 8, c

6 Penetrating Power of Radiation

Learning Objective ❯ Describe the nature of materials needed to block alpha, beta, and gamma radiation.

The danger of radiation to living organisms comes from its potential for damaging cells and tissues. The ability to inflict injury relates to the penetrating power of the radiation. The two aspects of nuclear medicine just discussed (therapeutic and diagnostic) are also dependent on the penetrating power of various types of radiation.

All other things being equal, the more massive the particle, the less its penetrating power. *Alpha particles*, which are helium nuclei with a mass of 4 u, are the least penetrating of the three main types of radiation. *Beta particles*, which are identical to the almost massless electrons, are somewhat more penetrating. *Gamma rays*, like X-rays, have no mass; they are considerably more penetrating than the other two types.

But all other things are not always equal. The faster a particle moves or the more energetic the radiation is, the more penetrating power it has.

It may seem contrary to common sense that the biggest particles make the least headway. But keep in mind that penetrating power reflects the ability of radiation to make its way through a sample of matter. It is as if you were trying to roll some rocks through a field of boulders. The alpha particle acts as if it were a boulder itself. Because of its size, it cannot get very far before it bumps into and is stopped by other boulders. The beta particle acts as if it were a small stone. It can sneak between and perhaps ricochet off boulders until it makes its way farther into the field. The gamma ray can be compared with a grain of sand that can get through the smallest openings.

The danger of a specific type of radiation to human tissue depends on the location of the radiation's source as well as on its penetrating power. If the radioactive substance is outside the body, alpha particles are the least dangerous; they have low penetrating power and are stopped by the outer layer of skin. Beta particles are also usually stopped before they reach vital organs. Gamma rays readily pass through tissues, and so an external gamma source can be quite dangerous. People working with radioactive materials can protect themselves through one or both of the following actions:

- Move away from the source. The intensity of radiation decreases with distance from the source.

- Use shielding. A sheet of paper can stop most alpha particles, and a block of wood or a thin sheet of aluminum can stop most beta particles, but it takes a meter of concrete or several centimeters of lead to stop most gamma rays (Figure 8).

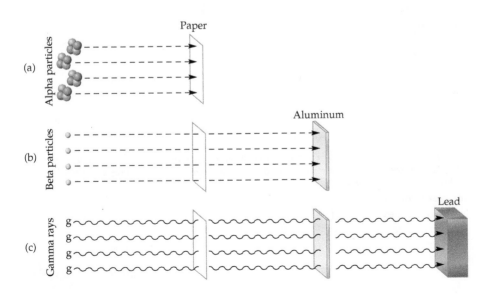

◀ **Figure 8** The relative penetrating power of alpha, beta, and gamma radiation. Alpha particles are stopped by a sheet of paper (a). Beta particles will not penetrate a sheet of aluminum (b). It takes several centimeters of lead to block gamma rays (c).

When the radioactive source is *inside* the body, as in the case of many medical applications, the situation is reversed. The nonpenetrating alpha particles can do great damage. All such particles are trapped within the body, which must then absorb all the energy the particles release. Alpha particles inflict all their damage in a tiny area because they do not travel far. Therefore, getting an alpha-emitting therapeutic radioisotope close to the targeted cells is vital.

Beta particles distribute their damage over a somewhat larger area because they travel farther. Tissue may recover from limited damage spread over a large area; it is less likely to survive concentrated damage.

Many diagnostic applications rely on the highly penetrating power of gamma rays. In most cases, the radiation created inside the body must be detected by instruments outside the body, so a minimum of absorption is desirable.

CONCEPTUAL Example 7   Radiation Hazard

Most modern smoke detectors contain a tiny amount of americium-241, a solid element that is an alpha emitter. The americium is in a chamber that includes thin aluminum shielding, and the device is usually mounted on a ceiling. Rate the radiation hazard of this device in normal use as (a) high, (b) moderate, or (c) very low. Explain your choice.

Solution
Alpha particles have very little penetrating ability—they are stopped by a sheet of paper or a layer of skin. The emitted alpha particles cannot exit the detector's chamber, because even thin metal is more than sufficient to absorb them. Even if alpha particles could escape, they would likely be stopped by the air after a short distance or by the dead cells of your skin. Therefore, the radiation hazard is rated (c)—very low.

■ EXERCISE 7
Radon-222 is a gas that can diffuse from the ground into homes. Like americium-241, it is an alpha emitter. Is the radiation hazard from radon-222 likely to be higher or lower than that from a smoke detector? Explain.

Self-Assessment Questions

1. Which of the following pairs represent the *most* and *least* (most/least) penetrating types of radiation?
   a. alpha/gamma
   b. beta/gamma
   c. gamma/alpha
   d. X-rays/beta

2. Which form of radiation could not readily penetrate a sheet of paper?
   a. alpha
   b. beta
   c. gamma
   d. all of these

3. A Geiger counter registered 50 Bq of activity from an unknown type of radiation. A piece of paper inserted between the source and the counter caused the reading to drop to about 2 Bq. The radiation was mostly
   a. alpha particles
   b. beta particles
   c. gamma rays
   d. X-rays

Answers: 1, c; 2, a; 3, a

7 Energy from the Nucleus

Learning Objectives ❯ Explain where nuclear energy comes from. ❯ Describe the difference between fission and fusion.

We have seen that radioactivity—quiet and invisible—can be beneficial or dangerous. A much more dramatic—and equally paradoxical—aspect of nuclear chemistry is the release of nuclear energy by either *fission* (splitting of heavy nuclei into smaller nuclei) or *fusion* (combining of light nuclei to form heavier ones).

Einstein and the Equivalence of Mass and Energy

The potential power in the nucleus was established by Albert Einstein, a famous and most unusual scientist. Whereas most scientists work with glassware and instruments in laboratories, Einstein worked with a pencil and a notepad. By 1905, at the age of 26, he had already worked out his special theory of relativity and developed his famous **mass–energy equation**, in which mass (m) is multiplied by the square of the speed of light (c).

$$E = mc^2$$

The equation suggests that mass and energy are equivalent—just two different aspects of the same thing—and that a little bit of mass can yield enormous energy. The atomic bombs that destroyed Hiroshima and Nagasaki (Section 8) in World War II converted less than an ounce of matter into energy.

A chemical reaction that gives off heat must lose mass in the process, but the change in mass is far too small to measure. Reaction energy must be enormous—at the level of the energy given off by nuclear explosions—for the mass loss to be measurable. (If every atom in a 1-kg lump of coal became energy, it could produce 25 billion kWh of electricity—enough to keep a 100-W lightbulb going for 29 million years. Burning 1 kg of coal in a conventional power plant produces only enough energy to keep the bulb shining for 67 hours.)

Binding Energy

Nuclear fission releases the tremendous amounts of energy produced by atomic bombs and in nuclear power plants. Where does all this energy come from? It is locked inside the atomic nucleus. When protons and neutrons combine to form atomic nuclei, a small amount of mass is converted to energy. This is the **binding energy** that holds the nucleons together in the nucleus. For example, the helium nucleus contains two protons and two neutrons. The masses of these four particles add up to $2 \times 1.0073\,u + 2 \times 1.0087\,u = 4.0320\,u$ (Figure 9). However, the actual mass of the helium nucleus is only 4.0015 u, and the missing mass—called the *mass defect*—amounts to 0.0305 u. Using Einstein's equation $E = mc^2$, we can calculate (see Problem 55) a value of 28.3 million electron volts (28 MeV; $1\,MeV = 1.6022 \times 10^{-13}\,J$) for the binding energy of the helium nucleus. This is the amount of energy it would take to separate one helium nucleus into two protons and two neutrons.

When the binding energy per nucleon is calculated for all the elements and plotted against nucleon number, a graph such as that in Figure 10 is obtained. The elements with the highest binding energies per nucleon have the most stable nuclei. They include iron and elements with nucleon members close to that of iron. When uranium atoms undergo nuclear fission, they split into atoms with higher binding energies. In other words, the fission reaction converts large atoms into smaller ones with greater nuclear stability.

We can also see from Figure 10 that even more energy can be obtained by combining small atoms, such as hydrogen or deuterium, to form larger atoms with more stable nuclei. This kind of reaction is called **nuclear fusion**. It is what happens when a hydrogen bomb explodes, and it is also the source of the sun's energy.

▲ Albert Einstein (1879–1955). Element 99 was named einsteinium (Es) in his honor.

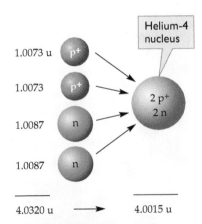

▲ **Figure 9** Nuclear binding energy in $_2^4$He. The mass of a helium-4 nucleus is 4.0015 u, which is 0.0305 u less than the masses of two protons and two neutrons. The missing mass is equivalent to the binding energy of the helium-4 nucleus.

▶ **Figure 10** Nuclear stability is greatest for iron and elements near iron in the periodic table. Fission of very large nuclei or fusion of very small ones results in greater nuclear stability.

Q: *Which process, fission of uranium nuclei or fusion of hydrogen nuclei, releases more energy?*

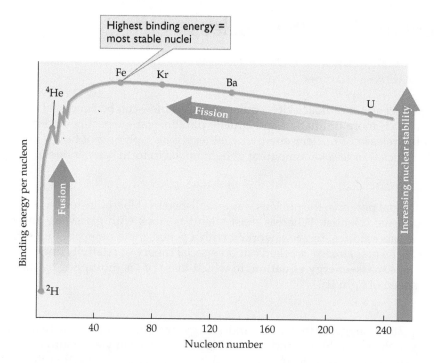

▲ Enrico Fermi (1901–1954). Element 100 was named fermium (Fm) in his honor.

▲ Lise Meitner (1878–1968). Element 109 was named meitnerium (Mt) in her honor.

Nuclear Fission

In 1934, the Italian scientists Enrico Fermi and Emilio Segrè (1905–1989) bombarded uranium atoms with neutrons. They were trying to make elements with higher atomic numbers than uranium, which then had the highest known atomic number. To their surprise, they found four radioactive species among the products. One was presumably element 93, formed by the initial conversion of uranium-238 to uranium-239, which then underwent beta decay.

$$^{238}_{92}\text{U} + ^{1}_{0}\text{n} \longrightarrow ^{239}_{92}\text{U}$$

$$^{239}_{92}\text{U} \longrightarrow ^{239}_{93}\text{Np} + ^{0}_{-1}\text{e}$$

They were unable to explain the remaining radioactivity.

When repeating the Fermi–Segrè experiment in 1938, German chemists Otto Hahn (1879–1968) and Fritz Strassman (1902–1980) were perplexed to find isotopes of barium among the many reaction products. Hahn wrote to Lise Meitner, his former longtime colleague, to ask what she thought about these strange results.

Lise Meitner was an Austrian physicist who had worked with Hahn in Berlin. Because she was Jewish, she fled to Sweden when the Nazis took over Austria in 1938. On hearing about Hahn's work, she noted that barium atoms were only about half the size of uranium atoms. Was it possible that the uranium nuclei might be splitting into fragments? She made some calculations that convinced her that the uranium nuclei had indeed been split apart. Her nephew, Otto Frisch (1904–1979), was visiting for the winter holidays, and they discussed this discovery with great excitement. It was Frisch who later coined the term **nuclear fission** (Figure 11).

Frisch was working with Niels Bohr at the University of Copenhagen, and when he returned to Denmark, he took the news of the fission reaction to Bohr, who happened to be going to the United States to attend a physics conference. The discussions in the corridors about this new reaction would be the most important talks to take place at that meeting.

Meanwhile, Enrico Fermi had just received the 1938 Nobel Prize in physics. Because Fermi's wife, Laura, was Jewish, and the fascist Italian dictator Mussolini was an ally of Hitler, Fermi accepted the award in Stockholm and then immediately fled with Laura and their children to the United States. Thus, by 1939, the United States had received news about the German discovery of nuclear fission and had also acquired from Italy one of the world's foremost nuclear scientists.

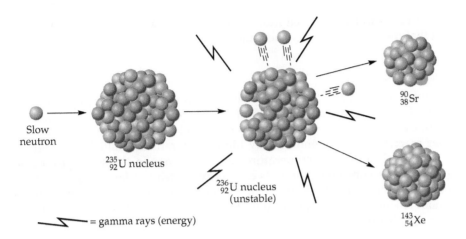

◀ Figure 11 One possible way a uranium nucleus can undergo fission. The neutrons produced by the fission reactions can split other uranium nuclei, thus sustaining a chain reaction.

Q: *If each of the neutrons emitted by the ^{236}U nucleus caused another ^{235}U nucleus to split in the way shown here, how many more neutrons would be released?*

Nuclear Chain Reaction

Leo Szilard (1898–1964) was one of the first scientists to realize that nuclear fission could occur as a chain reaction. Szilard had been born in Hungary and educated in Germany, but he came to the United States in 1937 as one of the many Jewish refugees. He saw that neutrons released in the fission of one atom could trigger the fission of other uranium atoms, thus setting off a **chain reaction** (Figure 12). Because massive amounts of energy could be obtained from the fission of uranium, he saw that the chain reaction might be used in a bomb with tremendous explosive force.

Aware of the destructive forces that could be produced and concerned that Germany might develop such a bomb, Szilard prevailed on Einstein to sign a letter to

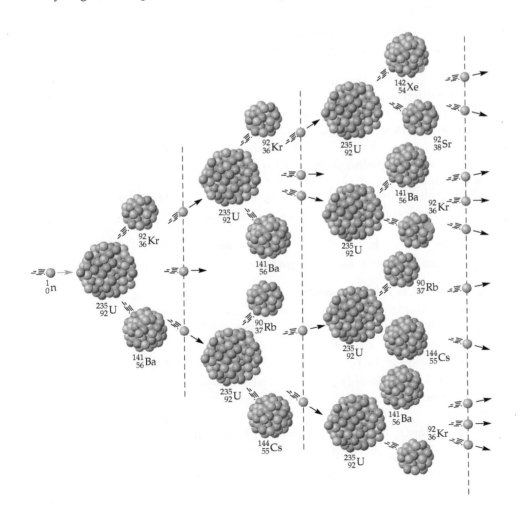

◀ Figure 12 Schematic representation of a nuclear chain reaction. Neutrons released in the fission of one uranium-235 nucleus can strike other uranium-235 nuclei, causing them to split and release more neutrons as well as a variety of other nuclei. For simplicity, some fission fragments are not shown.

President Franklin D. Roosevelt indicating the importance of the discovery. It was critical that the U.S. government act quickly.

Thermonuclear Reactions

The chapter opening mentioned that the sun is a nuclear power plant vital to life on Earth. However, the nuclear reactions that take place in the sun are somewhat different from the ones we have discussed throughout this chapter. These **thermonuclear reactions** require enormously high temperatures (millions of degrees) to initiate them. The intense temperatures and pressures in the sun cause nuclei to fuse and release enormous amounts of energy. Instead of large nuclei being split into smaller fragments (fission), small nuclei are fused into larger ones (fusion). The main reaction in the sun is thought to be the fusion of four hydrogen nuclei to produce one helium nucleus and two positrons.

$$4{}^{1}_{1}H \longrightarrow {}^{4}_{2}He + 2\ {}^{0}_{+1}e$$

Fusion of 1 g of hydrogen releases an amount of energy equivalent to the burning of nearly 20 tons of coal. Every second, the sun fuses 600 tons of hydrogen, producing millions of times more energy than has been produced on Earth in the entire history of humankind. Much current research is aimed at reproducing such a reaction in the laboratory, by using ultrapowerful magnets to contain the intense heat required for ignition. To date, however, fusion reactions on Earth have been limited to the uncontrolled reactions in explosion tests of hydrogen (thermonuclear) bombs and to small amounts of energy produced by very expensive experimental fusion reactors.

Self-Assessment Questions

Look at the graph in Figure 10 to answer questions 1–3.
1. Helium has a particularly high binding energy per nucleon, which means that it
   a. is especially unstable compared to H and Li
   b. is more stable than H and Li
   c. will readily fuse into larger nuclei
   d. will readily split into hydrogen-2 atoms

2. The most stable nuclei are those of
   a. Ba   b. He   c. Fe   d. U

3. Nuclei with nuclear numbers greater than that of iron are
   a. all radioactive   b. increasingly stable
   c. less stable than iron   d. easily split into smaller nuclei

4. Which equation explains why the products of fission have less mass than the original substances?
   a. $E = h\nu/\lambda$ b. $E = h\nu$ c. $E = mc^2$ d. $PV = nRT$

5. Which subatomic particles are responsible for carrying on the chain reactions characteristic of nuclear fission?
   a. alpha particles   b. beta particles   c. neutrons   d. protons

6. When uranium-235 absorbs a neutron and undergoes fission, barium-142 and krypton-91 are two possible fission fragments. How many neutrons are released?

$${}^{235}_{92}U + {}^{1}_{0}n \longrightarrow {}^{142}_{56}Ba + {}^{91}_{36}Kr + ?\ {}^{1}_{0}n$$

   a. 0   b. 1   c. 2   d. 3

7. What process is represented by the equation ${}^{2}_{1}H + {}^{2}_{1}H \longrightarrow {}^{4}_{2}He$ + energy?
   a. alpha decay   b. artificial transmutation
   c. fission   d. fusion

8. Hydrogen-2 and hydrogen-3 fuse to form helium-4. The other product is a(n)
   a. electron   b. neutron   c. positron   d. proton

Answers: 1. b; 2. c; 3. c; 4. c; 5. c; 6. d; 7. d; 8. b

8 Nuclear Bombs

Learning Objectives ❯ Describe how uranium and plutonium bombs are made.
❯ Identify the most hazardous fallout isotopes, and explain why they are particularly dangerous.

In 1939, President Roosevelt launched a highly secret research project for the study of atomic energy. Called the *Manhattan Project*, it eventually became a massive research effort involving more scientific brainpower than ever was or has been devoted to a single project. Amazingly, it was conducted under such extreme secrecy that even Vice President Harry Truman did not know of its existence until after Roosevelt's death.

The Manhattan Project included four separate research teams trying to learn how to

- sustain the nuclear-fission chain reaction,
- enrich uranium so that it contained about 90% of the fissionable isotope ^{235}U,
- make plutonium-239 (another fissionable isotope), and
- construct a bomb based on nuclear fission.

Sustainable Chain Reaction

By that time, it had been established that neutron bombardment could initiate the fission reaction, but many attributes of this reaction were unknown. Enrico Fermi and his group, working in a lab under the bleachers at Stagg Field on the campus of the University of Chicago, worked on the fission reaction itself and how to sustain it. They found that the neutrons used to trigger the reaction had to be slowed down to increase the probability that they would hit a uranium nucleus. Because graphite slows down neutrons, a large "pile" of graphite was built to house the reaction. Then the amount of uranium "fuel" was gradually increased. The major goal was to determine the **critical mass**—the amount of uranium-235 needed to sustain the fission reaction. There had to be enough fissionable nuclei in the "fuel" for the neutrons released in one fission process to have a good chance of being captured by another fissionable nucleus before escaping from the pile.

On December 2, 1942, Fermi and his group achieved the first sustained nuclear fission reaction. The critical mass of uranium (enriched to about 94% ^{235}U) for this reactor turned out to be about 16 kg.

Isotopic Enrichment

Natural uranium is 99.27% uranium-238, which does not undergo fission. Uranium-235, the fissionable isotope, makes up only 0.72% of natural uranium. Because making a bomb required *enriching* the uranium to about 90% uranium-235, it was necessary to find a way to separate the uranium isotopes. This was the job of the Manhattan Project research team in Oak Ridge, Tennessee.

Chemical separation was almost impossible; ^{235}U and ^{238}U are chemically almost identical. The separation method eventually used involved converting uranium to gaseous uranium hexafluoride, UF_6. Molecules of UF_6 containing uranium-235 are slightly lighter and therefore move slightly faster than molecules containing uranium-238. Uranium hexafluoride was allowed to pass through a series of thousands of pinholes, and the molecules containing uranium-235 gradually outdistanced the others. Enough enriched uranium-235 was finally obtained to make a small explosive device.

Synthesis of Plutonium

While the tedious work of separating uranium isotopes was underway at Oak Ridge, another research team, led by Glenn T. Seaborg, approached the problem of obtaining fissionable material by another route. Although uranium-238 would not fission when bombarded by neutrons, it was found that this more common isotope of uranium *would* decay to form a new element, named neptunium (Np). This product quickly decayed to another new element, plutonium (Pu).

$$^{238}_{92}\text{U} + ^{1}_{0}\text{n} \longrightarrow ^{239}_{92}\text{U}$$

$$^{239}_{92}\text{U} \longrightarrow ^{0}_{-1}\text{e} + ^{239}_{93}\text{Np}$$

$$^{239}_{93}\text{Np} \longrightarrow ^{239}_{94}\text{Pu} + ^{0}_{-1}\text{e}$$

Plutonium-239 was found to be fissionable and thus was suitable material for the making of a bomb. A group of large reactors was built near Hanford, Washington, to produce plutonium.

Bomb Construction

The actual building of the nuclear bombs was carried out at Los Alamos, New Mexico, under the direction of J. Robert Oppenheimer (1904–1967). In a top-secret laboratory at a remote site, a group of scientists planned and then constructed what would become known as atomic bombs. Two different models were developed, one based on ^{235}U and the other on ^{239}Pu.

The critical mass of uranium-235 could not be exceeded prematurely, so it was important that no single piece of fissionable material in the bomb be that large. The bomb was designed to contain pieces of uranium of subcritical mass, plus a neutron source to initiate the fission reaction. Then, at the chosen time, all the pieces would be forced together using an ordinary high explosive, thus triggering a runaway nuclear chain reaction.

The synthesis of plutonium turned out to be easier than the isotopic separation, and by July 1945, enough fissionable material had been made for three bombs to be assembled—two using plutonium, and one using uranium. The first atomic bomb (one of the plutonium devices) was tested in the desert near Alamogordo, New Mexico, on July 16, 1945. The heat from the explosion vaporized the 30-m steel tower on which the bomb was placed and melted the sand for several hectares around the site. The light produced was the brightest anyone had ever seen.

Some of the scientists were so awed by the force of the blast that they argued against using the bombs on Japan. A few, led by Leo Szilard, suggested a demonstration of the bombs' power at an uninhabited site. But fear of a well-publicized "dud" and the desire to avoid millions of casualties in an invasion of Japan led President Harry Truman to order the dropping of the bombs on Japanese cities. The lone uranium bomb, called "Little Boy" (Figure 13), was dropped on Hiroshima on August 6, 1945, and caused over 100,000 casualties. Three days later, the other plutonium bomb, called "Fat Man," was dropped on Nagasaki with comparable results (Figure 14). World War II ended with the surrender of Japan on August 14, 1945.

Radioactive Fallout

When a nuclear explosion occurs in the open atmosphere, radioactive materials can rain down on parts of Earth thousands of miles away, days and weeks later in what is called **radioactive fallout**. The uranium atom can split in several different ways.

▲ Glenn T. Seaborg (1912–1999). Element 106 was named seaborgium (Sg) in his honor. Seaborg is the only person to have had an element named for him while still alive. He is shown here pointing to his namesake element on the periodic table of elements.

▶ **Figure 13** An internal schematic of the atomic bomb "Little Boy" dropped on Hiroshima. Each of the cylinders of uranium-235 had less than the critical mass. The high explosive shot the cylindrical "bullet" down the gun barrel and onto the target spike. The result was about two critical masses of uranium-235, and a nuclear explosion occurred about a millisecond later.

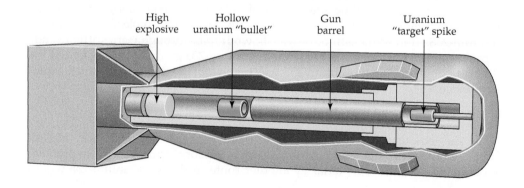

High explosive   Hollow uranium "bullet"   Gun barrel   Uranium "target" spike

$$^{235}_{92}U + ^{1}_{0}n \longrightarrow ^{90}_{38}Sr + ^{143}_{54}Xe + 3^{1}_{0}n$$

$$\longrightarrow ^{102}_{39}Y + ^{131}_{53}I + 3^{1}_{0}n$$

$$\longrightarrow ^{95}_{37}Rb + ^{137}_{55}Cs + 4^{1}_{0}n$$

▲ **Figure 14** The mushroom cloud over Nagasaki, following the detonation of "Fat Man" on August 9, 1945.

The primary (first) fission products are radioactive. These decay to daughter isotopes, many of which are also radioactive. In all, over 200 different fission products are produced, with half-lives that vary from less than a second to more than a billion years. Also, the neutrons produced in the explosion act on molecules in the atmosphere to produce carbon-14, tritium, and other radioisotopes. Fallout is therefore exceedingly complex. We consider three of the more worrisome isotopes here.

Of all the isotopes, strontium-90 (half-life 28.5 y) presents the greatest hazard to people. Strontium-90 reaches us primarily through dairy products and vegetables. Because of its similarity to calcium (both are group 2A elements), strontium-90 is incorporated into bone. There it remains an internal source of radiation for many years.

Iodine-131 may present a greater threat immediately after a nuclear explosion or reactor meltdown. Its half-life is only 8 days, but it is produced in relatively large amounts. Iodine-131 is readily transferred up the food chain. In the human body, it is concentrated in the thyroid gland, and it is precisely this characteristic that makes a trace of iodine-131 so useful for diagnostic scanning. However, for a healthy individual, larger amounts of radioactive iodine offer only damaging side effects. To minimize the absorption of radioactive iodine, many people in the areas of Chernobyl and Fukushima were given large amounts of potassium iodide, which effectively diluted the amount of radioactive iodine absorbed by their thyroid glands.

Cesium-137 (half-life 30.2 y) is, like strontium-90, capable of long-term effects. Because of its similarity to potassium (both are group 1A elements), it is taken up by living organisms as part of body fluids. It can be obtained from sources in the environment and reconcentrated in living organisms.

By the late 1950s, radioactive isotopes from atmospheric testing of nuclear weapons were detected in the environment. Concern over radiation damage from nuclear fallout led to a movement to ban atmospheric testing. Many scientists were leaders in the movement. Linus Pauling, who won the Nobel Prize in Chemistry in 1954 for his bonding theories and for his work in determining the structure of proteins, was a particularly articulate advocate of banning atmospheric tests. In 1963, a nuclear test ban treaty was signed by the major nations—with the exception of France and the People's Republic of China, which continued aboveground tests. Since the signing of the treaty, other countries have joined the nuclear club. Pauling, who had endured being called a communist and a traitor because of his outspoken position, was awarded the Nobel Peace Prize in 1962.

Self-Assessment Questions

1. The isotope used in uranium fission reactions is
   a. uranium-232
   b. uranium-234
   c. uranium-235
   d. uranium-238

2. What fraction of natural uranium is the fissionable isotope?
   a. <1%   b. 10%   c. 50%   d. >99%

3. Plutonium for fission reactions is
   a. made from uranium-238
   b. made from neptunium ores
   c. obtained from the dwarf planet Pluto
   d. obtained from plutonium ores

4. Strontium-90 substitutes for calcium in bones because Sr and Ca
   a. are in the same group of the periodic table
   b. are in the same period of the periodic table
   c. have identical electron configurations
   d. have identical half-lives

5. Which of the following radioisotopes in fallout is dangerous mainly because it becomes concentrated in the thyroid gland?
   a. cesium-137   b. iodine-131   c. strontium-90   d. radon-222

Answers: 1, c; 2, a; 3, a; 4, a; 5, b

9 Uses of Nuclear Energy

Learning Objective ❯ List some uses of nuclear energy.

A significant portion of the electricity we use today is generated by nuclear power plants. In the United States, one-fifth of all the electricity produced comes from nuclear power plants. Europeans rely even more on nuclear energy. France, for example, obtains 80% of its electric power from nuclear plants, while Belgium, Spain, Switzerland, and Sweden generate about one-third of their power from nuclear reactors.

Ironically, the same nuclear chain reaction that occurred in the detonation of the bomb dropped on Hiroshima is used extensively today under the familiar concrete containment tower of a nuclear power plant. The key difference is that the power plant employs a *slow, controlled* release of energy from the nuclear chain reaction, rather than an explosion. The slowness of the process is due to the use of uranium fuel that is much less enriched (2.5–3.5% ^{235}U rather than the 90% enrichment of weapons-grade uranium).

One of the main problems with the production of nuclear power arises from the products of the nuclear reactions. As in nuclear fallout, most of the daughter nuclei produced by the fission of uranium-235 are also radioactive, some with very long half-lives. We will discuss the problems associated with nuclear waste. Perhaps a more serious problem is the potential transformation of spent nuclear fuel into weapons-grade material (see the box titled "Nuclear Proliferation and Dirty Bombs").

▶ The core of a nuclear reactor contains hollow rods filled with uranium pellets. The heat generated by the fission reaction is used to boil water, which drives turbines to generate electricity in the same way as in coal-fired or gas-fired generating plant. Because the pellets are only about 3% uranium-235, a nuclear explosion cannot occur, though loss of coolant may lead to a reactor meltdown.

JIJI PRESS/AFP/Getty Images/Newscom

GREEN CHEMISTRY

Bevin W. Parks-Lee, *Industrial organic chemist*

Green Remediation of Nuclear Waste

You learned that a large amount of ^{239}Pu was manufactured in Hanford, Washington, for the Manhattan Project (Section 8). The plutonium was produced from uranium in a nuclear reactor much like the ones used to produce electricity today. After the uranium rods reacted long enough to produce usable amounts of plutonium, they were transferred from the reactor and prepared for reprocessing. The goal was to maximize the plutonium production. The waste, still highly radioactive, was stored in many million-gallon tanks. Some of these tanks have been in service for 70 years, and leaks have been detected. Green chemistry principles can guide the development of methods to handle this legacy waste responsibly.

The Manhattan Project generated more than 91 million gallons of extremely acidic radioactive waste left over from the recovery of Pu and U. The solutions, referred to as high-level liquid waste (HLLW), are radioactive because small amounts of U and Pu remain with many other radioactive *nuclides* (nuclei having specific mass numbers and atomic numbers) that were produced during the fission reactions, including Np, Am, and Nd (Sections 3 and 7). If this small amount of radioactive material (1–2% of the 91 million gallons) could be removed, the impact would be tremendous.

Spent fuel rods are made up of different metals that can be separated and reclaimed through reprocessing. The aim is to remove any remaining radioactive nuclides, but many steps are necessary to achieve this. To access the separate atoms and free them from the solid matrix, the fuel rods are dissolved in concentrated nitric acid. An oxidation-reduction reaction occurs between the acid and the metals. The protons from the acid are reduced to form hydrogen gas, and the metals are oxidized to produce cations. The radioactive metal cations remain in the acidic water. At this point, it is possible to selectively remove metals by using special organic solutions that bind specific nuclides.

Processes that reduce the amount of HLLW align with Green Chemistry Principles 1, 6, and 12. How can these principles be put into action? One way is to design remediation processes that target the radioactive parts of the waste. Specifically, isolating only the radioactive compounds that require treatment avoids the need to store millions of gallons of acidic solution. Also, since the half-lives of these nuclides are so long (Section 3), encasing the waste in glass (vitrification) has been proposed as a good storage approach. Decreasing the volume of waste, though, would minimize the use of vitrification, which is energy-intensive and expensive.

In reprocessing, specific molecules can be used to bind to the radioactive cations and to manipulate the properties (e.g., solubility) of the resulting metal compounds. The molecules react with the metals to make compounds soluble in organic solvents. This enables the radioactive materials to be removed from water and transferred into a small volume of organic solvent. If the molecules are selective for one metal over another, they will bind to and carry only that metal into the organic solvent. This reprocessing method offers the opportunity to separate and reclaim individual types of metals.

One type of organic molecule that can extract the radioactive nuclides is an *amide*. Amides are easy to synthesize, and they are stable in the highly acidic and radioactive environment. A way to further reduce the volume of radioactive waste would be to burn off the organic components—the molecules bound to the metals and the solvent carrying them—leaving only solid metal waste. Amides (composed of only C, H, N, and O) will burn completely, making them a good fit with Green Chemistry Principle 10—designing for degradation. The simple amides tested first did not bind the metal ions as well as other types of molecules, which were harder to synthesize, degraded in the waste solutions, could not be incinerated, and tended to be toxic. Further research uncovered that molecules containing two amide groups bound the metal ions very well. This example shows the application of Green Chemistry Principle 4 through the design of a safer chemical.

Overall, green chemistry principles can be used to dramatically reduce amounts of radioactive waste and to reprocess the waste in ways that are safer for human health and the environment.

▲ Construction of the storage tanks of HLLW that are buried on completion.

Nuclear Proliferation and Dirty Bombs

As power is generated in nuclear plants, important changes occur in the fuel. Neutron bombardment converts ^{235}U to radioactive daughter products. Eventually, the concentration of ^{235}U becomes too low to sustain the nuclear chain reaction. The fuel rods must be replaced about every three years. The rods then become high-level nuclear waste.

As ^{235}U undergo fission, the nonfissionable (and very concentrated) ^{238}U nuclei absorb neutrons and are converted to ^{239}Pu, a transmutation described in Section 8). In time, some ^{240}Pu is also formed. However, if the fuel rods are removed after only about three months, the fissionable plutonium-239 can be easily separated from the other fission products by chemical means. Plutonium bombs require less sophisticated technology to produce than is needed to make nuclear weapons from uranium. Plutonium is thus of greater concern with respect to weapons proliferation, because operation of a nuclear plant can produce materials suitable for use in a bomb. North Korea has nuclear power plants and a plutonium separation facility capable of producing enough ^{239}Pu for several weapons each year (Figure 15). Iran also has a facility for enriching uranium, which could lead to the production of nuclear bombs. The activities of these and other developing countries raise the fear of a dangerous proliferation of nuclear weapons.

Another security concern is a "dirty bomb," a device that uses a conventional explosive, such as dynamite, to disperse radioactive material that might be stolen from a hospital or other facility that uses radioactive isotopes. In most cases, the conventional bomb would do more immediate harm than the radioactive substances. At the levels most likely to be used, the dirty bomb would not contain enough radioactive material to kill people or cause severe illness.

GeoEye Inc.

▲ **Figure 15** Satellite photograph of the plutonium processing plant at Yongbyon, North Korea.

The Nuclear Age

The splitting of the atom made the Chinese curse "May you live in interesting times" seem quite appropriate. The goal of the alchemists, to change one element into another, has been achieved through the application of scientific principles. New elements have been formed, and the periodic table has been extended well beyond

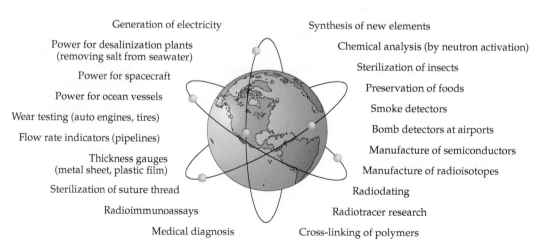

Generation of electricity

Power for desalinization plants (removing salt from seawater)

Power for spacecraft

Power for ocean vessels

Wear testing (auto engines, tires)

Flow rate indicators (pipelines)

Thickness gauges (metal sheet, plastic film)

Sterilization of suture thread

Radioimmunoassays

Medical diagnosis

Synthesis of new elements

Chemical analysis (by neutron activation)

Sterilization of insects

Preservation of foods

Smoke detectors

Bomb detectors at airports

Manufacture of semiconductors

Manufacture of radioisotopes

Radiodating

Radiotracer research

Cross-linking of polymers

▲ **Figure 16** Some constructive uses of nuclear energy.

uranium ($Z = 92$). This modern alchemy produces plutonium by the ton; neptunium ($Z = 93$), americium ($Z = 95$), and curium ($Z = 96$) by the kilogram; and berkelium ($Z = 97$) and einsteinium ($Z = 99$) by the milligram.

As we have seen, radioactive isotopes have many uses, from killing tiny but deadly cancer cells and harmful microorganisms in food to serving as tracers in a variety of biological experiments and imaging technologies and generating fearsome weapons. Figure 16 displays a number of other constructive uses of nuclear energy. We live in an age in which the extraordinary forces present in the atom have been unleashed as a true double-edged sword. The threat of nuclear war—and nuclear terrorism—has been a constant specter for the last six decades, yet it is hard to believe that the world would be a better place if we had not discovered the secrets of the atomic nucleus.

CRITICAL THINKING EXERCISES

Apply knowledge that you have gained in this chapter and one or more of the FLaReS principles to evaluate the following statements or claims.

1. Brazil nuts are known to absorb and concentrate the element barium. A nationally known laboratory announces that Brazil nuts contain tiny traces of radium.

2. For more than 600 years, it was alleged that the Shroud of Turin was the burial shroud of Jesus. In 1988, several laboratories carried out carbon-14 analyses indicating that the flax from which the shroud was made was grown between C.E. 1260 and 1390. Recently there have been claims that the 1988 analyses are unreliable because the shroud is contaminated with pollen from plants grown in the fourteenth century, and it is the age of this pollen that was actually measured in 1988. At least one of the scientists has offered to repeat the analysis on a very carefully cleaned sample of the cloth, but further access to the shroud has been refused.

3. A scientist reports that he has found an artifact that has been shown to be 80,000 years old by carbon-14 dating.

4. The americium in a smoke detector (see Conceptual Example 7) is encased in a chamber with aluminum shielding, about as thick as the wall of a soft-drink can. A woman who purchases a smoke detector mounts it at the highest point on the ceiling. She claims that this minimizes her exposure to the radiation.

5. A young girl refuses to visit her grandmother after the woman has undergone radiation therapy for breast cancer. The teenager is afraid that she will catch radiation sickness from her grandmother.

SUMMARY

Section 1—Some isotopes of elements have unstable nuclei, which undergo changes in nucleon number, atomic number, or energy; this process is called radioactive decay. The nuclei that undergo such changes are called radioisotopes. We are constantly exposed to naturally occurring radiation, called background radiation. Radiation that causes harm by dislodging electrons from living tissue and forming ions is called ionizing radiation and includes nuclear radiation and X-rays. Radiation can disrupt normal chemical processes in cells and can damage DNA, sometimes causing mutations.

Section 2—Nuclear equations are used to represent nuclear processes. These equations are balanced when the sum of nucleon numbers on each side is the same and the sum of atomic numbers on each side is the same. Four types of radioactive decay are alpha $\left(^{4}_{2}\text{He}\right)$ decay, beta $\left(^{0}_{-1}\text{e}\right)$

decay, gamma $\left(^{0}_{0}\gamma\right)$ decay, and emission of a positron $\left(^{0}_{+1}\text{e}\right)$. Electron capture (EC) is a fifth type of decay, in which a nucleus absorbs one of the atom's electrons. There are a number of important differences between nuclear reactions and chemical reactions.

Section 3—The rate of radioactive decay is measured in becquerels (Bq).

$$1 \text{ becquerel (Bq)} = 1 \text{ disintegration/s}$$

The **half-life** of a radioactive isotope is the time it takes for half of a sample to undergo radioactive decay. The fraction of a radioisotope remaining after n half-lives is given by the expression

$$\text{Fraction remaining} = \frac{1}{2^n}$$

3

Half-lives of certain isotopes can be used to estimate the ages of various objects. Carbon-14 dating is the best-known of the radioisotopic dating techniques. Relying on carbon-14's half-life of 5730 years, this technique can be used to estimate the age of once-living items up to 50,000 years old. The decay of tritium can be used to date items up to 100 years old. Other isotopes can be used to date rocks, the Earth's crust, and meteorites.

Section 4—Transmutation, the conversion of one element into another, cannot be carried out by chemical means but can be accomplished by nuclear processes. Bombarding a stable nucleus with energetic particles can cause artificial transmutation. These processes can be represented with nuclear equations.

Section 5—Radioisotopes have many uses. A radioisotope and a stable isotope of an element behave nearly the same chemically, so radioisotopes can be used as tracers in physical and biological systems. A radioactive atom in a molecule labels it so that it can be followed by a radiation detector. Radioisotopes have many uses in agriculture, including the production of useful mutations. Radiation can be used to irradiate foodstuffs as a method of preservation. Radiation therapy to destroy cancer cells depends on the fact that radiation is more damaging to those rapidly reproducing cells than to healthy cells. Radioisotopes are used in the diagnosis of various disorders. Iodine-131 is used for thyroid diagnoses, gadolinium-153 for bone mineralization examinations, and technetium-99m for a variety of diagnostic tests. Positron emission tomography (PET) involves radioisotopes that emit positrons, which are then annihilated by electrons in the body, producing gamma rays that can be used to form an image.

Section 6—Different types of radiation have different penetrating abilities. *Alpha particles* (helium nuclei) are relatively slow and have low penetrating power. *Beta particles* (electrons) are much faster and more penetrating. *Gamma rays* (high-energy photons) travel at the speed of light and have great penetrating power. How hazardous radiation is depends on the location of the source; alpha particles from a source inside the body are highly damaging. Radiation hazard can be decreased by moving away from the source or by using shielding.

Section 7—Einstein's mass–energy equation, $E = mc^2$ shows that mass and energy are different aspects of the same thing. The total mass of the nucleons in a nucleus is greater than the actual mass of the nucleus. The missing mass, or the mass defect, is equivalent to the binding energy holding the nucleons together. Binding energy can be released either by breaking down heavy nuclei into smaller ones, a process called nuclear fission, or by

joining small nuclei to form larger ones, called nuclear fusion.

Fermi and Segrè bombarded uranium atoms with neutrons and found radioactive species among the products, while Hahn and Strassman found light nuclei among the reaction products. Meitner, aided by Frisch, hypothesized that the uranium nuclei were undergoing fission. Szilard saw that neutrons released in the fission of one nucleus could trigger the fission of other nuclei, setting off a chain reaction.

Thermonuclear reactions (fusion reactions) combine small nuclei to form larger ones. Nuclear fusion produces even more energy than nuclear fission. Fusion is the basis of the hydrogen bomb and the source of the sun's energy. Much research is aimed at producing controlled fusion commercially.

Section 8—The nuclear fission reaction became the center of the Manhattan Project during World War II. Its goals were (1) to achieve sustained nuclear fission and determine the critical mass, or minimum amount, of fissionable material required; (2) to enrich the amount of fissionable uranium-235 in ordinary uranium; (3) to synthesize plutonium-239, which is also fissionable; and (4) to construct a nuclear fission bomb before the Germans were able to do so. World War II ended shortly after the dropping of atomic bombs on Hiroshima and Nagasaki.

In addition to the devastation at the site of a nuclear explosion, much radioactive debris, or radioactive fallout, is, produced. Strontium-90 and iodine-131 are particularly hazardous components of fallout. Partly because of fallout, a nuclear test ban treaty was signed by most of the major nations; only underground testing is not banned.

Section 9—Nuclear power plants use the same nuclear chain reaction as in atomic bombs, but the reaction is much slower and can be controlled because of the low concentration of fissionable material. Disposal of the products of nuclear fission in power plants is an important problem facing us, as is the potential conversion of nuclear fuel into weapons. The forces within the nucleus truly constitute a double-edged sword for civilization.

Green chemistry Radioactive waste must be handled responsibly, and green chemistry principles can guide the development of new methods. A greener approach is to selectively isolate and treat the small amounts of radioactive isotopes instead of the large volumes of liquid waste. This can now be accomplished using safer chemicals, thereby reducing the amount of hazardous waste and the need for expensive and energy-intensive processing or storage methods.

Learning Objectives

› Identify the sources of the natural radiation to which we are exposed.	Problems 15, 54
› List the sources and dangers of ionizing radiation.	Problem 15
› Balance nuclear equations.	Problems 19–25, 43
› Identify the products formed by various decay processes.	Problems 26–30, 47
› Solve simple half-life problems.	Problems 31–38, 51
› Use the concept of half-life to solve simple radioisotopic dating problems.	Problems 39–42
› Write a nuclear equation for a transmutation, and identify the product element formed.	Problems 45, 46, 58

❯ List some applications of radioisotopes.	Problems 39–42, 50
❯ Describe the nature of materials needed to block alpha, beta, and gamma radiation.	Problem 13
❯ Explain where nuclear energy comes from.	Problems 52, 55
❯ Describe the difference between fission and fusion.	Problem 17
❯ Describe how uranium and plutonium bombs are made.	Problem 18
❯ Identify the most hazardous fallout isotopes, and explain why they are particularly dangerous.	Problems 15, 52
❯ List some uses of nuclear energy.	Problems 31, 34, 39, 42, 44
❯ Identify green chemistry principles that can help solve existing problems in nuclear chemistry.	Problems 59, 62
❯ Explain how molecules used in nuclear waste processing can be designed to be safer, and give examples of such molecules.	Problems 60, 61

REVIEW QUESTIONS

1. Match each description with the type of change.
   (i) A new compound is formed.   **a.** nuclear
   (ii) A new element is formed.   **b.** chemical
   (iii) Size, shape, appearance,   **c.** physical
        or volume is changed without
        changing the composition.

2. Define or describe each of the following.
   a. half-life
   b. positron
   c. background radiation
   d. radioisotope

3. Write the nuclear symbols for protium, deuterium, and tritium (which are hydrogen-1, hydrogen-2, and hydrogen-3, respectively).

4. Why are isotopes important in nuclear reactions but not in most chemical reactions?

5. Write the nuclear symbols for the following isotopes. You may refer to the periodic table.
   a. cobalt-60
   b. iodine-127
   c. sodium-22
   d. calcium-42

6. Indicate the number of protons and the number of neutrons in atoms of the following isotopes.
   a. $^{65}_{30}Zn$ **b.** $^{236}_{93}Np$
   c. $^{101}_{43}Tc$ **d.** $^{81m}_{36}Kr$

7. Which of the following pairs represent isotopes? (X is a general symbol for an element.)
   a. $^{70}_{32}X$ and $^{70}_{32}X$
   b. $^{57}_{22}X$ and $^{52}_{22}X$
   c. $^{176}_{74}X$ and $^{167}_{74}X$
   d. $^{8}_{4}X$ and $^{16}_{8}X$

8. In which of the following atoms are there more protons than neutrons?
   a. ^{17}F **b.** ^{58}Ni **c.** ^{16}O **d.** ^{197}Au

9. The longest-lived isotope of einsteinium (Es) has a mass (nucleon) number of 254. How many neutrons are in the nucleus of an atom of this isotope?

10. The longest-lived isotope of polonium (Po) has 125 neutrons. What is a mass (nucleon) number of this isotope?

11. What changes occur in the nucleon number and the atomic number of a nucleus during emission of each of the following?
    a. alpha particle
    b. gamma ray
    c. proton

12. What changes occur in the nucleon number and atomic number of a nucleus during emission of each of the following?
    a. beta particle
    b. neutron
    c. positron

13. **(a)** From which type of radiation would a pair of gloves be sufficient to shield the hands: heavy alpha particles or massless gamma rays? **(b)** From which type of radiation would heavy lead shielding be necessary to protect a worker: alpha, beta, or gamma?

14. What are some of the characteristics that make technetium-99m such a useful radioisotope for diagnostic purposes?

15. Plutonium is especially hazardous when inhaled or ingested because it emits alpha particles. Why do alpha particles cause more damage to tissue than beta particles when their source is inside the body?

16. List two ways in which workers exposed to radioactive materials can protect themselves from radiation hazard.

17. Compare nuclear fission and nuclear fusion. Why is energy liberated in each case?

18. The compounds $^{235}UF_6$ and $^{238}UF_6$ are nearly chemically identical. How are they separated?

PROBLEMS

Nuclear Equations

19. Write a balanced equation for emission of (a) an alpha particle by californium-250, (b) a beta particle by bismuth-210, and (c) a positron by iodine-117.

20. Write a balanced equation for (a) alpha decay of gold-173, (b) beta decay of iodine-138, and (c) capture of an electron by cadmium-104.

21. Complete the following equations.
    a. $^{179}_{79}Au \longrightarrow ^{175}_{77}Ir + ?$
    b. $^{12}_{6}C + ^{2}_{1}H \longrightarrow ^{13}_{6}C + ?$
    c. $^{154}_{62}Sm + ^{1}_{0}n \longrightarrow ? + 2\,^{1}_{0}n$

22. Complete the following equations.
    a. $^{10}_{5}B + ^{1}_{0}n \longrightarrow ? + ^{4}_{2}He$
    b. $^{23}_{10}Ne \longrightarrow ^{23}_{11}Na + ?$
    c. $^{121}_{51}Sb + ? \longrightarrow ^{121}_{52}Te + ^{1}_{0}n$

23. Radiological laboratories often have a container of molybdenum-99, which decays to form technetium-99m. What other particle is formed? Complete the equation.
$$^{99}_{42}Mo \longrightarrow ^{99m}_{43}Tc + ?$$

24. Complete the equation for the decay of technetium-99m to technetium-99.
$$^{99m}_{43}Tc \longrightarrow ^{99}_{43}Tc + ?$$

25. When a magnesium-24 nucleus is bombarded with a neutron, a proton is ejected. What element is formed? (*Hint:* Write a balanced nuclear equation.)

26. A radioisotope decays to give an alpha particle and a protactinium-233 nucleus. What was the original nucleus?

27. A radioactive isotope decays to give an alpha particle and a bismuth-211 nucleus. What was the original nucleus?

28. When silver-107 is bombarded with a neutron, a different isotope of silver forms and then undergoes beta decay. What is the final product? (*Hint:* Write two separate nuclear equations.)

29. A nucleus of astatine-210 decays by beta emission, forming nucleus A. Nucleus A also decays by beta emission to nucleus B. Write the nuclear symbol for B.

30. A proposed method of making fissionable nuclear fuel is to bombard the relatively abundant isotope thorium-232 with a neutron. The product X of this bombardment decays quickly by beta emission to nucleus Y, and nucleus Y decays quickly to fissionable nucleus Z. Write the nuclear symbol for Z.

Half-Life

31. Gallium-67 is used in nuclear medicine (Table 6). After treatment, a patient's blood shows an activity of 20,000 counts per minute (counts/min). How long will it be before the activity decreases to about 5000 counts/min?

32. How long will it take for a 12.0-g sample of iodine-131 to decay to leave a total of 1.5 g of the isotope? The half-life of iodine-131 is 8.07 days.

33. A lab worker reports an activity of 80,000 counts/s for a sample of magnesium-21, whose half-life is 122 ms. Exactly 5.00 min later, another worker records an activity of 10 counts/min on the same sample. What best accounts for this difference? Magnesium-21
    a. gives off only neutrinos
    b. has a very short half-life, so almost every radioactive atom in the sample has decayed
    c. is an alpha emitter
    d. is a gamma emitter

34. A patient is injected with a radiopharmaceutical labeled with technetium-99m, half-life of 6.0 h, in preparation for a gamma ray scan to evaluate kidney function. If the original activity of the sample was 48 μCi, what activity (in μCi) remains (a) after 24 h and (b) after 48 h?

35. Krypton-81m is used for lung ventilation studies. Its half-life is 13 s. How long does it take the activity of this isotope to reach one-quarter of its original value?

36. Radium-223 has a half-life of 11.4 days. Approximately how long would it take for the activity of a sample of ^{223}Ra to decrease to 1% of its initial value?

37. In an experiment with dysprosium-197, half-life of 8.1 h, an activity of 500 counts/min was recorded at 4:00 p.m. on a Friday. What was the approximate activity of this sample at 8:30 a.m. the following Monday morning, when the experiment was resumed?

38. In determining the half-life of sulfur-35, students collected the following data, with the time in days and the activity in counts/s.

Time	Activity	Time	Activity
0	1000	80	525
20	851	100	446
40	725	120	380
60	616	140	323

Without doing detailed calculations, estimate a value for the half-life.

Radioisotopic Dating

39. Living matter has a carbon-14 activity of about 16 counts/min per gram of carbon. What is the age of an artifact for which the carbon-14 activity is 8 counts/min per gram of carbon?

40. A piece of wood from an Egyptian tomb has a carbon-14 activity of 980 counts/h. A piece of new wood of the same size shows 3920 counts/h. What is the age of the wood from the tomb?

41. The ratio of carbon-14 to carbon-12 in a piece of charcoal from an archaeological excavation is found to be one-half the ratio in a sample of modern wood. Approximately how old is the charcoal? How old would it be if the isotopic ratio were 25% of that in a sample of modern wood?

42. You are offered a great price on a case of brandy supposedly bottled during the lifetime of Napoleon (1769–1821). Before buying it, you insist on testing a sample of the brandy and find that its tritium content is 12.5% of that of newly produced brandy. How long ago was the brandy bottled? Is it likely to be authentic Napoleon-era brandy?

ADDITIONAL PROBLEMS

43. Write balanced nuclear equations for **(a)** the bombardment of $^{121}_{51}Sb$ by alpha particles to produce $^{124}_{53}I$, followed by **(b)** the radioactive decay of $^{124}_{53}I$ by positron emission.

44. A typical smoke detector contains about 0.25 mg of americium-241. The activity of 1 g of ^{241}Am is 1.26×10^{11} Bq. What is the activity of the americium-241 in the smoke detector?

45. In 2010, Russian and American scientists produced a few atoms of element 117 by shooting an intense beam of ions of the rare isotope calcium-48 at a target of berkelium-247. Two isotopes of element 117 were formed, one having 176 neutrons and the other 177 neutrons. Write two separate nuclear equations for the formation of the two isotopes. How many neutrons were released in each process?

46. Meitnerium undergoes alpha decay to form element 107, which in turn also emits an alpha particle. What are the atomic number and nucleon number of the isotope formed by these two steps? Write balanced nuclear equations for the two reactions.

47. Radium-223 nuclei usually decay by alpha emission. Once in every billion decays, a radium-223 nucleus emits a carbon-14 nucleus. Write a balanced nuclear equation for each type of emission.

48. A particular uranium alloy has a density of 18.75 g/cm³. What volume is occupied by a critical mass of 49 kg of this alloy? The critical mass can be decreased to 16 kg if the alloy is surrounded by a layer of natural uranium (which acts as a neutron reflector). What is the volume of the smaller mass? Compare your answers to the approximate volumes of a baseball, a volleyball, and a basketball.

49. Plutonium has a density of 19.1 g/cm³. What volume is occupied by a mass of 16.3 kg of plutonium? If a neutron-reflecting coating (made of beryllium) is used, the critical mass can be lowered to 2.5 kg. Compare the size of this mass to the volume of a baseball, a volleyball, and a basketball.

50. There are several technological applications for the transuranium elements ($Z > 92$). An important one is in smoke detectors, which can use the decay of a tiny amount of americium-241 to neptunium-237. What subatomic particle is emitted from that decay process?

51. The radioisotopic dating problems in this chapter are deceptively easy because they involve only integral numbers of half-lives. Calculations involving other than integral half-life values require a bit more complicated math. However, carbon-14 dating calculators that make the task quite easy can be accessed on the Web. Use one of those calculators to find **(a)** the age of a scrap of paper taken from the Dead Sea Scrolls that has a $^{14}C/^{12}C$ ratio that is 79.5% of that in living plants and **(b)** the age of a piece of charcoal from a Neanderthal site that has a $^{14}C/^{12}C$ ratio that is 17.5% of that in living plants.

52. In the first step of the chain reaction of a nuclear explosion, a ^{235}U nucleus absorbs a neutron. The resulting ^{236}U nucleus is unstable and can fission into ^{92}Kr and ^{141}Ba nuclei as shown in the figure. What are the other products of this reaction? After assessing this reaction, explain how the chain reaction can continue.

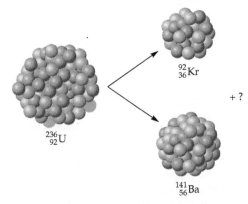

53. In 1932, James Chadwick discovered a new subatomic particle when he bombarded beryllium-9 with alpha particles. One of the products was carbon-12. What particle did Chadwick discover?

54. Several different radioisotopes can be used much like carbon-14 for determining the age of rocks and other matter. In the geosciences, the age of rocks may be determined using potassium-40, which decays to argon-40 with a half-life of 1.2 billion years. **(a)** Some rocks brought back from the moon were dated as being 3.6 billion years old. What percentage of the potassium-40 has decayed after that time? **(b)** Give a reason why uranium-238 (half-life of 4.6 billion years) is more useful for confirming this age than is carbon-14.

55. Einstein's mass–energy equation is $E = mc^2$, where mass is in kilograms and the speed of light is 3.00×10^8 m/s. The unit of energy is the joule (4.184 J = 1 cal; 1000 cal = 1 kcal).
    a. Calculate the energy released, in calories and kilocalories, when 1 g of matter is converted to energy.
    b. A bowl of cornflakes supplies 110 kcal (110 food calories). How many bowls of cornflakes would supply the same amount of energy as you calculated for 1 g of matter in part (a)?

56. Radioactive copper ($^{64}_{29}Cu$, half-life 12.7 h) is found in quantities exceeding the pollution standard in the sediments of a reservoir during a routine check on Monday, when 56 ppm/m³ was measured. The standard allows up to 14 ppm/m³. About when will the level of copper-64 return to 14 ppm/m³?

57. An unidentified corpse was discovered on April 21 at 7:00 a.m. The pathologist discovered that there were 1.24×10^{17} atoms of $^{32}_{15}P$ remaining in the victim's bones and placed the time of death sometime on March 15. The half-life of $^{32}_{15}P$ is 14.28 days. How much $^{32}_{15}P$ was present in the bones at the time of death?

58. Scientists have tried to make element 120. Three different combinations of projectile and target were used to try to produce the nucleus $^{302}_{120}X$: **(a)** nickel-64 and uranium-238, **(b)** iron-58 and plutonium-244, and **(c)** chromium-54 and curium-248. However, after 120 days, no sign of element 120 was found. Write nuclear equations for the three expected reactions.

59. True or False? Green chemistry principles can be applied only as a process is being developed.

60. List four elements of which a compound that can be completely incinerated may be composed.

61. What is the benefit of having two amide groups on one molecule that binds radioactive metal ions?

62. Vitrification is an expensive and energy-intensive method involving encasing waste in glass. What portion of HLLW is radioactive, and why is that important with respect to vitrification?

COLLABORATIVE GROUP PROJECTS

Prepare a PowerPoint, poster, or other presentation (as directed by your instructor) to share with the class.

1. Write a brief report on the impact of nuclear science on one of the following.
   a. war and peace
   b. industrial progress
   c. medicine
   d. agriculture
   e. human, animal, and plant genetics

2. Write an essay on radioisotopic dating using one or more of the isotopes in Table 5 other than carbon-14 or tritium.

3. Write a brief biography of one of the following scientists.
   a. Otto Hahn   **b.** Enrico Fermi
   c. Glenn T. Seaborg   **d.** J. Robert Oppenheimer
   e. Lise Meitner   **f.** Albert Einstein

4. The positron is a particle of antimatter. Search the Web for information about antimatter, and the positron in particular.

5. Find a Web site that is strongly in favor of nuclear power plants and one that is strongly opposed. Note the sites' sponsors, and analyze their viewpoints. Try to find a Web site with a balanced viewpoint.

6. In July 1999, researchers at Lawrence Berkeley Laboratory reported the creation of the heaviest element to date, element 118. Two years later, that report was found to be fraudulent. Report on the scientific ethical questions raised by this episode.

7. Find the location of the nuclear power plant closest to where you live. Try to determine risks and benefits of the plant. To how many houses does it provide power? What are the environmental impacts of the plant under normal operating conditions?

8. Assemble two teams of two to four people each to debate the following resolution: The dropping of the atomic bombs on Hiroshima and Nagasaki was justified. Decide beforehand which team will take the affirmative and which the negative. Each team member is to give a three- to six-minute speech followed by a cross-examination by the opposing team members. Have the rest of the class judge the debate and give written or oral comments.

BRIEF ANSWERS TO SELECTED PROBLEMS

Answers are provided for *all in-chapter exercises*. Brief answers are given for *odd-numbered Review Questions*; more complete answers can be obtained by reviewing the text. Answers are provided for *all odd-numbered Problems and Additional Problems*.

NOTE: For numerical problems, your answer may differ slightly from ours because of rounding and the use of significant figures.

1 **a.** $^{235}_{92}U \longrightarrow ^{4}_{2}He + ^{231}_{90}Th$ **b.** $^{210}_{82}Pb \longrightarrow ^{0}_{-1}e + ^{210}_{83}Bi$
   c. $^{18}_{9}F \longrightarrow ^{0}_{+1}e + ^{18}_{8}O$ **d.** $^{13}_{8}O + ^{0}_{-1}e \longrightarrow ^{13}_{7}N$

2 **A.** 6.25%   **B.** 500 Bq; 4 Bq

3 **a.** yes (3 Bq left)   **b.** no (4.0×10^{10} Bq remain)

4 **a.** 11,460 y;   **b.** 49 y

5 **a.** A neutron ($^{1}_{0}n$)   **b.** Thorium-232 ($^{232}_{90}Th$)

6 Silicon-30 ($^{30}_{14}Si$)

7 Higher; the gas can be absorbed by inhalation and decay in the body.

1. (i), (b); (ii), (a); (iii), (c)

3. $^{1}_{1}H$, $^{2}_{1}H$, $^{3}_{1}H$

5. **a.** $^{60}_{27}Co$ **b.** $^{127}_{53}I$ **c.** $^{22}_{11}Na$ **d.** $^{42}_{20}Ca$

7. Isotopes: b, c

9. 155

11. **a.** A, down 4; Z, down 2 **b.** no change in either
   c. A, down 1; Z, down 1

13. **a.** alpha   **b.** gamma

15. more massive; energy dissipated over a short distance

17. Fission is the splitting of large atoms. Fusion is the joining of small atoms. Both liberate energy because, in each case, the nuclei formed have greater nuclear stability than the reacting nuclei (Fig. 11.10).

19. **a.** $^{250}_{98}Cf \longrightarrow ^{4}_{2}He + ^{246}_{96}Cm$
   b. $^{210}_{83}Bi \longrightarrow ^{210}_{84}Po + ^{0}_{-1}e$

21. **a.** $^{179}_{79}Au \longrightarrow ^{175}_{77}Ir + ^{4}_{2}He$
   b. $^{12}_{6}C + ^{2}_{1}H \longrightarrow ^{13}_{6}C + ^{1}_{1}H$
   c. $^{154}_{62}Sm + ^{1}_{0}n \longrightarrow 2\,^{1}_{0}n + ^{153}_{62}Sm$

23. beta particle; $^{99}_{42}Mo \longrightarrow ^{99m}_{43}Tc + ^{0}_{-1}e$

25. $^{24}_{12}Mg + ^{1}_{0}n \longrightarrow ^{1}_{1}H + ^{24}_{11}Na$; sodium-24

27. $^{215}_{85}At \longrightarrow ^{4}_{2}He + ^{211}_{83}Bi$; astatine-215

29. $^{210}_{87}Fr$

31. 156 h (6.5 d)

33. b

35. 26 s

37. 2 counts/min

39. 5730 y

41. 5730 y; 11,460 y

43. **a.** $^{121}_{51}Sb + ^{4}_{2}He \longrightarrow ^{124}_{53}I + ^{1}_{0}n$ **b.** $^{124}_{53}I \longrightarrow ^{124}_{52}Te + ^{0}_{+1}e$

45. $^{247}_{97}Bk + ^{48}_{20}Ca \longrightarrow ^{293}_{117}117 + 2\,^{1}_{0}n$; $^{247}_{97}Bk + ^{48}_{20}Ca \longrightarrow ^{294}_{117}117 + ^{1}_{0}n$

47. $^{223}_{88}Ra \longrightarrow ^{219}_{86}Rn + ^{4}_{2}He$; $^{223}_{88}Ra \longrightarrow ^{209}_{82}Pb + ^{14}_{6}C$

49. 853 cm³; 131 cm³; smaller than a baseball (~200 cm³)

51. **a.** 1900 y   **b.** 14,400 y

53. the neutron, $^{1}_{0}n$

55. **a.** 2.2×10^{13} cal; 2.2×10^{10} kcal
   b. 2.0×10^{8} bowls

57. 7.5×10^{17} atoms

59. false

61. The presence of two amides increases the ability to bind to metal ions without losing the benefits of using this type of molecule.

Biochemistry

From Chapter 16 of *Chemistry for Changing Times*, Thirteenth Edition. John W. Hill, Terry W. McCreary, Doris K. Kolb.

Tiago Sá Brito/Shutterstock

Learning Objectives

❭ List the major parts of a cell, and describe the function of each part. (1)

❭ Name the primary source of energy for plants and three classes of substances that are the sources of energy for animals. (1)

❭ Compare and contrast starch, glycogen, and cellulose. (2)

❭ Describe the fundamental structure of a fatty acid and of a fat. (3)

❭ Classify fats as saturated, monounsaturated, or polyunsaturated. (3)

❭ Draw the fundamental structure of an amino acid, and show how amino acids combine to make proteins. (4)

❭ Describe the four levels of protein structure, and give an example of each. (5)

❭ Describe how enzymes work as catalysts. (5)

❭ Name the two types of nucleic acids, and describe the function of each type. (6)

❭ Explain complementary base pairing, and describe how a copy of DNA is synthesized. (6)

❭ Explain how mRNA is synthesized from DNA and how a protein is synthesized from mRNA. (7)

❭ List important characteristics of the genetic code. (7)

❭ Describe recombinant DNA technology, and explain how it is used. (8)

❭ Name some advantages of using biochemistry to create useful molecules.

❭ Give examples of the use of biochemistry for energy production and other applications.

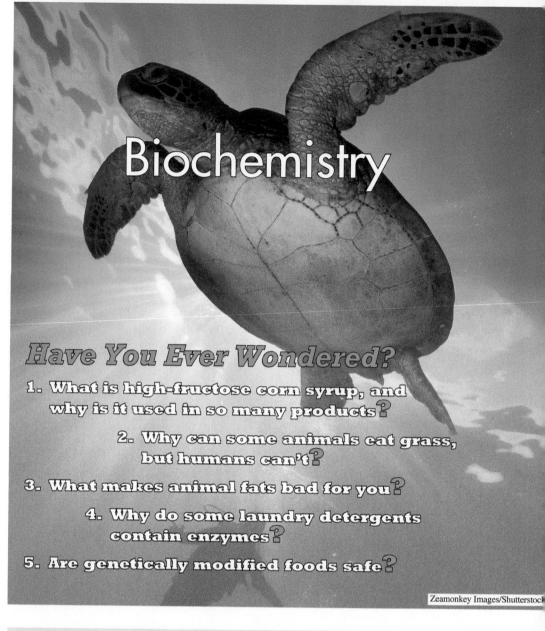

Biochemistry

Have You Ever Wondered?

1. **What is high-fructose corn syrup, and why is it used in so many products?**

2. **Why can some animals eat grass, but humans can't?**

3. **What makes animal fats bad for you?**

4. **Why do some laundry detergents contain enzymes?**

5. **Are genetically modified foods safe?**

Zeamonkey Images/Shutterstock

A Molecular View of Life

The human body is an incredible chemical factory, far more complex than any industrial plant. To stay in good condition and perform its varied tasks, it needs many specific chemical compounds—most of which it manufactures in an exquisitely organized network of chemical production lines.

Every minute of every day, thousands of chemical reactions take place within each of the 100 trillion tiny cells in your body. The study of these reactions and the chemicals they produce is called *biochemistry*.

picturepartners/Shutterstock

Every form of life is chemical in nature. The substances and reactions that occur in living organisms are often more complex than the ones we have already studied. Nonetheless, basic chemical concepts such as acid-base reactions, intermolecular forces, and the reactivity of organic functional groups all apply to living organisms. In this chapter, we will examine acid-base reactions that govern the behavior of proteins in our bodies. We will look at intermolecular forces that influence the properties and behavior of DNA and RNA. And we will see that the functional groups on fats are the same as those on other organic compounds we have studied.

1 Energy and the Living Cell

Learning Objectives ❭ List the major parts of a cell, and describe the function of each part. ❭ Name the primary source of energy for plants and three classes of substances that are the sources of energy for animals.

Biochemistry is the chemistry of living things and life processes. The structural unit of all living things is the *cell*. Every cell is enclosed in a *cell membrane*, through which it gains nutrients and gets rid of wastes. Plant cells (Figure 1) also have walls made of cellulose. Animal cells (see Figure 2) do not have cell walls. Cells have a variety of interior structures that serve a multiplicity of functions. We can consider only a few of them here.

The largest interior structure of a cell is usually the *nucleus*, which contains the material that controls heredity. Protein synthesis takes place in the *ribosomes*. The *mitochondria* are the cell's "batteries," where energy is produced. Plant cells (but not animal cells) also contain *chloroplasts*, in which energy from the Sun is converted to chemical energy, which is stored in the plant in the form of carbohydrates.

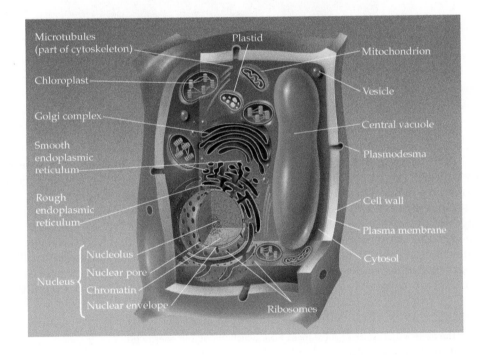

Microtubules (part of cytoskeleton)
Plastid
Mitochondrion
Chloroplast
Vesicle
Golgi complex
Central vacuole
Smooth endoplasmic reticulum
Plasmodesma
Rough endoplasmic reticulum
Cell wall
Plasma membrane
Cytosol
Nucleolus
Nuclear pore
Chromatin
Nuclear envelope
Nucleus
Ribosomes

◀ **Figure 1** The general form of a plant cell. Not all the structures shown here occur in every type of plant cell.

Energy in Biological Systems

Life requires energy. Living cells are inherently unstable, and only a continued input of energy keeps them from falling apart. Living organisms are restricted to using certain forms of energy. Supplying a plant with heat energy by holding it in a flame will do little to prolong its life. On the other hand, a green plant is uniquely able to use sunlight, the richest source of energy on Earth. Chloroplasts in green plant cells capture the radiant energy of the Sun and convert it to chemical energy, which is then stored in carbohydrate molecules. The photosynthesis of glucose is represented by the equation

$$6\,CO_2 + 6\,H_2O \longrightarrow C_6H_{12}O_6 + 6\,O_2$$

Plant cells can also convert the carbohydrate molecules to fat molecules and, given the proper inorganic nutrients, to protein molecules.

Biochemistry

▶ **Figure 2** An animal cell. The entire range of structures shown here seldom occurs in a single cell, and only a few of them are discussed in this text. Each kind of plant or animal tissue has cells specific to the function of that tissue. Muscle cells differ from nerve cells, nerve cells differ from red blood cells, and so on.

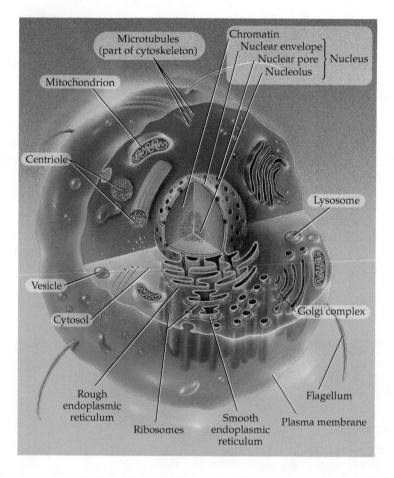

This chapter, deals mainly with the synthesis and structure of carbohydrates, fats, and protiens.

Animals cannot directly use the energy of sunlight. They must get their energy by eating plants or by eating other animals that eat plants. Animals obtain energy from three major types of substances: carbohydrates, fats, and proteins.

Once digested and transported to a cell, a food molecule can be used as a building block to make new cell parts or to repair old ones, or it can be "burned" for energy. The entire series of coordinated chemical reactions that keep cells alive is called **metabolism**. In general, metabolic reactions are divided into two classes: The degrading of molecules to provide energy is called **catabolism**, and the process of building up, or synthesizing, the molecules of living systems is termed **anabolism**.

Self-Assessment Questions

1. The three major types of substances from which we obtain energy are
   a. amino acids, proteins, and carbohydrates
   b. burgers, pizza, and soft drinks
   c. carbohydrates, fats, and proteins
   d. proteins, nucleic acids, and oils

2. The process of degrading molecules to provide energy within a living cell is called
   a. anabolism
   b. catabolism
   c. depolymerization
   d. transcription

3. The overall set of chemical reactions that keep cells alive is called
   a. anabolism
   b. enzymology
   c. metabolism
   d. proteolysis

Answers: 1, c; 2, b; 3, c

2 Carbohydrates: A Storehouse of Energy

Learning Objectives > Compare and contrast starch, glycogen, and cellulose.

It is difficult to give a simple formal definition of *carbohydrates*. Chemically, **carbohydrates** are polyhydroxy aldehydes or ketones or compounds that can be hydrolyzed (split by water) to form such aldehydes and ketones. Composed of the elements carbon, hydrogen, and oxygen, carbohydrates include sugars, starches, and cellulose. Usually, the atoms of these elements are present in a ratio expressed by the formula $C_x(H_2O)_y$. Glucose, a simple sugar, has the formula $C_6H_{12}O_6$, which we can write as $C_6(H_2O)_6$. The term *carbohydrate* is derived from formulas written in this way, but keep in mind that carbohydrates are not actually hydrates of carbon.

Some Simple Sugars

Sugars are sweet-tasting carbohydrates. The simplest sugars are **monosaccharides**, carbohydrates that cannot be further hydrolyzed. Three familiar dietary monosaccharides are shown in Figure 3. They are *glucose* (also called *dextrose*), *galactose* (a component of lactose, the sugar in milk), and *fructose* (fruit sugar). Glucose and galactose are **aldoses**, monosaccharides with an aldehyde functional group. Fructose is a **ketose**, a monosaccharide with a ketone functional group. Pure fructose is about 25% sweeter than table sugar (sucrose, shown on the next page); glucose is about 25% less sweet than table sugar.

CONCEPTUAL Example 1 | Classification of Monosaccharides

Shown below are structures of (left to right) erythrulose, used in some sunless tanning lotions; mannose, a sugar found in some fruits, including cranberries; and ribose, a component of ribonucleic acid (RNA; Section 7).

Classify erythrulose and ribose as an aldose or a ketose.

Solution
Erythrulose is a ketose. The carbonyl (C=O) group is on the second C atom from the top; it is between two other C atoms, an arrangement that defines a ketone. Ribose is an aldose. The carbonyl group includes a chain-ending carbon atom, as in all aldehydes.

■ EXERCISE 1
How does the structure of mannose (shown above) differ from that of glucose?

The monosaccharides glucose, galactose, and fructose are represented in Figure 3 as open-chain compounds to show the aldehyde or ketone functional groups. However, these sugars exist in solution mainly as cyclic molecules (see Figure 4).

1. What is high-fructose corn syrup, and why is it used in so many products? High-fructose corn syrup (HFCS) has had some of its glucose enzymatically converted to fructose. This makes it significantly sweeter than ordinary corn syrup, because fructose is sweeter than glucose. HFCS is quite cheap in the United States. Unfortunately, like table sugar, it provides little more than empty calories.

▶ **Figure 3** Three common monosaccharides. All have hydroxyl groups. Glucose and galactose have aldehyde functional groups, and fructose has a ketone group. Glucose and galactose differ only in the arrangement of the H and OH on the fourth carbon (green) from the top. Living cells use glucose as a source of energy. Fructose is fruit sugar, and galactose is a component of milk sugar.

Q: *What is the molecular formula of each of the three monosaccharides? How are the three compounds related?*

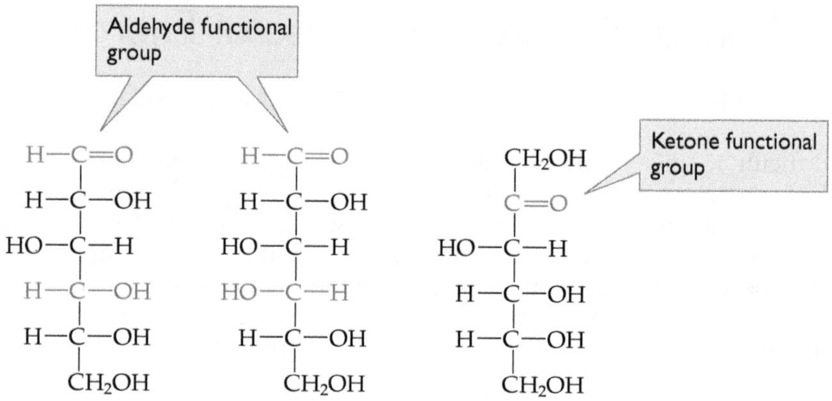

Aldehyde functional group

Ketone functional group

Glucose   Galactose   Fructose

Aldoses   **A ketose**

▶ **Figure 4** Cyclic structures for glucose, galactose, and fructose. A corner with no letter represents a carbon atom. Glucose and galactose differ only in the arrangement of the H and OH (green) on the fourth carbon. Some sugars exist in more than one cyclic form, but, for simplicity, only one form of each is shown here.

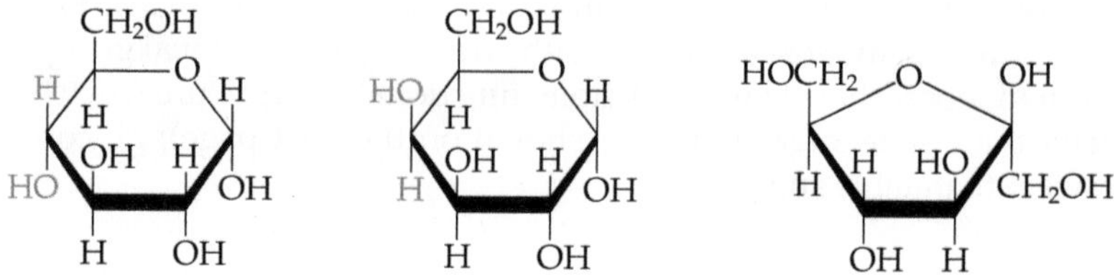

Glucose   Galactose   Fructose

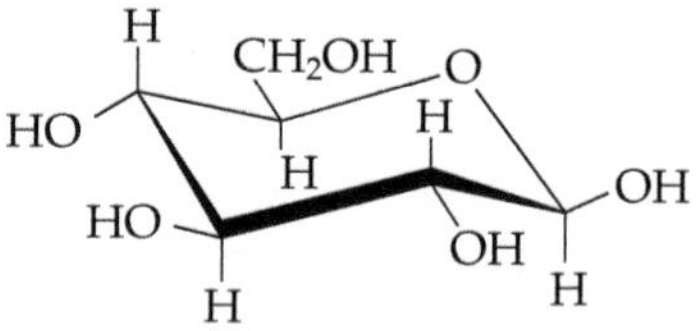

▲ Although we have represented the cyclic monosaccharides as flat hexagons, they are actually three-dimensional. Most assume a conformation (shape) called a *chair conformation* because it somewhat resembles a reclining chair.

Sucrose and lactose are examples of **disaccharides**, carbohydrates whose molecules can be hydrolyzed to yield two monosaccharide units (Figure 5). Sucrose is split into glucose and fructose. Hydrolysis of lactose yields glucose and galactose.

$$Sucrose + H_2O \longrightarrow Glucose + Fructose$$

$$Lactose + H_2O \longrightarrow Glucose + Galactose$$

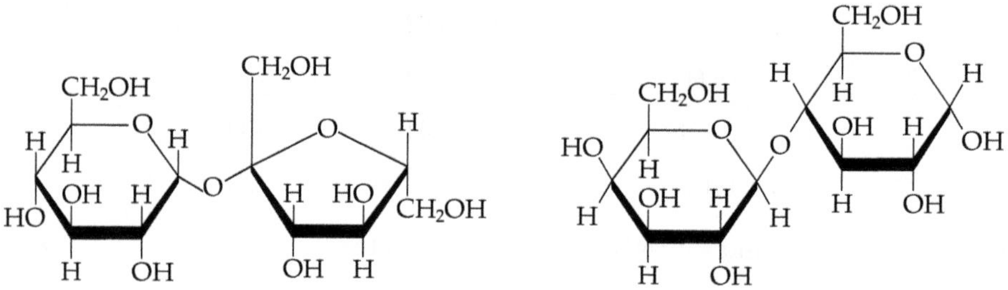

Sucrose   Lactose

▲ **Figure 5** Sucrose and lactose are disaccharides. On hydrolysis, sucrose yields glucose and fructose, whereas lactose yields glucose and galactose. Sucrose is cane or beet sugar, and lactose is milk sugar.

Q: *What is the molecular formula of each of these disaccharides? How are the two compounds related? Label the two monosaccharide units in each as fructose, galactose, or glucose.*

Polysaccharides: Starch and Cellulose

Polysaccharides are composed of large molecules that yield many monosaccharide units on hydrolysis. Polysaccharides include starches, which comprise the main energy-storage system of many plants, and cellulose, which is the structural material of plants. Figure 6 shows short segments of starch and cellulose molecules.

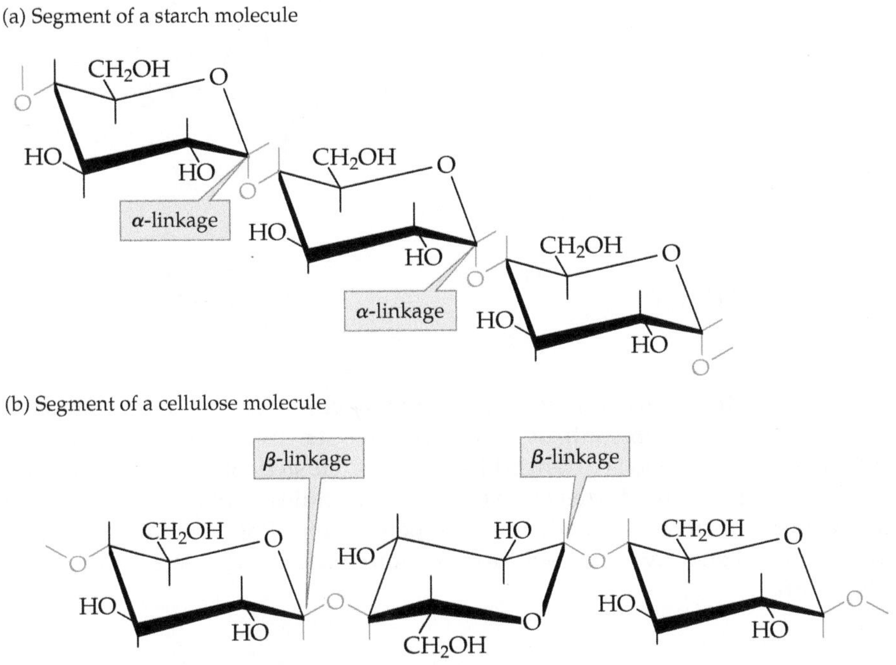

(a) Segment of a starch molecule

CH₂OH

α-linkage

CH₂OH

α-linkage

CH₂OH

(b) Segment of a cellulose molecule

β-linkage

β-linkage

CH₂OH

HO

HO

CH₂OH

CH₂OH

HO

HO

HO

HO

CH₂OH

◄ **Figure 6** Both starch and cellulose are polymers of glucose. They differ in that the glucose units are joined by alpha linkages (blue) in starch and by beta linkages (red) in cellulose.

Q: *The formulas for most polymers can be written in condensed form. Write a condensed formula for starch. How would the condensed formula for cellulose differ from that of starch?*

Notice that both are polymers of glucose. Starch molecules generally have from 100 to about 6000 glucose units. Cellulose molecules are composed of 1800–3000 or more glucose units.

A crucial structural difference between starch and cellulose is the way the glucose units are hooked together. In starch, with the —CH₂OH group at the top as a reference, the oxygen atom joining the glucose units is pointed *down*. This arrangement is called an *alpha linkage*. In cellulose, again with the —CH₂OH group as the point of reference, the oxygen atom connecting the glucose units is pointed *up*, an arrangement called a *beta linkage*.

This subtle but important difference in linkage determines whether the material can be digested by humans. The different linkages also result in different three-dimensional forms for cellulose and starch. For example, cellulose in the cell walls of plants is arranged in *fibrils*, bundles of parallel chains. As shown in Figure 7(a), these fibrils lie parallel to each other in each layer of the cell wall. In alternate layers, the fibrils are perpendicular, an arrangement that imparts great strength to the cell wall.

There are two kinds of starches found in plants. One, called *amylose*, has glucose units joined in a continuous chain like beads on a string. The other kind, *amylopectin*, has branched chains of glucose units. These starches are perhaps best represented schematically, as in Figure 8, where each glucose unit is represented by filled circles.

2. Why can some animals eat grass, but humans can't? Although both cellulose and starch are glucose polymers, humans do not have the enzyme to break the beta linkages in cellulose. The digestive systems of cows, horses, and deer contain bacteria that can break these linkages, allowing these ruminants to digest the cellulose in grass.

◄ **Figure 7** Cellulose molecules form fibers, whereas starch molecules (glycogen) form granules. Electron micrographs of (a) the cell wall of an alga, made up of successive layers of cellulose fibers in parallel arrangement, and (b) glycogen granules in a liver cell of a rat.

Biophoto Associates/Photo Researchers, Inc.

(a)

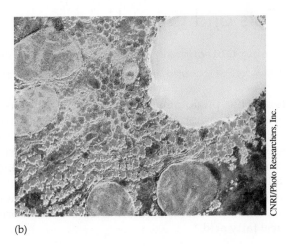

CNRI/Photo Researchers, Inc.

(b)

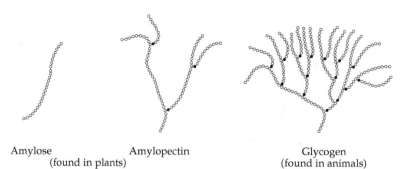

Amylose
(found in plants)

Amylopectin

Glycogen
(found in animals)

► Figure 8 Schematic representations of amylose, amylopectin, and glycogen. Amylose is unbranched. Amylopectin has a branch approximately every 25 glucose units. Glycogen branches about every 10 glucose units.

When cornstarch is heated at about 400 °F for an hour, the starch polymers are broken down into shorter chains to form a product called *dextrin*, which has properties intermediate between those of sugars and starches. Mixed with water, dextrin makes a slightly thick, sticky mixture. Starch and dextrin adhesives account for about 58% of the U.S. packaging market.

Animal starch is called *glycogen*. Like amylopectin, it is composed of branched chains of glucose units. In contrast to cellulose, we see in Figure 7(b) that glycogen in muscle and liver tissue is arranged in granules, clusters of small particles. Plant starch, on the other hand, forms large granules. Granules of plant starch rupture in boiling water to form a paste, which gels when it cools. Potatoes and cereal grains form this type of starchy broth. All forms of starch are hydrolyzed to glucose during digestion.

Self-Assessment Questions

1. A monosaccharide with an aldehyde group is called
   a. an aldol
   b. an aldose
   c. aldicarb
   d. aldosterol

2. A ketose is a monosaccharide
   a. diet aid
   b. that forms polyhydroxy cellulose
   c. that causes ketosis
   d. with a ketone group

3. When most monosaccharides dissolve in water, they form
   a. branched polysaccharides
   b. disaccharides
   c. ring structures
   d. polysaccharides

4. The two monosaccharide units that make up a lactose molecule are
   a. both glucose
   b. fructose and galactose
   c. glucose and fructose
   d. glucose and galactose

5. Which of these polysaccharide molecules consists of branched chains of glucose units?
   a. amylose and amylopectin
   b. amylose and cellulose
   c. amylose and glycogen
   d. amylopectin and glycogen

6. Carbohydrates are stored in the liver and muscle tissue as
   a. amylose
   b. amylopectin
   c. cellulose
   d. glycogen

Answers: 1. b; 2. d; 3. c; 4. d; 5. d; 6. d

3 Fats and Other Lipids

Learning Objectives ❯ Describe the fundamental structure of a fatty acid and of a fat.
❯ Classify fats as saturated, monounsaturated, or polyunsaturated.

Fats are the predominant forms of a class of compounds called *lipids*. These substances are not defined by a functional group, as are most other families of organic compounds. Rather, lipids have common solubility properties. A **lipid** is a cellular component that is insoluble in water but soluble in organic solvents of low polarity, such as hexane, diethyl ether, and chloroform. In addition to fats, the lipid family includes **fatty acids** (long-chain carboxylic acids), steroids such as cholesterol and sex hormones, fat-soluble vitamins, and other substances. Figure 9 shows three representations of palmitic acid, a typical fatty acid.

$$CH_3CH_2CH_2CH_2CH_2CH_2CH_2CH_2CH_2CH_2CH_2CH_2CH_2CH_2CH_2COOH$$

(a)

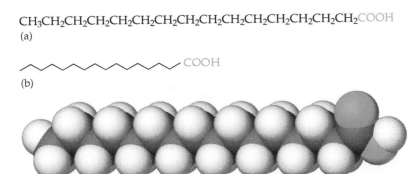

(b)

(c)

◀ **Figure 9** Three representations of palmitic acid: (a) Condensed structural formula. (b) Line-angle formula, in which the lines denote bonds and each intersection of lines or end of a line represents a carbon atom. (c) Space-filling model.

A **fat** is an ester of fatty acids and the trihydroxy alcohol glycerol (Figure 10). A fat has three fatty acid chains joined to glycerol through ester linkages (which is why fats are often called *triglycerides*, or *triacylglycerols*). Related compounds are also classified according to the number of fatty acid chains they contain: A *monoglyceride* has one fatty acid chain joined to glycerol, and a *diglyceride* has two.

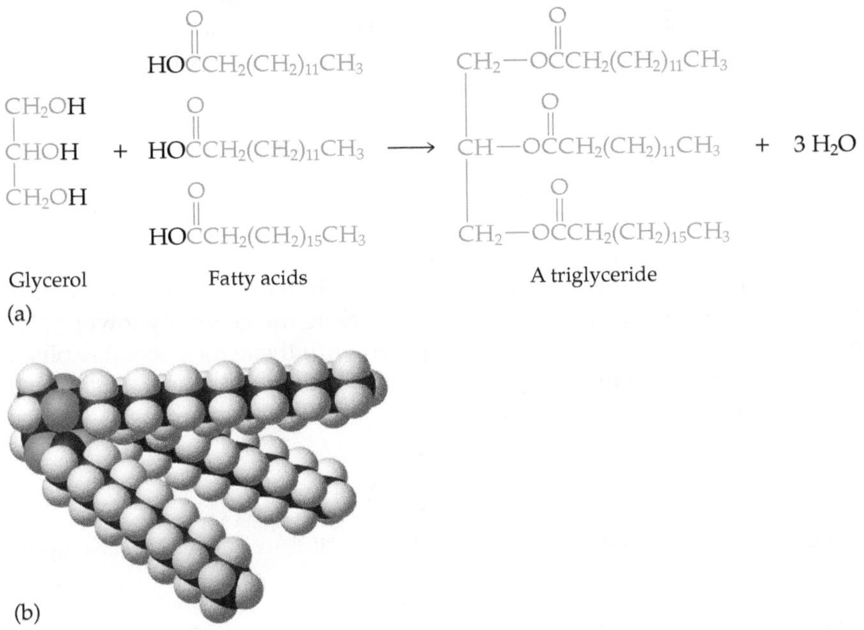

◀ **Figure 10** Triglycerides (triacylglycerols) are esters in which the trihydroxy (having three OH groups) alcohol glycerol is esterified with three fatty acid groups. (a) The equation for the formation of a triglyceride. (b) Space-filling model of a triglyceride.

Glycerol   Fatty acids   A triglyceride

(a)

(b)

Naturally occurring fatty acids nearly always have an even number of carbon atoms. Representative ones are listed in Table 1. Animal fats are generally rich in saturated fatty acids (fatty acids with no carbon-to-carbon double bonds) and have a smaller proportion of unsaturated fatty acids. At room temperature, most animal fats are solids. Liquid fats, called *oils*, are obtained mainly from vegetable sources. Oils typically have a higher proportion of unsaturated fatty acid units than do fats. Fats and oils feel greasy. They are less dense than water and float on it.

Fats are often classified according to the degree of unsaturation of the fatty acids they incorporate. A *saturated fatty acid* contains no carbon-to-carbon double bonds, a *monounsaturated fatty acid* has one carbon-to-carbon double bond per molecule, and a *polyunsaturated fatty acid* has two or more carbon-to-carbon double bonds. A *saturated fat* contains a high proportion of saturated fatty acids; these fat molecules have relatively few carbon-to-carbon double bonds. A *polyunsaturated fat* (oil) incorporates mainly unsaturated fatty acids; these fat molecules have many double bonds.

Table 1 — Some Fatty Acids in Natural Fats

Number of Carbon Atoms	Condensed Structural Formula	Name	Source
4	$CH_3CH_2CH_2COOH$	Butyric acid	Butter
6	$CH_3(CH_2)_4COOH$	Caproic acid	Butter
8	$CH_3(CH_2)_6COOH$	Caprylic acid	Coconut oil
10	$CH_3(CH_2)_8COOH$	Capric acid	Coconut oil
12	$CH_3(CH_2)_{10}COOH$	Lauric acid	Palm kernel oil
14	$CH_3(CH_2)_{12}COOH$	Myristic acid	Oil of nutmeg
16	$CH_3(CH_2)_{14}COOH$	Palmitic acid	Palm oil
18	$CH_3(CH_2)_{16}COOH$	Stearic acid	Beef tallow
18	$CH_3(CH_2)_7CH{=}CH(CH_2)_7COOH$	Oleic acid	Olive oil
18	$CH_3(CH_2)_4CH{=}CHCH_2CH{=}CH(CH_2)_7COOH$	Linoleic acid	Soybean oil
18	$CH_3CH_2(CH{=}CHCH_2)_3(CH_2)_6COOH$	Linolenic acid	Fish oils
20	$CH_3(CH_2)_4(CH{=}CHCH_2)_4CH_2CH_2COOH$	Arachidonic acid	Liver

The iodine number is a measure of the degree of unsaturation of a fat or oil. The **iodine number** is the mass in grams of iodine that is consumed by 100 g of fat or oil. Iodine, like other halogens, adds to a carbon-to-carbon double bond.

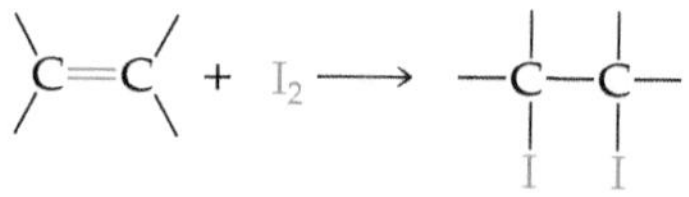

$$\ce{>C=C< + I2 -> -\underset{|}{\overset{|}{C}}-\underset{|}{\overset{|}{C}}-}$$

3. What makes animal fats bad for you? The saturated fats found in most animal fats can pack closely together to form artery-clogging plaque, which contributes to heart disease. The structures of unsaturated fats do not stack neatly and do not form this plaque.

The more double bonds a fat contains, the more iodine is required for the addition reaction. Thus, a high iodine number means a high degree of unsaturation. Representative iodine numbers are listed in Table 2. Note the generally lower values for animal fats (butter, tallow, and lard) compared with those for vegetable oils. Coconut oil, which is highly saturated, and fish oils, which are relatively unsaturated, are notable exceptions to the general rule.

Table 2 — Typical Iodine Numbers for Some Fats and Oils[a]

Fat or Oil	Iodine Number	Fat or Oil	Iodine Number
Coconut oil	8–10	Cottonseed oil	100–117
Butter	25–40	Corn oil	115–130
Beef tallow	30–45	Fish oils	120–180
Palm oil	37–54	Canola oil	125–135
Lard	45–70	Soybean oil	125–140
Olive oil	75–95	Safflower oil	130–140
Peanut oil	85–100	Sunflower oil	130–145

[a]Oils shown in blue are from plant sources.

Shutterstock

▲ Many salad dressings are made of an oil and vinegar. The one shown here has olive oil floating on balsamic vinegar, an aqueous solution of acetic acid.

Self-Assessment Questions

1. Lipids are defined by their
   a. chemical reactivity
   b. functional group
   c. function in the body
   d. solubility properties

Questions 2–6 refer to the structures S, T, U, and V.

   S: CH$_3$(CH$_2$)$_{10}$COOH   T: CH$_3$(CH$_2$)$_{16}$COOH

   U: CH$_3$(CH$_2$)$_7$CH=CH(CH$_2$)$_7$COOH   V: CH$_3$CH$_2$(CH=CHCH$_2$)$_3$(CH$_2$)$_6$COOH

2. Which are saturated fatty acids?
   a. S and T   **b.** S and U   **c.** T and U   **d.** U and V

3. Which is a monounsaturated fatty acid?
   a. S   **b.** T   **c.** U   **d.** V

4. Which is a polyunsaturated fatty acid?
   a. S   **b.** T   **c.** U   **d.** V

5. Saturated fats often have a high proportion of
   a. S and T   **b.** S and U   **c.** T and U   **d.** U and V

6. Polyunsaturated fats (oils) often have a high proportion of
   a. S   **b.** T   **c.** U   **d.** V

7. The iodine number of a fat or oil expresses its
   a. calories per gram
   b. degree of acidity
   c. degree of unsaturation
   d. digestibility

8. In general, animal fats differ from vegetable oils in that the fat molecules
   a. are higher in calories
   b. are shorter
   c. have fewer C=C bonds
   d. have more C=C bonds

Answers: 1, d; 2, a; 3, c; 4, d; 5, c; 6, d; 7, c; 8, c

4 Proteins: Polymers of Amino Acids

Learning Objective ❯ Draw the fundamental structure of an amino acid, and show how amino acids combine to make proteins.

Proteins are vital components of all life. No living part of the human body—or of any other organism, for that matter—is completely without protein. There is protein in blood, muscles, brain, and even tooth enamel. The smallest cellular organisms—bacteria—contain protein. Viruses, so small that they make bacteria look like giants, are little more than proteins and nucleic acids, a combination that is the stuff of life itself.

Each type of cell makes its own kinds of proteins. Proteins serve as the structural materials of animals, much as cellulose does in plants. Muscle tissue is largely protein, and so are skin and hair. Silk, wool, nails, claws, feathers, horns, and hooves are proteins. All proteins contain the elements carbon, hydrogen, oxygen, and nitrogen, and most also contain sulfur. The structure of a short segment of a typical protein molecule is shown in Figure 11.

Like starch and cellulose, *proteins* are polymers. They differ from other polymers that we have studied in that the monomer units are about 20 different amino acids (Table 3). The amino acids differ in their side chains (shown in green). An **amino acid** has two functional groups, an amino group (—NH$_2$) and a carboxyl group (—COOH), attached to the same carbon atom (called the *alpha carbon*).

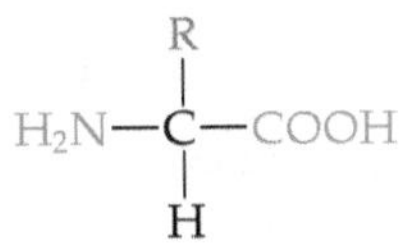

$$H_2N-\overset{\overset{\displaystyle R}{|}}{\underset{\underset{\displaystyle H}{|}}{C}}-COOH$$

Biochemistry

▶ **Figure 11** Space-filling model (a) and structural formula (b) of a short segment of a protein molecule. In the structural formula, hydrocarbon side chains (green), an acidic side chain (red), a basic side chain (blue), and a sulfur-containing side chain (amber shading) are highlighted. The dashed lines crossing the formula indicate where two amino-acid units join (see Section 5).

Q: *The formulas for most polymers can be written in condensed form. Those for natural proteins cannot. Explain.*

(a)   (b)

Richard Megna/Fundamental Photographs

In this formula, the R can be a hydrogen atom (as it is in glycine, the simplest amino acid) or any of the groups shown in green in Table 3. The formula shows the proper placement of the groups, but it is not really correct. Acids react with bases to form salts. The carboxyl group is acidic, and the amino group is basic. The two functional groups interact, the acid transferring a proton to the base. The resulting product is an inner salt, or **zwitterion**, a compound in which the negative charge and the positive charge are on different parts of the same molecule.

$$H_3N^+ - \overset{\overset{\displaystyle R}{|}}{\underset{\underset{\displaystyle H}{|}}{C}} - COO^-$$

A zwitterion

Plants can synthesize proteins from carbon dioxide, water, and minerals such as nitrates (NO_3^-) and sulfates (SO_4^{2-}). Animals need to consume proteins in their foods. Humans can synthesize some of the amino acids in Table 3. Others must be part of the proteins consumed in a normal diet. The latter are called *essential amino acids*.

The Peptide Bond: Peptides and Proteins

The human body contains tens of thousands of different proteins. Each of us has a tailor-made set. Proteins are polyamides. The amide linkage is called a **peptide bond** (shaded part of the structure below) when it joins two amino-acid units.

$$H_2N - \overset{\overset{\displaystyle R_1}{|}}{\underset{\underset{\displaystyle H}{|}}{C}} - \overset{\overset{\displaystyle }{|}}{\underset{\underset{\displaystyle O}{||}}{C}} - \overset{\overset{\displaystyle H}{|}}{N} - \overset{\overset{\displaystyle H}{|}}{\underset{\underset{\displaystyle R_2}{|}}{C}} - COOH$$

108

Table 3 The 20 Amino Acids Specified by the Human Genetic Code

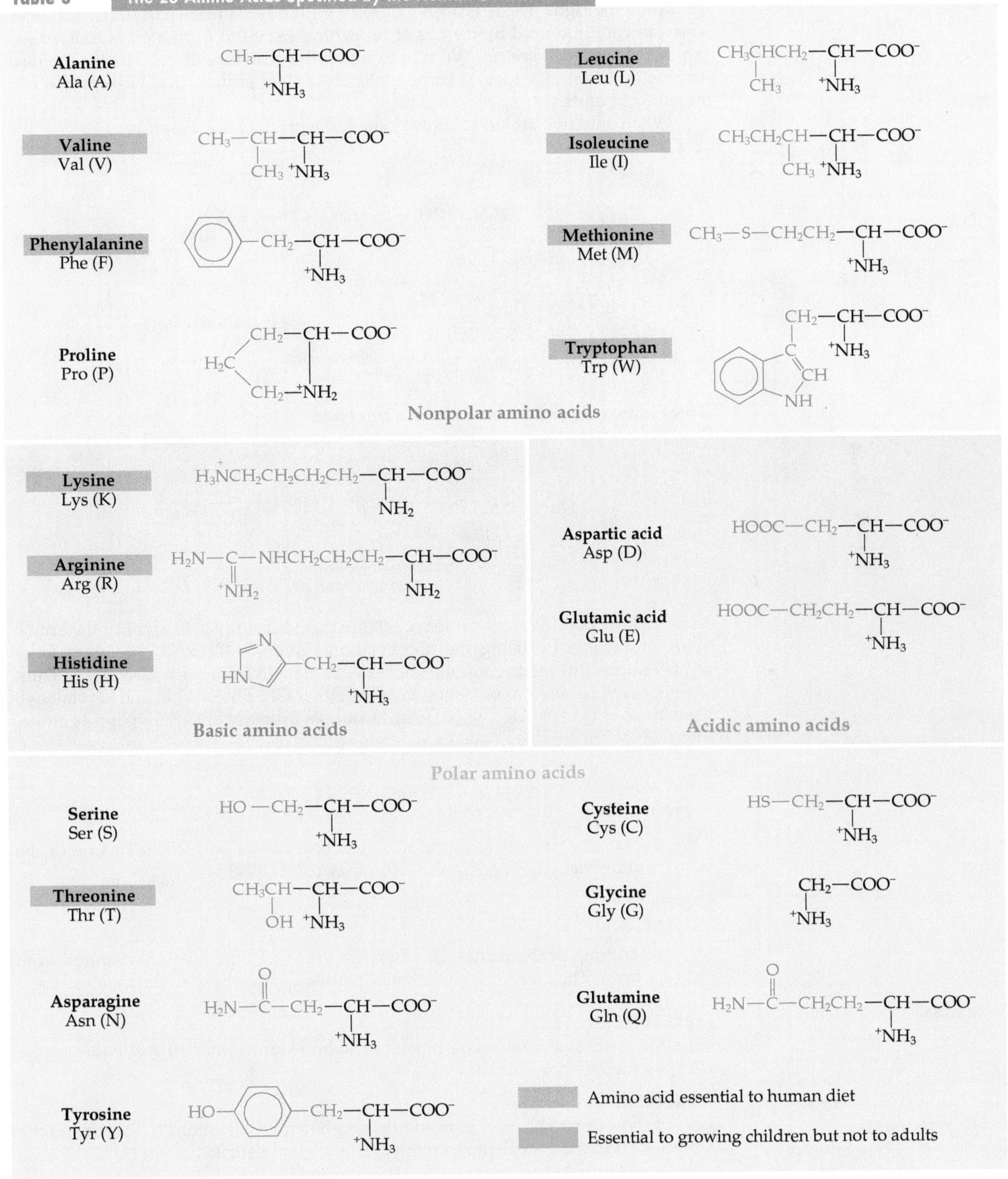

Alanine
Ala (A)

$$CH_3-CH-COO^-$$
$$\quad\quad\; ^+NH_3$$

Leucine
Leu (L)

$$CH_3CHCH_2-CH-COO^-$$
$$\quad\; CH_3 \quad\; ^+NH_3$$

Valine
Val (V)

$$CH_3-CH-CH-COO^-$$
$$\quad\quad CH_3\; ^+NH_3$$

Isoleucine
Ile (I)

$$CH_3CH_2CH-CH-COO^-$$
$$\quad\quad\; CH_3\; ^+NH_3$$

Phenylalanine
Phe (F)

$$\bigcirc-CH_2-CH-COO^-$$
$$\quad\quad\quad\; ^+NH_3$$

Methionine
Met (M)

$$CH_3-S-CH_2CH_2-CH-COO^-$$
$$\quad\quad\quad\quad\quad\; ^+NH_3$$

Proline
Pro (P)

$$CH_2-CH-COO^-$$
$$H_2C \quad\quad\; ^+NH_2$$
$$CH_2$$

Tryptophan
Trp (W)

$$CH_2-CH-COO^-$$
$$C \quad\quad\; ^+NH_3$$
$$CH$$
$$NH$$

Nonpolar amino acids

Lysine
Lys (K)

$$H_3NCH_2CH_2CH_2CH_2-CH-COO^-$$
$$\quad\quad\quad\quad\quad\quad NH_2$$

Arginine
Arg (R)

$$H_2N-C-NHCH_2CH_2CH_2-CH-COO^-$$
$$\quad\; ^+NH_2 \quad\quad\quad\quad NH_2$$

Histidine
His (H)

$$N$$
$$HN \quad -CH_2-CH-COO^-$$
$$\quad\quad\quad\quad\; ^+NH_3$$

Aspartic acid
Asp (D)

$$HOOC-CH_2-CH-COO^-$$
$$\quad\quad\quad\quad ^+NH_3$$

Glutamic acid
Glu (E)

$$HOOC-CH_2CH_2-CH-COO^-$$
$$\quad\quad\quad\quad\quad ^+NH_3$$

Basic amino acids

Acidic amino acids

Polar amino acids

Serine
Ser (S)

$$HO-CH_2-CH-COO^-$$
$$\quad\quad\quad ^+NH_3$$

Cysteine
Cys (C)

$$HS-CH_2-CH-COO^-$$
$$\quad\quad\quad ^+NH_3$$

Threonine
Thr (T)

$$CH_3CH-CH-COO^-$$
$$\quad OH \; ^+NH_3$$

Glycine
Gly (G)

$$CH_2-COO^-$$
$$^+NH_3$$

Asparagine
Asn (N)

$$O$$
$$H_2N-C-CH_2-CH-COO^-$$
$$\quad\quad\quad\quad ^+NH_3$$

Glutamine
Gln (Q)

$$O$$
$$H_2N-C-CH_2CH_2-CH-COO^-$$
$$\quad\quad\quad\quad\quad ^+NH_3$$

Tyrosine
Tyr (Y)

$$HO-\bigcirc-CH_2-CH-COO^-$$
$$\quad\quad\quad\quad\quad ^+NH_3$$

Amino acid essential to human diet

Essential to growing children but not to adults

Note that this molecule still has a reactive amino group on the left and a carboxyl group on the right. These groups can react with other amino-acid units. This process can continue until thousands of units have joined to form a giant molecule—a polymer called a *protein*. We will examine the structure of proteins in the next section, but first let's look at some molecules called *peptides* that have only a few amino-acid units.

When only two amino acids are joined, the product is a *dipeptide*.

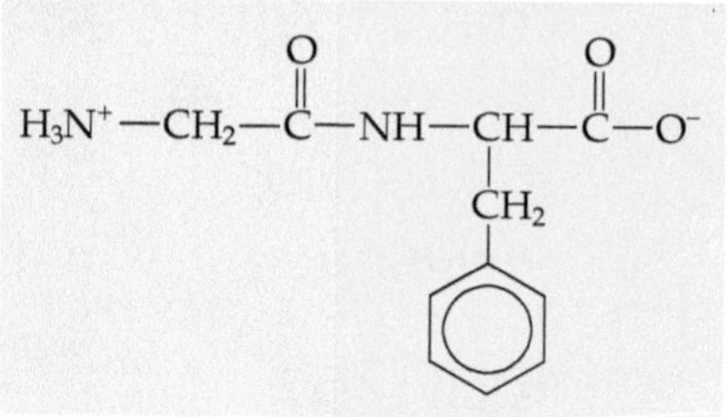

Glycylphenylalanine
(a dipeptide)

Three amino acids combine to form a *tripeptide*.

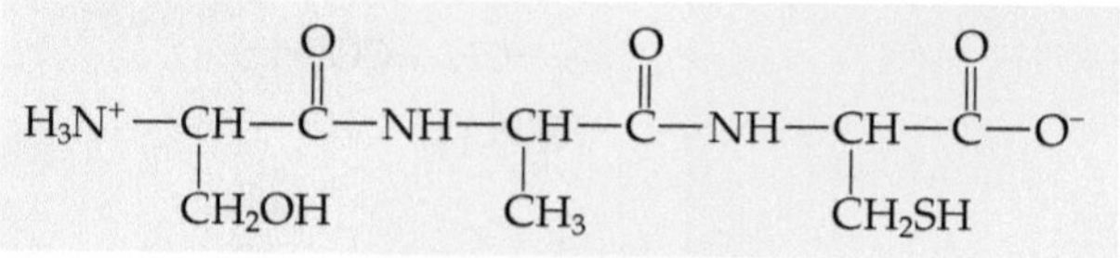

Serylalanylcysteine
(a tripeptide)

In describing peptides and proteins, scientists find it simpler to identify the amino acids in a chain by using the abbreviations given in Table 3. The three-letter abbreviations are more common, but the single-letter ones are also used. Thus, glycylphenylalanine can be abbreviated as either Gly-Phe or G-F, and serylalanyl-cysteine as either Ser-Ala-Cys or S-A-C. Example 2 further illustrates peptide names and their abbreviations.

Example 2   Names of Peptides

Give the **(a)** designation using one-letter abbreviations and **(b)** full name of the pentapeptide Met-Gly-Phe-Ala-Cys. You may use Table 3.

Solution

a. M-G-F-A-C

b. The endings of the names for all except the last amino acid are changed from -*ine* to -*yl*. The name is therefore methionylglycylphenylalanylalanylcysteine.

■ EXERCISE 2A

Give the **(a)** designation using one-letter abbreviations and **(b)** full name of the tetrapeptide His-Pro-Val-Ala.

■ EXERCISE 2B

Use **(a)** three-letter abbreviations and **(b)** one-letter abbreviations to identify all the amino acids in the peptide threonylglycylalanylalanylleucine.

A molecule with more than 10 amino-acid units is often simply called a **polypeptide**. When the molecular weight of a polypeptide exceeds about 10,000, it is called a **protein**. These distinctions are arbitrary and not always precisely applied.

Some protein molecules are enormous, with molecular weights in the tens of thousands. The molecular formula for hemoglobin, the oxygen-carrying protein in red blood cells, is $C_{3032}H_{4816}O_{780}N_{780}S_8Fe_4$, corresponding to a molar mass of 64,450 g/mol. Although they are huge compared with ordinary molecules, a billion average-sized protein molecules could still fit on the head of a pin.

GREEN CHEMISTRY

Principles 1, 2, 3, 4, 5, 6, 7, 8, 9, 10, 12

David A. Vosburg, *Harvey Mudd College*

Green Chemistry and Biochemistry

Chemistry has gone on constantly for millions of years in plants, animals, and bacteria. These living systems perform many chemical reactions, and plants have evolved to harness energy from the Sun using photosynthesis. Living things store energy in the form of carbohydrates (like glucose, sucrose, and cellulose, Section 2) and lipids (fats and oils, Section 3). These renewable feedstocks (Principle 7) hold great potential for supplying human energy needs in the future.

Chemists are devising ways of converting these natural energy reservoirs into substitutes for nonrenewable petroleum fuels, and biochemists are engineering existing biochemical pathways in various microorganisms to directly produce usable fuels. In 2009 and 2010, three Presidential Green Chemistry Challenge Awards were given for work in this area to Virent Energy Systems, James Liao, and LS9. Virent's process transforms plant carbohydrates into gasoline, which could reduce U.S. dependence on fossil fuels. Liao and coworkers (UCLA and Easel Biotechnologies) have engineered bacteria to turn carbohydrates and carbon dioxide into alcohols that can be used as fuels. The LS9 company developed microorganisms that directly produce hydrocarbon fuels. All of these achievements use the products or processes of biochemistry to address the energy needs of tomorrow.

Using biochemistry to make molecules has several distinct advantages over traditional chemical synthesis and invokes many of the green chemistry principles. The reactions normally occur in water, a ubiquitous, nontoxic, and nonflammable solvent (Principle 5). When reaction products are nonpolar, they can often be separated easily from the more polar water. In contrast to many current industrial reactions that are performed at very high temperatures and pressures, most biochemical reactions are extremely rapid and occur at mild temperatures and atmospheric pressure. These reactions reduce both energy costs and potential hazards (Principles 6 and 12). The atom economy of biochemical reactions is very high, as protecting groups and auxiliaries are not necessary (Principles 2 and 8), and toxic reagents and products can also be avoided in most cases (Principles 3 and 4). Biological reactions are frequently catalytic, using a single enzyme (Section 5) for thousands or millions of repeated reactions to selectively generate products with very little waste produced (Principles 1 and 9). Furthermore, the products formed (and the biological catalysts themselves) are generally biodegradable and innocuous (Principle 10). Also, when compounds are not themselves biodegradable, other biochemical pathways may be employed to degrade molecules that would otherwise persist in the environment. This bioremediation of environmental waste by cleaning up toxins and purifying water is a very important advantage of using biochemistry.

A common challenge associated with organic reactions is the production of specific isomers of molecules. Although these processes traditionally have relied on metal compounds as catalysts, new biochemical routes are increasingly preferred. For example, Merck and Codexis received a Presidential Green Chemistry Challenge Award in 2010 for their development of an enzyme catalyst for the production of the diabetes drug Januvia. As an example of the pace of innovation, the new method replaced a high-pressure reaction that used hydrogen gas and an expensive rhodium catalyst, a process that had been recognized with a Presidential Green Chemistry Challenge Award in 2006. The new biochemical pathway increases the yield of the drug and dramatically reduces the amount of waste produced. These innovations benefit the pharmaceutical companies, diabetics, the environment, and society at large.

The self-replicating nature of the cell and its DNA and the self-assembling (folding) properties of proteins (Section 5) make biological systems ideal candidates for the discovery and implementation of novel chemical processes. One of the greatest strengths of biochemical reactions is also the greatest challenge: specificity. Biological catalysts have evolved to have exquisite selectivity for their natural substrate(s), so adapting these catalysts to have more general function for a wider range of (potentially unnatural) substrates is difficult. Yet this is precisely what was done by Merck and Codexis for the synthesis of Januvia, so there is hope that similar approaches could lead to other successes.

▲ Genetic engineering of bacteria may transform natural energy sources into materials that will be energy-rich for human use. *Synechococcus elongatus*, shown here, may be particularly useful because of its small genome and its aptitude for photosynthesis.

UCLA Henry Samueli School of Engineering and Applied Science

The Sequence of Amino Acids

For peptides and proteins to function properly, it is not enough that they incorporate certain *amounts* of specific amino acids. The order, or *sequence*, in which the amino acids are connected, is also of critical importance. The sequence is written starting at the free amino group ($-NH_3^+$), called the *N-terminal* end, and continuing to the free carboxyl group ($-COO^-$), called the *C-terminal* end.

$$H_3N^+ \; CHC-NHCHC\left(NHCHC\right)_n NHCHC-NHCHC-O^-$$

N-terminal end   C-terminal end

Glycylalanine (Gly-Ala) is therefore different from alanylglycine (Ala-Gly). Although the difference seems minor, the structures are different, and the two substances behave differently in the body.

$$H_3N^+ \; CH_2CO-NHCHCOO^- \qquad H_3N^+ \; CHCO-NHCH_2COO^-$$
$$CH_3 \qquad\qquad\qquad CH_3$$

Glycylalanine   Alanylglycine

As the length of a peptide chain increases, the number of possible sequential variations becomes enormous. Just as millions of different words can be made from the 26 letters of the English alphabet, millions of different proteins can be made from the 20 amino acids. And just as we can write gibberish with the English alphabet, nonfunctioning proteins can be formed by putting together the wrong sequence of amino acids.

Example 3   Numbers of Peptides

How many different tripeptides can be made from one unit each of the three amino acids methionine, valine, and phenylalanine? Write the sequences of these tripeptides, using the three-letter abbreviations in Table 3.

Solution
We write the various possibilities. Two begin with Met, two start with Val, and two with Phe:

Met-Val-Phe	Val-Met-Phe	Phe-Val-Met
Met-Phe-Val	Val-Phe-Met	Phe-Met-Val

There are six possible tripeptides.

■ EXERCISE 3A
How many different tripeptides can be made from two methionine units and one valine unit?

■ EXERCISE 3B
How many different tetrapeptides can be made from one unit each of the four amino acids methionine, valine, tyrosine, and phenylalanine?

Although the correct sequence is ordinarily of utmost importance, it is not always absolutely required. Just as you can sometimes make sense of incorrectly spelled English words, a protein with a small percentage of "incorrect" amino acids may function, but just not as well. And sometimes a seemingly minor difference can have a disastrous effect. Some people have hemoglobin with one incorrect amino-acid unit out of about 300. That "minor" error is responsible for sickle cell anemia, an inherited condition that often proves fatal.

Self-Assessment Questions

1. Proteins are polymers of
   a. amino acids
   b. fatty acids
   c. monoacylglycerides
   d. monosaccharides

2. The 20 amino acids that make up proteins differ mainly in their
   a. alpha carbon atoms
   b. amino groups
   c. carboxyl groups
   d. side chains

3. Which of the following is *not* an alpha amino acid?
   a. $CH_3C(CH_3)(NH_2)COOH$
   b. $(CH_3)_2CHCH(NH_2)COOH$
   c. H_2NCH_2COOH
   d. $H_2NCH_2CH_2CH_2COOH$

4. Which of the following is a zwitterion?
   a. $H_2NCH_2COO^-$
   b. $^-NHCH_2COO^-$
   c. $H_3N^+CH_2COOH$
   d. $^+H_3NCH_2COO^-$

5. In a dipeptide, two amino acids are joined through a(n)
   a. amide linkage
   b. dipolar interaction
   c. ionic bond
   d. hydrogen bond

6. The N-terminal amino acid and the C-terminal amino acid of the peptide Met-Ile-Val-Glu-Cys-Tyr-Gln-Trp-Asp are, respectively,
   a. Asp and Met
   b. Met and Asp
   c. Met and Ile
   d. Trp and Asp

7. How many different tripeptides can be formed from alanine, valine, and lysine, when each appears only once in each product?
   a. 1   b. 3   c. 6   d. 9

8. The tripeptides represented as Ala-Val-Lys and Lys-Val-Ala are
   a. different only in name
   b. different in molar mass
   c. exactly the same
   d. two different peptides

Answers: 1, a; 2, d; 3, d; 4, d; 5, a; 6, b; 7, c; 8, d

5 Structure and Function of Proteins

Learning Objectives ❯ Describe the four levels of protein structure, and give an example of each. ❯ Describe how enzymes work as catalysts.

The structures of proteins have four organizational levels:

- **Primary structure.** Amino acids are linked by peptide bonds to form polypeptide chains. The primary structure of a protein molecule is simply the order of its amino acids. By convention, this order is written from the amino (N-terminal end) to the carboxyl (C-terminal end).
- **Secondary structure.** Polypeptide chains can fold into regular structures such as the alpha helix and the beta pleated sheet (described in this section).
- **Tertiary structure.** Protein folding creates spatial relationships between amino-acid units that are relatively far apart in the protein chain.
- **Quaternary structure.** Two or more polypeptide chains can assemble into multiunit structures.

To specify the primary structure, we write out the sequence of amino acids. For even a small protein molecule, this sequence can be quite long. For example, it takes about two pages, using the one-letter abbreviations, to give the sequence of the 1927 amino-acid units in lactase, the enzyme that catalyzes the hydrolysis of the disaccharide lactose into galactose and glucose. The primary structure of angiotensin II, a peptide that causes powerful constriction of blood vessels and is produced in the kidneys, is

Asp-Arg-Val-Tyr-Ile-His-Pro-Phe

► **Figure 12** Beta pleated sheet structure consisting of protein chains. (a) Ball-and-stick model. (b) Model emphasizing the pleats. The side chains extend above or below the sheet and alternate along the chain. The protein chains are held together by interchain hydrogen bonds.

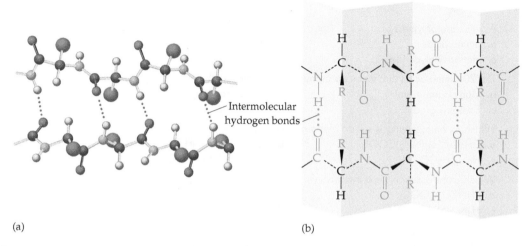

(a)

(b)

Intermolecular hydrogen bonds

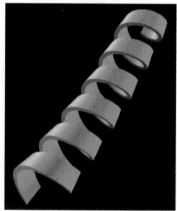

▲ The protein strands in an alpha helix are often represented as coiled ribbons.

▲ The protein strands in a pleated sheet are often represented as ribbons.

This sequence specifies an octapeptide with aspartic acid at the N-terminal end, followed by arginine, valine, tyrosine, isoleucine, histidine, proline, and then phenylalanine at the C-terminal end.

The secondary structure of a protein refers to the arrangement of chains about an axis. The two main types of secondary structure are a *pleated sheet*, as in silk, and a *helix*, as in wool.

In the pleated-sheet conformation (Figure 12), protein chains are arranged in an extended zigzag arrangement, with hydrogen bonds holding adjacent chains together. The appearance gives this type of secondary structure its name, the **beta (β) pleated sheet**. This structure, with its multitude of hydrogen bonds, makes silk strong and flexible.

The protein molecules in wool, hair, and muscle contain large segments arranged in the form of a right-handed helix, or **alpha (α) helix** (Figure 13). Each turn of the helix requires 3.6 amino-acid units. The N—H group at one turn forms a hydrogen bond to a carbonyl (C=O) group at another turn. These helices wrap around one another in threes or sevens like strands of a rope. Unlike

► **Figure 13** Two representations of the α-helical conformation of a protein chain. (a) Intrachain hydrogen bonding between turns of the helix is shown in the ball-and-stick model. (b) The skeletal representation better shows the helix.

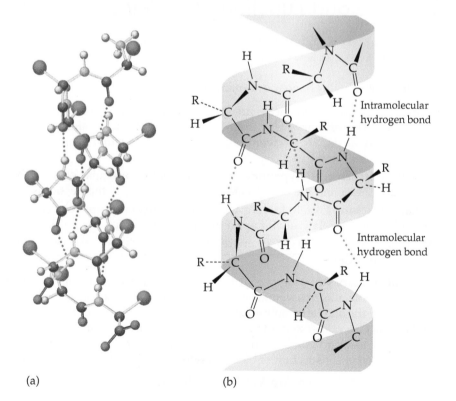

(a)

(b)

Intramolecular hydrogen bond

Intramolecular hydrogen bond

Protein chain   Heme group

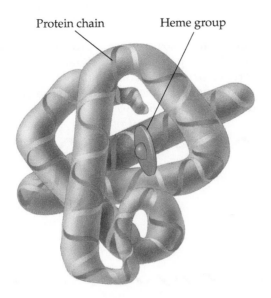

◀ **Figure 14** The tertiary structure of myoglobin. The protein chain is folded to form a globular structure, much as a string can be wound into a ball. The disk shape represents the heme group, which binds the oxygen carried by myoglobin (or hemoglobin).

silk, wool can be stretched, much like stretching a spring by pulling the coils apart.

The tertiary structure of a protein refers to folding that affects the spatial relationships between amino-acid units that are relatively far apart in the chain. An example is the protein chain in a **globular protein**. Figure 14 shows the tertiary structure of myoglobin, which is folded into a compact, spherical shape.

Quaternary structure exists only if there are two or more polypeptide chains, which can form an aggregate of subunits. Hemoglobin is the most familiar example. A single hemoglobin molecule contains four polypeptide units, and each unit is roughly comparable to a myoglobin molecule. The four units are arranged in a specific pattern (Figure 15). The quaternary structure of hemoglobin is this arrangement of the four units.

Protein chain   Protein chain

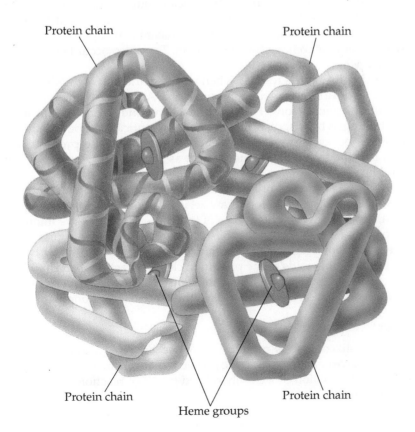

Protein chain   Protein chain

Heme groups

◀ **Figure 15** The quaternary structure of hemoglobin has four coiled protein chains, each analogous to myoglobin (Figure 14), grouped in a nearly tetrahedral arrangement.

Four Ways to Link Protein Chains

As we noted earlier, the primary structure of a protein is the order of the amino acids, which are held together by peptide bonds. What forces determine the secondary, tertiary, and quaternary structures? Four kinds of forces operate between protein chains: hydrogen bonds, ionic bonds, disulfide linkages, and dispersion forces. These forces are illustrated in Figure 16.

▶ **Figure 16** The tertiary structure of proteins is maintained by four different types of forces.

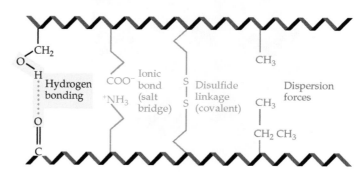

Hydrogen bonds and dispersion forces, introduced as intermolecular forces, can also be intramolecular, as occurs in proteins.

The most important hydrogen bonding in a protein involves an interaction between the atoms of one peptide bond and those of another. The amide hydrogen (N—H) of one peptide bond can form a hydrogen bond to a carbonyl (C=O) oxygen located (a) some distance away on the same chain, an arrangement that occurs in the secondary structure of wool (alpha helix), or (b) on an entirely different chain, as in the secondary structure of silk (beta pleated sheet). In either case, there is usually a pattern of such interactions. Because peptide bonds are regularly spaced along the chain, the hydrogen bonds also occur in a regular pattern, both intramolecularly (in wool) and intermolecularly (in silk). Other types of hydrogen bonding can occur (between side chains of amino acids, for example) but are less important.

Ionic bonds, sometimes called *salt bridges*, occur when an amino acid with a basic side chain is located near one with an acidic side chain. Proton transfer results in opposite charges, which then attract one another. These interactions can occur between groups that ordinarily are relatively distant that happen to come in contact because of folding or coiling of a single chain. They also occur between groups on adjacent chains.

A **disulfide linkage** is formed when two cysteine units (whether on the same chain or on two different chains) are oxidized. A disulfide linkage is a covalent bond, and thus much stronger than a hydrogen bond. Although far less numerous than hydrogen bonds, disulfide linkages are critically important in determining the shape of some proteins (for example, many of the proteins that act as enzymes) and the strength of others (such as the fibrous proteins in connective tissue and hair).

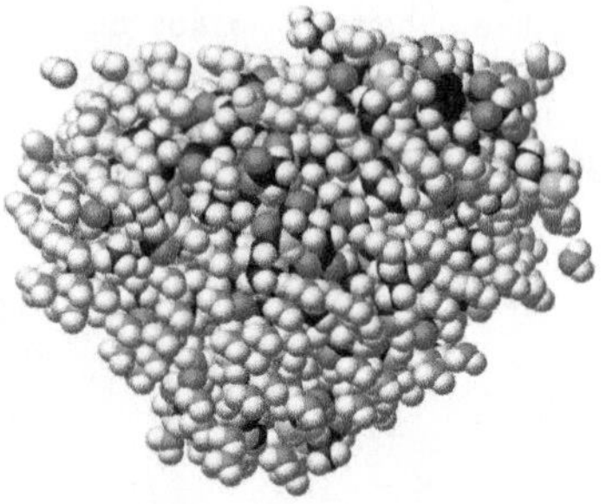

Dispersion forces are the only kind of forces that exist between nonpolar side chains. Recall that dispersion forces are relatively weak. These interactions can be important, however, when other types of forces are missing or are minimized. Dispersion forces are increased by the cohesiveness of the water molecules surrounding the protein. Nonpolar side chains minimize their exposure to water by clustering together on the inside folds of the protein in close contact with one another (Figure 17). Dispersion forces become fairly significant in structures such as that of silk, in which a high proportion of amino acids in the protein have nonpolar side chains.

▲ **Figure 17** A protein chain often folds with its nonpolar groups on the inside, where they are held together by dispersion forces. The outside has polar groups, visible in this space-filling model of a myoglobin molecule as oxygen atoms (red) and nitrogen atoms (blue). The carbon atoms (black) are mainly on the inside.

Enzymes: Exquisite Precision Machines

A highly specialized class of proteins, **enzymes**, are biological catalysts produced by cells. They have enormous catalytic power and are ordinarily highly specific, catalyzing only one reaction or a closely related group of reactions. Nearly all known enzymes are proteins.

Infectious Prions: Deadly Protein

In the early years of the twenty-first century, a malady called *mad cow disease* cast a shadow over the beef industry, causing concern over the safety of beef. Two cows in the United States were found to have the disease, properly called *bovine spongiform encephalopathy (BSE)*.

BSE is not a bacterial disease like anthrax or cholera, nor is it a viral disease like influenza and AIDS. Rather, BSE seems to be caused by an infectious *prion*, an abnormal form of a protein. Because they are simple proteins rather than living organisms, prions can remain unchanged when subjected to considerable heat, disinfectants, or antibiotics, conditions that are used to destroy bacteria and viruses.

Much of the fear over BSE is unfounded, because it is not contagious like bacterial and viral diseases. It is generally spread by consumption of contaminated feed. The U.S. Department of Agriculture has imposed restrictions on the materials that may be used in cattle feed, which have been quite effective. The incidence of prion-caused diseases is extremely low among people. The best-known example is *kuru*, or laughing sickness, which seems to arise from cannibalistic practices in certain societies. Nonetheless, the U.S. government continues to be vigilant in avoiding any potential spread of BSE because it is impossible to treat the disease once it is contracted.

Enzymes enable reactions to occur at much more rapid rates and lower temperatures than they otherwise would. They do this by changing the reaction path. The reacting substance, called the **substrate**, attaches to an area on the enzyme called the **active site**, to form an enzyme–substrate complex. Biochemists often use the model pictured in Figure 18, called the *induced-fit model*, to explain enzyme action. In this model, the shapes of the substrate and the active site are not perfectly complementary, but the active site adapts to fit the substrate, much as a glove molds to fit the hand that is inserted into it. The enzyme–substrate complex decomposes to form products, and the enzyme is regenerated. We can represent the process as follows.

Enzyme + Substrate $\longrightarrow$ Enzyme–substrate complex $\rightleftharpoons$ Enzyme + Products

An enzyme–substrate complex is also usually held together by electrical attraction. Certain charged groups on the enzyme complement certain charged or partially charged groups on the substrate. The formation of new bonds between enzyme and substrate weakens bonds within the substrate, and these weakened bonds can then be more easily broken to form products.

Portions of the enzyme molecule other than the active site may be involved in the catalytic process. Some interaction at a position remote from the active site can change the shape of the enzyme and thus change its effectiveness as a catalyst. In this way, it is possible to slow or stop the catalytic action. Figure 19 illustrates a model for the inhibition of enzyme catalysis. An inhibitor molecule attaches to the enzyme at a position (called the *allosteric site*) away from the active site where the substrate is bound. The enzyme changes shape as it accommodates the inhibitor, and the substrate is no longer able to bind to the enzyme. This is one of the mechanisms by which cells "turn off" enzymes when their work is done.

Some enzymes consist entirely of protein chains. In others, another chemical component, called a **cofactor**, is necessary for proper function of the enzyme. This cofactor may be a metal ion such as zinc (Zn^{2+}), manganese (Mn^{2+}), magnesium (Mg^{2+}), iron(II) (Fe^{2+}), or copper(II) (Cu^{2+}). An organic cofactor is called a **coenzyme**. By definition, coenzymes are nonprotein. The pure protein part of an enzyme is called the **apoenzyme**. Both the coenzyme and the apoenzyme must be present for enzymatic activity to take place.

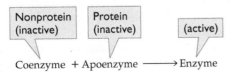

Coenzyme + Apoenzyme $\longrightarrow$ Enzyme

Many coenzymes are vitamins or are derived from vitamin molecules. Enzymes are essential to the function of every living cell.

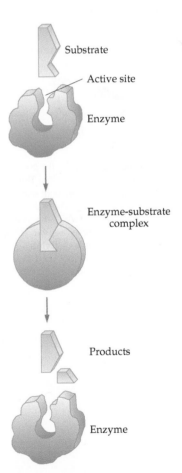

▲ **Figure 18** The induced-fit model of enzyme action. In this case, a single substrate molecule is broken into two product molecules.

Enzymes as Green Catalysts

Scientists are hard at work trying to find enzymes to carry out all kinds of chemical conversions. Enzymes are often more efficient than the usual chemical catalysts, and they are more specific in that they produce more of the desired product and fewer by-products that have to be disposed of. Further, processes involving enzymes do not require toxic solvents and thus produce less waste.

Companies have spent hundreds of millions of dollars studying the special characteristics of the enzymes inside *extremophiles*, microorganisms that live in harsh environments that would kill other creatures. Scientists hope to replace ordinary enzymes with enzymes from extremophiles. They are already finding uses for these enzymes in specialty chemicals and new drugs. Many industrial processes can only be carried out at high temperatures and pressures. Enzymes make it possible to carry out some of these processes at fairly low temperatures and atmospheric pressure, thus reducing the energy used and the need for expensive equipment.

Another area of enzyme use is in cleaning up pollution. For example, polychlorinated biphenyls (PCBs), notoriously persistent pollutants, are usually destroyed by incineration at 1200 °C. Microorganisms have been isolated that can degrade PCBs and thus have the potential to destroy these toxic pollutants. However, much research is still needed to make them cost-effective.

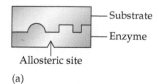

Allosteric site

(a)

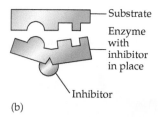

(b)

▲ **Figure 19** A model for the inhibition of an enzyme. (a) The enzyme and its substrate fit exactly. (The allosteric site is where the inhibitor binds.) (b) With the inhibitor bound to the enzyme, the active site of the enzyme is distorted, and the enzyme cannot bind to its substrate.

Applications of Enzymes

Enzymes find many uses in medicine, industry, and everyday life. One widespread use is in the test strips used by diabetics. Each strip contains *glucose oxidase*, an enzyme that catalyzes the oxidation of glucose at an electrode. The reaction generates an electrical current that is proportional to the amount of glucose in the blood that has reacted with the enzyme. The result is displayed directly on an external meter.

Clinical analysis for enzymes in body fluids or tissues is a common diagnostic technique in medicine. For example, enzymes normally found only in the liver may leak into the bloodstream from a diseased or damaged liver. The presence of these enzymes in blood confirms liver damage.

Enzymes are used to break up blood clots after a heart attack. If these medicines are given immediately after an attack, the patients' survival rate increases significantly. Other enzymes are used to do just the opposite: Blood-clotting factors are used to treat hemophilia, a disease in which the blood fails to clot normally.

Enzymes are widely used in a variety of industries, from baby foods to beer. Enzymes in intact microorganisms have long been used to make bread, beer, wine, yogurt, and cheese. Now the use of enzymes has been broadened to include such things as the following:

- Enzymes that act on proteins (called *proteases*) are used in the manufacture of baby foods to predigest complex proteins and make them easier for infants to digest.

- Enzymes that act on starches (*carbohydrases*) are used to convert corn starch to corn syrup (mainly glucose) for use as a sweetener.

- Enzymes called *isomerases* are used to convert the glucose in corn syrup into fructose, which is sweeter than glucose and can be used in smaller amounts to give the same sweetness. (Glucose and fructose are isomers, both having the molecular formula $C_6H_{12}O_6$.)

- Protease enzymes are used to make beer and fruit juices clear by breaking down the proteins that cause cloudiness.

- Enzymes that degrade cellulose (*cellulases*) are used in stonewashing blue jeans. These enzymes break down the cellulose polymers of cotton fibers. By carefully controlling their activity, manufacturers can get the desired effect without destroying the cotton material. Varying the cellulase enzymes creates different effects to make true "designer jeans."

- Proteases and carbohydrases are added to animal feed to make nutrients more easily absorbed and improve the animals' digestion.

Biochemistry

Enzymes are important components in some detergents. Enzymes called *lipases* attack the fats and grease that make up many stains. Proteases attack the proteins in certain types of stains, such as those from blood, meat juice, and dairy products, breaking them down into smaller, water-soluble molecules. Total worldwide production of enzymes is worth more than $1 billion per year.

Klaudia Steiner/iStockphoto

Self-Assessment Questions

1. Hydrogen bonds form between the N—H group of one amino acid and the C=O group of another, giving a protein molecule the form of an alpha helix or a beta pleated sheet. What level of protein structure do those forms represent?
   a. primary   **b.** quaternary   **c.** secondary   **d.** tertiary

2. The folding of a protein chain into a globular form is an example of
   a. primary structure
   c. secondary structure
   b. quaternary structure
   d. tertiary structure

3. The arrangement of several protein subunits into a specific pattern, as in hemoglobin, is an example of
   a. primary structure
   c. secondary structure
   b. quaternary structure
   d. tertiary structure

4. The cross-links between cysteine units in protein chains of fibrous proteins such as those in hair are
   a. dispersion linkages
   c. hydrogen bonds
   b. disulfide linkages
   d. salt bridges

5. An acidic side chain of an amino-acid unit on a protein chain reacts with the basic side chain of an amino-acid unit on another chain or at some distance away on the same chain to form a
   a. dispersion linkage
   c. hydrogen bond
   b. disulfide linkage
   d. salt bridge

6. When nonpolar side chains of amino-acid units in a protein chain interact with other nonpolar side chains of amino-acid units on another chain or at some distance away on the same chain, the interactions are
   a. dispersion forces
   b. a disulfide linkage
   c. a hydrogen bond
   d. a salt bridge

7. The molecule on which an enzyme acts is called the enzyme's
   a. catalyst   **b.** coenzyme   **c.** cofactor   **d.** substrate

8. According to the induced fit model of enzyme action, the
   a. action of an enzyme is enhanced by an inhibitor
   b. active site is the same as the allosteric site
   c. shapes of active sites are rigid and only fit substrates with exact complementary shapes
   d. shape of the active site can change somewhat to fit a substrate

9. An organic, nonprotein component of an enzyme molecule is called a(n)
   a. accessory enzyme
   b. allosteric group
   c. coenzyme
   d. stimulator

10. Enzyme cofactors are
    a. always ions such as Ca^{2+}, Mg^{2+}, and K^+
    b. always nonprotein organic molecules
    c. either ions such as Zn^{2+}, Mg^{2+}, and Mn^{2+} or nonprotein organic molecules
    d. small protein molecules

11. The pure protein part of an enzyme is called a(n)
    a. apoenzyme
    c. holoenzyme
    b. coenzyme
    d. ribozyme

▲ It DOES Matter!
You can demonstrate protein hydrolysis. Mix a gelatin-dessert powder according to directions. Divide into two parts. Add fresh pineapple, kiwi, or papaya to one portion. Add cooked fruit or none at all to the other. The portion with the fresh fruit will not gel! These fruits contain a protease enzyme that breaks down proteins (gelatin is a protein). The enzyme is inactivated by cooking, so canned pineapple is perfectly fine in gelatin. (Why do you think cooking ham with pineapple tenderizes the ham, and eating too much raw pineapple can "burn" the lips?)

4. Why do some laundry detergents contain enzymes?
Enzymes in laundry detergents catalytically break down proteins that used to be difficult for detergents and bleaches to remove. Years ago, grass stains in children's clothing were almost impossible to remove, because the proteins of grass have a strong attraction for cotton and other cloth. Enzymes have alleviated that problem.

Answers: 1, c; 2, d; 3, b; 4, b; 5, d; 6, a; 7 d; 8, d; 9, c; 10, c; 11, a

6 Nucleic Acids: Parts, Structure, and Function

Learning Objectives ❯ Name the two types of nucleic acids, and describe the function of each type. ❯ Explain complementary base pairing, and describe how a copy of DNA is synthesized.

Life on Earth has a fantastic range of forms, but all life arises from the same molecular ingredients: five nucleotides that serve as the building blocks for nucleic acids, and 20 amino acids (Section 4) that are the building blocks for proteins. These components limit the chemical reactions that can occur in cells and thus determine what Earth's living things are like.

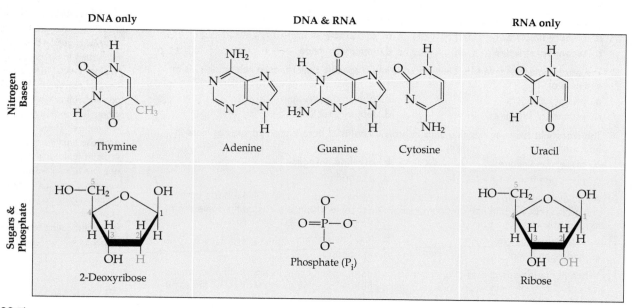

▲ **Figure 20** The components of nucleic acids. The sugars are 2-deoxyribose (in DNA) and ribose (in RNA). Note that deoxyribose differs from ribose in that it lacks an oxygen atom on the second carbon atom. *Deoxy* indicates that an oxygen atom is "missing." Phosphate units are often abbreviated as P_i ("inorganic phosphate"). Heterocyclic bases in nucleic acids are adenine, guanine, and cytosine in both DNA and RNA. Thymine occurs only in DNA, and uracil only in RNA. Note that thymine has a methyl group (red) that is lacking in uracil.

Nucleic acids serve as the information and control centers of the cell. There are two kinds of nucleic acids: *Deoxyribonucleic acid* (*DNA*) provides a mechanism for heredity and serves as the blueprint for all the proteins of an organism. *Ribonucleic acid* (*RNA*) carries out protein assembly. DNA is a coiled threadlike molecule found primarily in the cell nucleus. RNA is found in all parts of the cell, where different forms do different jobs. Both DNA and RNA are chains of repeating units called **nucleotides**. Each nucleotide in turn consists of three parts (Figure 20): a pentose (five-carbon sugar), a phosphate unit, and a heterocyclic amine base. The sugar is either ribose (in RNA) or deoxyribose (in DNA). Looking at the sugar in the nucleotide, note that the hydroxyl group on the first carbon atom is replaced by one of five bases. The bases with two fused rings, adenine and guanine, are classified as **purines**. The **pyrimidines**, cytosine, thymine, and uracil, have only one ring.

The hydroxyl group on the fifth carbon of the sugar unit is converted to a phosphate ester group. Adenosine monophosphate (AMP) is a representative nucleotide. In AMP, the base (blue) is adenine and the sugar (black) is ribose.

Adenosine monophosphate

120

Nucleotides can be represented schematically as in the following, where P_i is biochemists' designation for "inorganic phosphate." A general representation is shown on the left, and a specific schematic for AMP on the right.

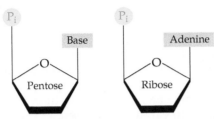

Nucleotides are joined to one another through the phosphate group to form nucleic acid chains. The phosphate unit on one nucleotide forms an ester linkage with the hydroxyl group on the third carbon atom of the sugar unit in a second nucleotide. This unit is in turn joined to another nucleotide, and the process is repeated to build up a long nucleic acid chain (Figure 21). The backbone of the chain consists of alternating phosphate and sugar units, and the heterocyclic bases are branches off this backbone.

$$\sim\text{sugar-}P_i\text{-sugar-}P_i\text{-sugar-}P_i\text{-sugar-}P_i\text{-sugar-}P_i\text{-sugar-}P_i\sim$$

| base | base | base | base | base | base |

The numbers in Figure 21 refer to positions on the pentose sugar ring (look again at Figure 20). The 3′ end has a hydroxyl group and the 5′ end has a phosphate group. If the above diagram represents DNA, the sugar is deoxyribose and the bases are adenine, guanine, cytosine, and thymine. In RNA, the sugar is ribose and the bases are adenine, guanine, cytosine, and uracil.

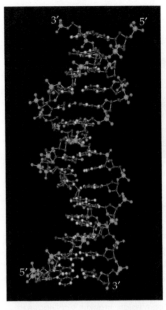

▲ **Figure 21** A DNA molecule. Each repeating unit is composed of a sugar, a phosphate unit, and a base. The sugar and phosphate units form backbones on the outside. The bases are attached to the sugar units. Pairs of bases make "steps" on the inside of the spiral staircase.

Example 4   Nucleotides

Consider the following nucleotide. Identify the sugar and the base. State whether it is found in DNA or RNA.

Solution
The sugar has two H atoms on the second C atom and therefore is deoxyribose, found in DNA. The base is a pyrimidine (one ring). The amino group ($-NH_2$) helps identify it as cytosine.

■ EXERCISE 4A
Consider the following nucleotide. Identify the sugar and the base. State whether it is found in DNA or RNA.

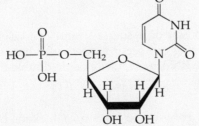

(continued)

Francis H. C. Crick (1916–2004) (seated) and James D. Watson (b. 1928) used data obtained by British chemist Rosalind Franklin (1920–1958) to propose a double helix model of DNA in 1953. Franklin used a technique called X-ray diffraction, which showed DNA's helical structure. Without her permission, Franklin's colleague Maurice Wilkins shared her work with Watson and Crick. The data helped Watson and Crick decipher DNA's structure. Wilkins, Watson, and Crick were awarded the Nobel Prize for this discovery in 1962, a prize Franklin might have shared had she lived.

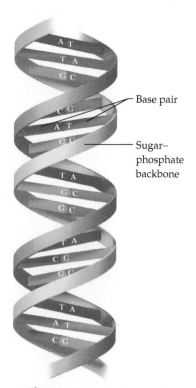

Base pair

Sugar–phosphate backbone

Figure 22 A model of a portion of a DNA double helix is shown in Figure 21. This schematic representation of the double helix shows the sugar–phosphate backbones as ribbons and the complementary base pairs as steps on the spiral staircase.

■ **EXERCISE 4B**
A nucleotide is composed of a phosphate unit, ribose, and thymine. Is it found in DNA, RNA, or neither? Explain.

The vast amount of genetic information needed to build living organisms is stored in a primary structure, the *sequence* of the four bases along the nucleic acid strand. Not surprisingly, these molecules are huge, with molecular masses ranging into the billions for mammalian DNA. Along these chains, the four bases can be arranged in almost infinite variations. We will examine this aspect of nucleic acid chemistry shortly, after considering another important feature of nucleic acid structure.

The Double Helix

The three-dimensional, or secondary, structure of DNA was the subject of an intensive research effort in the late 1940s and early 1950s. Experiments showed that the molar amount of adenine (A) in DNA corresponds to the molar amount of thymine (T). Similarly, the molar amount of guanine (G) is the same as that of cytosine (C). To maintain this balance, researchers concluded the bases in DNA must be paired, A to T and G to C. But how?

At the midpoint of the twentieth century, it was clear that whoever answered this question would win a Nobel Prize. Many illustrious scientists worked on the problem, but two who were relatively unknown announced in 1953 that they had worked out the structure of DNA. Using data that involved quite sophisticated chemistry, physics, and mathematics, and working with models not unlike a child's construction set, James D. Watson and Francis H. C. Crick determined that DNA must be composed of two helices wound about one another. The two strands are antiparallel; they run in opposite directions. The phosphate and sugar backbones of the polymer chains form the outside of the structure, which is rather like a spiral staircase. The heterocyclic amines are paired on the inside—with guanine always opposite cytosine and adenine always opposite thymine. In the spiral staircase analogy, these base pairs are the steps (Figure 22).

Why do the bases pair in this precise pattern, always A to T and T to A and always G to C and C to G? The answers: hydrogen bonding, and a truly elegant molecular arrangement. Figure 23 shows the two sets of base pairs. You should notice two things. First, a pyrimidine is paired with a purine in each case, and the long dimensions of both pairs are identical (1.085 nm).

Second, notice the hydrogen bonding between the bases in each pair. When guanine is paired with cytosine, three hydrogen bonds can be formed between the bases. No other pyrimidine–purine pairing permits such extensive interaction. Indeed, in the combinations shown in the figure, each pair of bases fits like a lock and a key.

Other scientists around the world quickly accepted the Watson–Crick structure because it answered so many crucial questions: how cells are able to divide and go on functioning, how genetic data are passed on to new generations, and even how proteins are built to required specifications. All of these processes depend on the base pairing.

Structure of RNA

Most RNA molecules consist of a single strand of nucleic acids. Some internal (intramolecular) base pairing can occur in sections where the molecule folds back on itself. Portions of some RNA molecules exist in double-helical form (Figure 24).

DNA: Self-Replication

Dogs have puppies that grow up to be dogs. Chickens lay eggs that hatch and grow up to be chickens. How is it that each species reproduces its own kind?

(a)

1.085 nm

Thymine   To chain   Adenine   To chain

(b)

1.085 nm

Cytosine   To chain   Guanine   To chain

▲ **Figure 23** Pairing of the complementary bases thymine and adenine (a) and cytosine and guanine (b). The pairing involves hydrogen bonding.

James D. Watson gave a personal account of the discovery of the structure of DNA in his book *The Double Helix* (New York: New American Library, 1968).

How does a fertilized egg "know" that it should develop into a kangaroo and not a koala?

The physical basis of heredity has been known for a long time. Most higher organisms reproduce sexually. A sperm cell from the male unites with an egg cell from the female. The fertilized egg that results must carry all the information needed to make the various cells, tissues, and organs necessary for the functioning of a new individual. Further, if the species is to survive, information must be passed along in the germ cells—both sperm and egg—for the production of new individuals.

The hereditary material is found in the nuclei of all cells, concentrated in elongated, threadlike bodies called *chromosomes*. Chromosomes form compressed X-shaped structures when strands of DNA coil up tightly just before a cell divides. The number of chromosomes varies with the species. In sexual reproduction, chromosomes come in pairs, with one member of each pair provided by each parent. Each human inherits 23 pairs and so has 46 chromosomes in his or her body's cells. Thus, the entire complement of chromosomes is achieved only when the egg's 23 chromosomes combine with a like number from the sperm.

Chromosomes are made of DNA and proteins. Arranged along the chromosomes are the basic units of heredity, the genes. Structurally, a **gene** is a section of the DNA molecule, although some viral genes contain only RNA. Genes control the synthesis of proteins, which tell cells, organs, and organisms how to function in their surroundings. The environment helps determine which genes become active at a particular time. The complete set of genes of an organism is called its *genome*. When cell division occurs, each chromosome produces an exact duplicate of itself. Transmission of genetic information therefore requires the **replication** (copying or duplication) of DNA molecules.

The double helix provides a precise model for replication. If the two chains of the double helix are pulled apart, each chain can direct the synthesis of a new DNA chain using nucleotides from the cellular fluid surrounding the DNA. Each of the separating chains serves as a template, or pattern, for the formation of a new complementary chain. The two DNA strands are *antiparallel*. One chain runs in the direction labeled $3' \rightarrow 5'$, and the other runs in the appropriate direction labeled $5' \rightarrow 3'$. Synthesis begins with a base on a nucleotide pairing with its complementary base on the DNA strand—adenine with thymine and guanine with cytosine (Figure 25). Each base unit in the separated strand can only pick up a base unit identical to the one with which it was paired before. For example, if a 12-base-pair strand

▲ **Figure 24** RNA occurs as single strands that can form double-helical portions through internal pairing of bases.

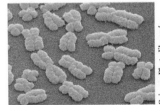

▲ Human chromosomes before cell division have a distinctive X-shape.

Genes have functional regions called *exons* interspersed with inactive portions called *introns*. During protein synthesis, introns are snipped out and not translated. Some genes, called *housekeeping genes*, are expressed in all cells at all times and are essential for the most basic cellular functions. Other genes are expressed only in specific types of cells or at certain stages of development. For example, the genes that encode brain nerve cells are expressed only in brain cells, not in the liver.

running in the 5′ → 3′ direction has guanine as the third base, the guanine will pick up base cytosine as the tenth base of the complementary 12-base-pair strand running in the opposite direction.

3′-ATGGGTCTATAT-5′

5′-TACCCAGATATA-3′

As the nucleotides align, enzymes connect them to form the new chain. In this way, each strand of the original DNA molecule forms a duplicate of its former partner. Whatever information was encoded in the original DNA double helix is now contained in each of the replications. When the cell divides, each daughter cell gets one of the DNA molecules and thus has all the information that was available to the parent cell.

How is information stored in DNA? The code for the directions for building all the proteins that comprise an organism and enable it to function resides in the *sequence* of bases along the DNA chain. Just as *cat* means one thing in English and *act* means another, the sequence of bases CGT means one amino acid and GCT means another. Although there are only four "letters"—the four bases—in the genetic code of DNA, their sequence along the long strands can vary so widely that unlimited information storage is available. Each cell carries in its DNA all the information that determines its hereditary characteristics.

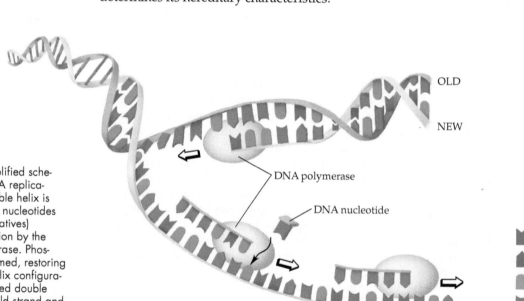

▶ **Figure 25** A simplified schematic diagram of DNA replication. The original double helix is "unzipped," and new nucleotides (as triphosphate derivatives) are brought into position by the enzyme DNA polymerase. Phosphate bridges are formed, restoring the original double-helix configuration. Each newly formed double helix consists of one old strand and one new strand.

Key

Adenine
Thymine
Guanine
Cytosine

Self-Assessment Questions

1. The monomer units of nucleic acids are
   a. amino acids
   c. nucleosomes
   b. monosaccharides
   d. nucleotides

2. A DNA nucleotide could contain
   a. A, P_i, and ribose
   c. T, P_i, and deoxyribose
   b. G, P_i, and glucose
   d. U, P_i, and deoxyribose

3. A possible base pair in DNA is
   a. A-G   **b.** A-T   **c.** A-U   **d.** T-G

4. A possible base pair in RNA is
   a. A-G   **b.** A-T   **c.** A-U   **d.** T-G

5. Nucleic acid base pairs are joined by
   a. amide bonds
   c. glucosidic bonds
   b. ester bonds
   d. hydrogen bonds

6. Replication of a DNA molecule involves breaking bonds between the
   a. base pairs
   b. pentose sugars
   c. phosphate units
   d. bases and pentoses

7. The first step of DNA replication involves
   a. bonding of free nucleotides in the correct sequence
   b. formation of a single-stranded RNA molecule
   c. linking of a phosphate group to an amino acid
   d. unzipping of the DNA molecule when the hydrogen bonds break

8. If an original DNA strand has the base sequence 3'-TAGC-5', the complementary strand will have the base sequence
   a. 5'-ATCG-3'
   b. 5'-GCAT-3'
   c. 5'-TACG-3'
   d. 5'-UACG-3'

9. If a portion of a gene has the base sequence 3'-TCGAAT-5', what base sequence appears in the complementary DNA strand when the gene is replicated?
   a. 5'-ACGTTA-3'
   b. 5'-AGCTTA-3'
   c. 5'-TCGAAT-3'
   d. 5'-UGCAAU-3'

Answers: 1, d; 2, c; 3, b; 4, c; 5, d; 6, a; 7, d; 8, a; 9, b

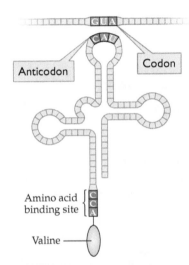

Anticodon

Codon

Amino acid binding site

Valine

▲ **Figure 26** A transfer RNA (tRNA) molecule doubles back on itself, forming three loops with intermolecular hydrogen bonding between complementary bases. The anticodon triplet at the head of the molecule joins with a complementary codon triplet on mRNA. Here the base triplet CAU in the anticodon specifies the amino acid valine.

7 RNA: Protein Synthesis and the Genetic Code

Learning Objectives ❯ Explain how mRNA is synthesized from DNA and how a protein is synthesized from mRNA. ❯ List important characteristics of the genetic code.

DNA carries a message that must somehow be transmitted and then acted on in a cell. Because DNA does not leave the cell nucleus, its information, or "blueprint," must be transported by something else, and it is. In the first step, called **transcription**, a segment of DNA called the *template strand* transfers its information to a special RNA molecule called *messenger RNA (mRNA)*. The base sequence of DNA specifies the base sequence of mRNA. Thymine in DNA calls for adenine in mRNA, cytosine specifies guanine, guanine calls for cytosine, and adenine requires uracil (Table 4). Remember that in RNA molecules, uracil appears in place of DNA's thymine. Notice the similarity in the structure of these two bases (revisit Figure 20). When transcription is completed, the RNA is released, and the DNA helix reforms.

Why is a code that must specify 20 different amino acids based on a triplet of bases? Four "letters" can be arranged in $4 \times 4 \times 4 = 64$ possible three-letter "words." A "doublet" code of four letters would have only $4 \times 4 = 16$ different words, and a "quadruplet" code of four letters can be arranged in $4 \times 4 \times 4 \times 4 = 256$ different ways. A triplet code specifies 20 different amino acids with some redundancy, a doublet code is inadequate, and a quadruplet code would provide too much redundancy.

Table 4 DNA Bases and Their Complementary RNA Bases

DNA Base	Complementary RNA Base
Adenine (A)	Uracil (U)
Thymine (T)	Adenine (A)
Cytosine (C)	Guanine (G)
Guanine (G)	Cytosine (C)

The next step in creating a protein involves deciphering the code copied by mRNA followed by **translation** of that code into a specific protein structure. The decoding occurs when the mRNA travels from the nucleus and attaches itself to a ribosome in the cytoplasm of the cell. Ribosomes are constructed of about 65% RNA and 35% proteins.

Another type of RNA molecule, called *transfer RNA (tRNA)*, carries amino acids from the cell fluid to the ribosomes. A tRNA molecule has the looped structure shown in Figure 26. At the head of the molecule is a set of three base units, a *base triplet* called the *anticodon*, that pairs with a set of three complementary bases on mRNA, called the **codon**. The codon triplet determines which amino acid is car-

Errors can occur at each step in the replication–transcription–translation process. In replication alone, each time a human cell divides, 4 billion bases are copied to make a new strand of DNA, and there may be up to 2000 errors. Most such errors are corrected, and others are un-important, but some have terrible consequences: genetic disease or even death may result.

Angela Waye/Shutterstock

▲ It DOES Matter!

Blue eyes result from a genetic muta-tion that involved the change of a single base in the code, from A to G. This change is thought to have occurred between 6000 and 10,000 years ago; before that time, no humans had blue eyes. The mutation turned off a gene involved in the pro-duction of melanin, the pigment that gives color to hair, eyes, and skin. Only people who inherit this gene from both parents have blue eyes.

ried at the tail of the tRNA. In Figure 26, for example, the codon GUA on the seg-ment of mRNA pairs with the anticodon base triplet CAU on the tRNA molecule. All tRNA molecules with the base triplet CAU always carry the amino acid valine. Once the tRNA has paired with the base triplet of mRNA, it releases its amino acid and returns to the cell fluid to pick up another amino acid molecule.

Each of the 61 different tRNA molecules carries a specific amino acid into place on a growing peptide chain. The protein chain gradually built up in this way is released from the tRNA as it is formed. A complete dictionary of the genetic code has been compiled (Table 5). It shows which amino acids are specified by all the possible mRNA base triplets. There are 64 possible triplets and only 20 amino acids, so there is some redundancy in the code. Three amino acids (serine, arginine, and leucine) are each specified by six different codons. Two others (tryptophan and methionine) have only one codon each. Three base triplets on mRNA are "stop" signals that call for termina-tion of the protein chain. The codon AUG signals "start" as well as specifying methio-nine in the chain. Figure 27 provides an overall summary of protein synthesis.

Table 5 — The Genetic Code

		SECOND BASE				
		U	C	A	G	
FIRST BASE	U	UUU=Phe UUC=Phe UUA=Leu UUG=Leu	UCU=Ser UCC=Ser UCA=Ser UCG=Ser	UAU=Tyr UAC=Tyr UAA=Termination UAG=Termination	UGU=Cys UGC=Cys UGA=Termination UGG=Trp	U C A G
	C	CUU=Leu CUC=Leu CUA=Leu CUG=Leu	CCU=Pro CCC=Pro CCA=Pro CCG=Pro	CAU=His CAC=His CAA=Gln CAG=Gln	CGU=Arg CGC=Arg CGA=Arg CGG=Arg	U C A G
	A	AUU=Ile AUC=Ile AUA=Ile AUG=Met	ACU=Thr ACC=Thr ACA=Thr ACG=Thr	AAU=Asn AAC=Asn AAA=Lys AAG=Lys	AGU=Ser AGC=Ser AGA=Arg AGG=Arg	U C A G
	G	GUU=Val GUC=Val GUA=Val GUG=Val	GCU=Ala GCC=Ala GCA=Ala GCG=Ala	GAU=Asp GAC=Asp GAA=Glu GAG=Glu	GGU=Gly GGC=Gly GGA=Gly GGG=Gly	U C A G

THIRD BASE

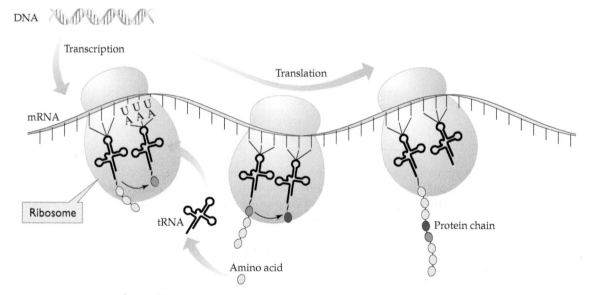

▲ **Figure 27** Protein synthesis occurs by transcription from DNA to mRNA, translation by tRNA, and building of a protein.

Biochemistry

Self-Assessment Questions

1. The synthesis of mRNA from a strand of DNA is called
   a. transaction **b.** transcription **c.** transition **d.** translation

2. The base sequence of a strand of mRNA that is transcribed from a segment of DNA that has the base sequence 5'-TACG-3' is
   a. 3'-AUGC-5' **b.** 3'-CGAU-5' **c.** 3'-TAGC-5' **d.** 3'-UAGC-5'

3. The anticodon base triplet is found on the
   a. original DNA **b.** ribosome **c.** mRNA **d.** tRNA

4. How many amino acids and how many codons are involved in the genetic code
   a. 20 amino acids, 20 codons **b.** 20 amino acids, 64 codons
   c. 64 amino acids, 20 codons **d.** 64 amino acids, 64 codons

5. Each amino acid except tryptophan and methionine is coded for by more than one codon, indicating that the genetic code has
   a. evolved **b.** redundancy
   c. sequence assurance **d.** translation equability

6. Refer to Table 5; the codon UUA
   a. codes for Leu and signals "start" **b.** codes for Leu and signals "stop"
   c. codes for Leu only **d.** signals "stop" only

Answers: 1, b; 2, a; 3, d; 4, b; 5, b; 6, c

8 The Human Genome

Learning Objective ❯ Describe recombinant DNA technology, and explain how it is used.

In 1990, scientists set out to determine the sequence of all 3 billion base pairs in the human genome. The Human Genome Project was completed in 2003 at a cost of about $2.7 billion. We can now read the complete genetic blueprint for a human. This project has driven a worldwide revolution in biotechnology—and today a genome can be sequenced in a few days at a cost of a few hundred dollars.

Many human diseases have clear genetic components. Some are directly caused by one defective gene, and others arise through involvement of several genes. The Human Genome Project has already led to the discovery of 2000 or more genes related to disease, allowing the development of more than 2000 genetic tests for human disorders. These tests enable patients to learn their genetic risk for certain diseases and also help health-care professionals to diagnose these diseases.

A gene suspected of causing an inherited disease can be located on the human genome map in a few days, instead of the years it took before the genome sequence was known. Once the genes are identified, the ability to use this information to diagnose and cure genetic diseases will revolutionize medicine.

DNA is sequenced by using enzymes to cleave it into segments of a few to several hundred nucleotides each. These fragments differ in length from each other by a single base that is identified in a later step. The pieces are duplicated and amplified by a technique called the *polymerase chain reaction (PCR)*. PCR employs enzymes called *DNA polymerases* to amplify the small amount of DNA by making millions of copies of each fragment. This builds a minuscule sample into a far larger quantity, which is needed for DNA sequencing. An electric current is used to sort the DNA segments by length, and the base at the end of each fragment is identified. Computers are then used to compile the short sequences into longer segments that recreate the original sequence of bases for the short pieces generated in the first step.

Humans were long thought to have 80,000 or more active genes. When scientists completed the Human Genome Project in 2003, they had found only about 20,000 to 25,000 genes in the human genome.

127

DNA Profiling

About 99.9% of DNA sequences are the same in every human, yet the 0.1% difference is enough to distinguish one person from another (except for identical twins). DNA profiling does not require sequencing of an entire genome. Rather, it uses *short tandem repeats*, or *STRs*, at 13 particular locations on the human genome. An STR is typically from two to five base units long and is repeated several times. An example is ACGT-ACGT-ACGT. The number of such repeats at the key points differs from one person to another. This is the key to a DNA fingerprint. When all 13 points are considered, each person has a different profile.

DNA fingerprinting is used to screen newborn babies for inherited disorders such as cystic fibrosis, sickle cell anemia, Huntington's disease, hemophilia, and many others. Early detection of such disorders enables doctors and parents to choose and initiate proper treatment of the child.

Because children inherit half their DNA from each parent, DNA fingerprinting is also used to establish parentage when there is a question about paternity.

The odds of identifying the father through DNA fingerprinting are at least 99.99%, and they are 100% for excluding a man as a possible father.

British scientist Alec Jeffreys invented DNA fingerprinting in 1985 and gave it its name. Like fingerprints, each person's DNA is unique. Any cells—skin, blood, semen, saliva, and so on—can supply the necessary DNA sample.

DNA fingerprinting was a major advance in criminal investigation, allowing thousands of criminal cases to be solved. DNA samples from evidence found at a crime scene are amplified by PCR and compared with DNA obtained from suspects and other people known to have been at the scene.

This technique has led to many criminal convictions, but perhaps more important, it can readily prove someone innocent. If the DNA does not match, the suspect could not have left the biological sample. Nearly 300 people have been shown to be innocent and freed, some after spending years in prison, including 17 who had been condemned to death. The technique is a major advance in the search for justice.

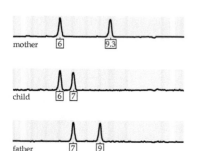

▲ This DNA test included samples from the mother (top), the child (middle), and the alleged father (bottom). The maternal marker 6 has been passed to the child. This means that marker 7 of the child must have come from the father, and the alleged father does indeed have a marker 7.

Recombinant DNA: Using Organisms as Chemical Factories

All living organisms (except some viruses) have DNA as their hereditary material. *Recombinant DNA* is DNA that has been created artificially. DNA from two different sources is incorporated into a single recombinant DNA molecule. The first step is to cut the DNA to extract a fragment of it, which scientists accomplish with an enzyme obtained from bacteria called an *endonuclease*. Endonuclease is a type of *restriction enzyme*, so called because its ability to cleave DNA is restricted to certain short sequences of DNA called *restriction sites*. This enzyme cuts two DNA molecules at the same site. There are three different methods by which recombinant DNA is made. We will consider just one of them here.

After scientists determine the base sequence of the gene that codes for a particular protein, they can isolate it and amplify it by PCR. The gene can then be spliced into a special kind of bacterial DNA called a *plasmid*. The recombined plasmid is then inserted into the host organism, the bacteria from which the plasmids came (Figure 28). Once inside the host bacteria, the plasmids replicate, making multiple exact copies of themselves, a process called *cloning*. As the engineered bacteria multiply, they become effective factories for producing the desired protein.

What kinds of proteins might scientists wish to produce using biotechnology? Insulin, a protein coded by DNA, is required for the proper use of glucose by cells. People with diabetes, an insulin-deficiency disease, formerly had to use insulin from pigs or cattle. Now human insulin is made using recombinant DNA technology. Scientists take the human gene for insulin production and paste it into the DNA of *Escherichia coli*, a bacterium commonly found in the human digestive tract. Expression factors, signals that provide instructions for transcription and translation of the gene by the cell, are also added. The bacterial cells multiply rapidly, making billions of copies of themselves, and each new *E. coli* cell carries in its DNA a replica of the gene for human insulin. The hope for the future is that a functioning gene for insulin can be incorporated directly into the cells of insulin-dependent diabetics.

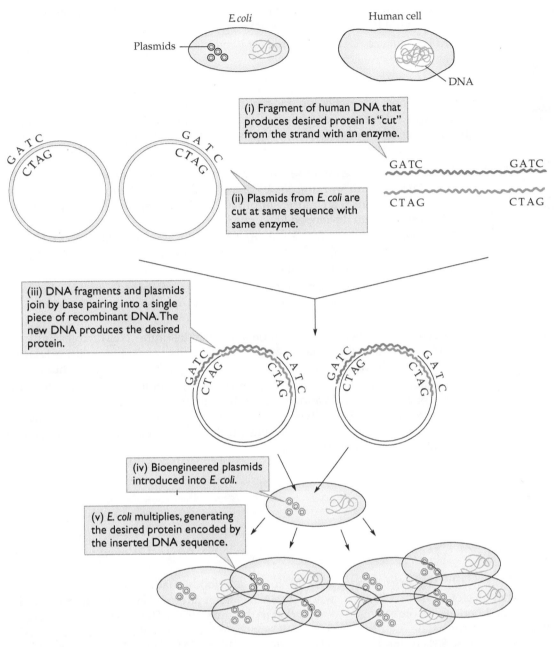

▲ **Figure 28** Recombinant DNA: cloning a human gene into a bacterial plasmid. The bacteria multiply and, in doing so, make multiple copies of the recombinant gene. The gene can be one that codes for insulin, human growth hormone, or another valuable protein. Potentially, a gene from any organism—microbe, plant, or animal—can be incorporated into any other organism.

In addition to insulin, many other valuable materials that are used in human therapy and are difficult to obtain in any other way can now be made using recombinant DNA technology. Some examples are

- *human growth hormone* (HGH), which replaced cadaver-harvested HGH for treating children who fail to grow properly;
- *erythropoietin* (EPO) for treating anemia resulting from chronic kidney disease and from treatment for cancer;
- *factor VIII* (formerly harvested from blood), a clotting agent for treating males with hemophilia;
- *tissue plasminogen activator* (TPA) for dissolving blood clots associated with diseases such as heart attack and stroke;

- *interferons*, which assist the immune response and induce the resistance of host cells to viral infection and are promising anticancer agents; and
- *recombinant vaccines*, such as that for hepatitis B.

Gene Therapy

In gene therapy, a functioning gene is introduced into a person's cells to correct the action of a defective gene. Viruses are commonly used to carry DNA into cells. Current gene therapy is experimental, and human gene transplants so far have had only modest success.

- In 1999, ten children with severe combined immunodeficiency disease (SCID) were injected with working copies of a gene that helps the immune system develop. Almost all the children improved and most are healthy today, but in 2002, two of them developed leukemia.
- Four severely blind young adults had a curative gene injected into their eyes. They can now see more light and have enough vision to walk without help. Two of them can read several lines of an eye chart.
- Genetically altered cells injected into the brain of patients with Alzheimer's disease appear to nourish ailing neurons and may slow cognitive decline in these people.
- In 2006, researchers at the National Cancer Institute (NCI) successfully re-engineered immune cells to attack cancer cells in patients with advanced melanoma, the first successful use of gene therapy to treat cancer in humans.
- Researchers have genetically engineered the formation of new beta cells in the liver of mice. They also added a gene that inhibits activity of the T cells around the new beta cells in the liver and not in the rest of the body. (The T cells would otherwise destroy the new beta cells.) If this works in humans, diabetics could produce their own insulin.

▲ It DOES Matter!

GM rice ("golden rice"), developed in 1999, has new genes implanted from daffodils and a bacterium. Golden rice was developed as a fortified food containing high amounts of β-carotene, a precursor of vitamin A. It was to be used in areas where children face a shortage of dietary vitamin A to help them overcome vitamin A deficiency. An estimated 124 million people in Africa and Southeast Asia are affected by vitamin A deficiency, which has caused 1–2 million deaths and 500,000 cases of blindness. Opposition to and complex regulation of transgenic crops have prevented golden rice from being grown on farms; it is still in field trials.

Genetically Modified Organisms: Controversy and Promise

Genes can be transferred from nearly any organism to any other. New animals can be cloned from cells in adult animals. Genetically modified (GM) organisms are in widespread—and often controversial—use. For example, by 2010 in the United States, 93% of the soybeans, 93% of the cotton, and 86% of the maize (corn) planted were GM varieties.

- Genes for herbicide resistance are now incorporated into soybeans so that herbicide application will kill weeds without killing the soybean plants. People worry that these genes will escape into wild plants (weeds), making them resistant to herbicides.
- Genes from the bacteria *Bacillus thuringiensis* (Bt) are incorporated into corn and cotton plants. The genes cause the plants to produce a protein toxin that kills caterpillars that would otherwise feed on the plants. People worry that insects will quickly become resistant to the toxin and that butterflies and other desirable insects will also be killed by it.

GM foods are foods made from GM organisms whose DNA has been altered. GM foods first entered the market in the early 1990s. The most common modified foods—soybeans, corn, canola oil, and cottonseed oil—are derived from GM plants. People worry that GM foods will have proteins that will cause allergic reactions in some people. To protect against such developments, strict guidelines for recombinant DNA research have been instituted. Some people think that these are not strict enough.

Molecular genetics has already resulted in some impressive achievements. Its possibilities are mind-boggling—elimination of genetic defects, a cure for cancer, and who knows what else? Knowledge gives power, but it does not necessarily give wisdom. Who will decide what sort of creature the human species should be? The greatest problem we are likely to face in our use of bioengineering is choosing who is to play God with the new "secret of life."

Many problems remain, including getting the gene in the right place and targeting it so that it inserts itself only into the cells where it is needed. The stakes in gene therapy are huge. We all carry some defective genes. About one in ten people either has or will develop an inherited genetic disorder. Gene therapy could become an efficient way of curing many diseases.

Self-Assessment Questions

1. Recombinant DNA cloning involves
   a. combining DNA from two different organisms to make a single new organism
   b. creating a genetically identical organism from a skin cell
   c. isolation of a genetically pure colony of cells
   d. splitting of a fertilized egg into two cells to generate identical twins

2. In producing recombinant DNA, the DNA from the two sources is cut with
   a. DNA ligase
   b. phages
   c. restriction enzymes
   d. vectors

3. Recombinant DNA is currently used in the biotechnology industry to
   a. create new species of animals
   b. eliminate all infectious diseases in domestic animals
   c. increase the frequency of mutations
   d. synthesize insulin, interferon, and human growth hormone

4. Some geneticists suggest transferring some genes that direct photosynthesis from an efficient crop plant to a less efficient one, thus producing a more productive plant variety. This project would most likely involve
   a. genetic profiling
   b. genetic engineering
   c. genetic screening
   d. transcription

Answers: 1, a; 2, c; 3, d; 4, b

5. Are genetically modified foods safe? There are potential problems with today's genetically modified foods, but in practice we have been using genetically modified foods for over a century—ever since Mendel discovered the concept of genetics. Most of today's foods are hybrids, the result of genetic modification by cross-breeding. Of course, sometimes a hybrid tomato isn't tasty or is too small. Likewise, some genetically modified plants aren't exactly what we'd like.

CRITICAL THINKING EXERCISES

Apply knowledge that you have gained in this chapter and one or more of the FLaReS principles to evaluate the following statements or claims.

1. The wrapper of an energy bar claims, in large print, "21,000 mg of amino acids in each bar!"

2. DNA is an essential component of every living cell. An advertisement claims that DNA is a useful diet supplement.

3. A restaurant menu states, "Other restaurants use saturated beef fat for frying. We use only pure vegetable oil to fry our fish and french fries, for healthier eating."

4. The label on a bag of sugar says, "NOW CERTIFIED CARBON FREE."

5. A dietician states that a recommendation of 60 g of protein per day for an adult is somewhat misleading. She claims that the right kinds of proteins, with the proper amino acids in them, must be consumed; otherwise, even a much larger amount of protein per day may be insufficient to maintain health.

6. A man convicted of rape claims that he is innocent because DNA fingerprinting of a semen sample taken from the rape victim showed that it contains DNA from another man.

SUMMARY

Section 1—**Biochemistry** is the chemistry of life processes. Life requires chemical energy. **Metabolism** is the set of chemical reactions that keep cells alive. Metabolism includes many processes of both **anabolism** (building up of molecules) and **catabolism** (breaking down of molecules). Substances that provide animals with energy are carbohydrates, fats, and proteins.

Section 2—A carbohydrate is a compound whose formula can be written as a hydrate of carbon. Sugars, starches, and cellulose are carbohydrates. The simplest sugars are monosaccharides, carbohydrates that cannot be further hydrolyzed. A monosaccharide is either an aldose (having an aldehyde functional group) or a ketose (having a ketone functional group). Glucose and fructose are monosaccharides. A disaccharide can be hydrolyzed to yield two monosaccharide units. Sucrose and lactose are disaccharides. Polysaccharides contain many monosaccharide units linked together. Starches and cellulose are polysaccharides. Starches are polymers of glucose units held together by alpha linkages; cellulose is a glucose polymer held together by beta linkages. There are two kinds of plant starches, amylose and amylopectin. Animal starch is called glycogen.

Section 3—A lipid is a cellular component that is insoluble in water and soluble in solvents of low polarity. Lipids include solid fats and liquid oils; both are triglycerides (esters of fatty acids with glycerol). Lipids also include steroids, hormones, and fatty acids (long-chain carboxylic acids). A fat is an ester of fatty acids and glycerol. Fats may be saturated (all carbon-to-carbon bonds in the fatty acid are single bonds), monounsaturated (one $C=C$), or polyunsaturated (more than one $C=C$). The iodine number of a fat or oil is the mass in grams of iodine that reacts with 100 g of the fat or oil. Oils tend to have higher iodine numbers than fats because there are more double bonds in oils.

Section 4—An amino acid contains an amino ($-NH_2$) group and a carboxyl ($-COOH$) group. An amino acid exists as a zwitterion, in which a proton from the carboxyl group has been transferred to the amino group. Proteins are polymers of amino acids, with 20 amino acids forming millions of different proteins. Plants can synthesize proteins from CO_2, water, and minerals, but animals require proteins in their diets.

The bond that joins two amino-acid units in a protein is called a peptide bond. Two amino acids form a dipeptide, three forms a tripeptide, and more than 10 forms a polypeptide. When the molecular weight of a polypeptide exceeds about 10,000, it is called a protein. The sequence of the amino acids in a protein is of great importance to its function. Three-letter or single-letter abbreviations are used to designate amino acids.

Section 5—Protein structure has four levels. The primary structure of a protein is simply the sequence of its amino acids. The secondary structure is the arrangement of polypeptide chains about an axis. Two such arrangements are the beta pleated sheet, in which the arrays of chains form zigzag sheets, and the alpha helix, in which protein chains coil around one another. The tertiary structure of a protein is its folding pattern; globular proteins such as myoglobin are folded into compact shapes. Some proteins have a quaternary structure consisting of an aggregate of subunits arranged in a specific pattern.

There are four types of forces that determine the secondary, tertiary, and quaternary structures of proteins: (a) hydrogen bonds; (b) ionic bonds formed between acidic and basic side chains; (c) disulfide linkages, which are S—S bonds formed between cysteine groups; and (d) dispersion forces arising between nonpolar side chains.

Enzymes are biological catalysts. In operation, the reacting substance, or substrate, attaches to the active site of the enzyme to form a complex, which then decomposes to the products. An enzyme is often made up of an apoenzyme (a protein) and a cofactor that is necessary for proper function and that may be a metal ion. An organic cofactor (such as a vitamin) is called a coenzyme.

Section 6—Nucleic acids are the information and control centers of a cell. DNA (deoxyribonucleic acid) and RNA (ribonucleic acid) are polymers of nucleotides. Each nucleotide contains a pentose sugar unit, a phosphate unit, and one of four amine bases. Bases with one ring are called pyrimidines, and those with two fused rings are purines. In DNA, the sugar is deoxyribose and the bases are adenine, thymine, guanine, and cytosine. In RNA, the sugar is ribose and the bases are the same as those in DNA, except that uracil replaces thymine. Nucleotides are joined through their phosphate groups to form nucleic acid chains. In DNA, the bases thymine and adenine are always paired, as are the bases cytosine and guanine. Pairing occurs via hydrogen bonding between the bases and gives rise to the double-helix structure of DNA. RNA consists of single strands of nucleic acids, some parts of which may hydrogen bond to form double helixes. Chromosomes are made of DNA and proteins. A gene is a section of DNA. Genetic information is stored in the base sequence; a three-base sequence code for a particular amino acid. Transmission of genetic information requires replication, or copying, of the DNA molecules. When the chains of DNA are pulled apart, each half can replicate using nucleotides in the cellular fluid. Each base unit picks up a unit identical to that with which it was paired before. Enzymes connect the paired nucleotides to form the new chain. When a cell divides, one DNA molecule goes to each daughter cell, providing all the necessary genetic information.

Section 7—In transcription, a segment of DNA transfers its information to messenger RNA (mRNA). The next step is the translation of the code into a specific protein structure. Transfer RNA (tRNA) delivers amino acids to the growing protein chain. Each base triplet on a tRNA pairs with a set of three complementary bases on mRNA, called the codon, which codes for a specific amino acid.

Section 8—Many diseases have genetic components. In genetic testing, DNA is cleaved and duplicated. The patterns of DNA fragments are examined and compared to those of individuals with genetic diseases, to identify and predict the occurrence of such diseases. A similar technique is used to compare DNA from different sources in DNA fingerprinting. In recombinant DNA technology, the base sequence for the gene that codes for a desired protein is determined and amplified; the gene is then spliced into a plasmid. The recombined plasmid is inserted into a host organism, which generates the protein as it reproduces. Gene therapy—replacement of defective genes—could be used to cure diseases. Genetic engineering holds great promise and carries with it great responsibility.

Green chemistry Biochemistry has important applications in renewable energy and offers several advantages over traditional chemical synthesis, including the use of water as the solvent and the low levels of waste and energy use. Drugs and fuels are examples of products that may be made using biochemical methods.

Learning Objectives

❯ List the major parts of a cell, and describe the function of each part.	Problem 2
❯ Name the primary source of energy for plants and three classes of substances that are the sources of energy for animals.	Problems 1, 4, 8
❯ Compare and contrast starch, glycogen, and cellulose.	Problems 19, 20
❯ Describe the fundamental structure of a fatty acid and of a fat.	Problems 31, 32, 35, 36
❯ Classify fats as saturated, monounsaturated, or polyunsaturated.	Problems 33, 34
❯ Draw the fundamental structure of an amino acid, and show how amino acids combine to make proteins.	Problems 39, 40, 42–48, 70
❯ Describe the four levels of protein structure, and give an example of each.	Problem 69
❯ Describe how enzymes work as catalysts.	Problem 50
❯ Name the two types of nucleic acids, and describe the function of each type.	Problems 51, 52
❯ Explain complementary base pairing, and describe how a copy of DNA is synthesized.	Problems 55, 56–58, 74
❯ Explain how mRNA is synthesized from DNA and how a protein is synthesized from mRNA.	Problems 59–68, 77
❯ List important characteristics of the genetic code.	Problems 14, 59
❯ Describe recombinant DNA technology, and explain how it is used.	Problem 15
❯ Name some advantages of using biochemistry to create useful molecules.	Problems 79, 82
❯ Give examples of the use of biochemistry for energy production and other applications.	Problems 80, 81

 REVIEW QUESTIONS

1. What is the importance of photosynthesis to plants and animals?

2. Briefly identify and state a function of each of the following parts of a cell.
   a. cell membrane
   b. cell nucleus
   c. chloroplasts
   d. mitochondria
   e. ribosomes

3. In what parts of the body are proteins found? What tissues are largely proteins?

4. How does the elemental composition of proteins differ from those of carbohydrates and fats?

5. What is the chemical nature of proteins?

6. Amino-acid units in a protein are linked by peptide bonds. What is another name for this kind of bond?

7. What is the difference between a polypeptide and a protein?

8. What provides most of the energy for plants? Write the equation for the reaction that is driven by that energy.

9. What kind of intermolecular force is involved in base pairing?

10. Describe how replication and transcription are similar and how they differ.

11. How do DNA and RNA differ in structure?

12. What is the relationship among the cell parts called chromosomes, the units of heredity called genes, and the nucleic acid DNA?

13. What is the polymerase chain reaction (PCR)?

14. Explain what is meant by redundancy in the genetic code. Does redundancy exist for every amino acid?

15. List the steps in recombinant DNA technology.

   How can a virus be used to replace a defective gene in a human being?

 PROBLEMS

Carbohydrates

17. What is a monosaccharide? Name three common ones.

18. What is a disaccharide? Name three common ones.

19. What is glycogen? How does it differ from amylose? From amylopectin?

20. In what way are amylose and cellulose similar? What is the main structural difference between starch and cellulose?

21. Which of the following are monosaccharides?
   a. amylose
   b. cellulose
   c. mannose
   d. glucose

22. Which of the following are monosaccharides?
a. sucrose   b. galactose
c. fructose   d. lactose

23. Which of the carbohydrates in Problems 21 and 22 are disaccharides?

24. Which of the carbohydrates in Problems 21 and 22 are polysaccharides?

25. What are the hydrolysis products of each of the following?
a. amylose   b. glycogen

26. What are the hydrolysis products of each of the following?
a. amylopectin   b. cellulose

27. What functional groups are present in the formula for the open-chain form of fructose?

28. Write the formula for the open-chain form of glucose. What functional groups are present?

29. What functional groups are present in the formula for the open-chain form of galactose? How does the structure of galactose differ from that of glucose?

30. Mannose differs from glucose only in having the positions of the H and OH on the second carbon atom reversed. Write the formula for the open-chain form of mannose. What functional groups are present?

Lipids: Fats and Oils

31. How do fats and oils differ in structure? In properties?

32. Define *monoglyceride*, *diglyceride*, and *triglyceride*.

33. Which of the following fatty acids are saturated? Which are unsaturated?
a. palmitic acid   b. linoleic acid
c. oleic acid   d. stearic acid

34. Which of the fatty acids in Problem 33 are monounsaturated? Which are polyunsaturated?

35. How many carbon atoms are in a molecule of each of the following fatty acids?
a. linoleic acid   b. palmitic acid
c. stearic acid

36. How many carbon atoms are in a molecule of each of the following fatty acids?
a. linoleic acid   b. oleic acid
c. butyric acid

37. Which of the two foodstuffs shown below would you expect to have a higher iodine number? Explain your reasoning.

38. Which of the two fats shown below is likely to have a lower iodine number? Explain your reasoning.

Proteins

39. What functional groups does amino acid have? What is a zwitterion?

40. What is a dipeptide? A tripeptide? A polypeptide?

41. Of the amino acids glutamic acid, lysine, serine, leucine, and glycine, which are essential to the human diet?

42. Examine Table 3, and write the condensed structural formula for the part of each structure that is identical for 19 of the 20 amino acids. Which amino acid does not have this particular structural feature?

43. Write structural formulas for the following amino acids.
a. alanine   b. cysteine

44. Identify the following amino acids.

$$HOOC-CH_2CH_2-\underset{\underset{{}^+NH_3}{|}}{CH}-COO^-$$

(a)

$$HS-CH_2-\underset{\underset{{}^+NH_3}{|}}{CH}-COO^-$$

(b)

45. Write structural formulas for the following dipeptides.
a. glycylalanine   b. alanylserine

46. Identify the following dipeptides.

$$\underset{{}^+NH_3}{\overset{OH-CH_2}{|}}-CH-CONH-\underset{}{\overset{CH_2CH(CH_3)_2}{|}}CH-COO^-$$

(a)

$$^+NH_3-CH_2-CONH-\underset{}{\overset{HS-CH_2}{|}}CH-COO^-$$

(b)

47. The sweetener *aspartame* has the structure shown below, in which a CH_3O- group (at right) is attached to a dipeptide. Identify the dipeptide.

$$H_2N-\underset{\underset{COOH}{\overset{|}{CH_2}}}{CH}-\overset{\overset{O}{\|}}{C}-NH-\underset{\underset{\bigcirc}{\overset{|}{CH_2}}}{CH}-\overset{\overset{O}{\|}}{C}-OCH_3$$

48. Refer to Problem 47, and draw the structure of the other dipeptide that contains the same amino acids as aspartame.

49. List the four different forces that link protein chains.

50. Describe **(a)** the induced-fit model of enzyme action and **(b)** how an inhibitor deactivates an enzyme.

Nucleic Acids: Parts and Structure

51. Which of the following nucleotides can be found in DNA, which in RNA, and which in neither?

thymine
a. deoxyribose—P_i

adenine
b. ribose—P_i

cytosine
c. ribose—P_i

52. Which of the following nucleotides can be found in DNA, which in RNA, and which in neither?

uracil
a. ribose—P_i

adenine
b. deoxyribose—P_i

cytosine
c. deoxyribose—P_i

53. Identify the sugar and the base in the following nucleotide.

54. Identify the sugar and the base in the following nucleotide.

55. In DNA, which base would be paired with the base listed?
a. cytosine   **b.** adenine
c. guanine   **d.** thymine

56. In RNA, which base would be paired with the base listed?
a. adenine   **b.** guanine
c. uracil   **d.** cytosine

DNA: Self-Replication

57. In replication, a DNA molecule produces two daughter molecules. What is the fate of each strand of the original double helix?

58. DNA controls protein synthesis, yet most DNA resides within the cell nucleus and protein synthesis occurs outside the nucleus. How does DNA exercise its control?

RNA: Protein Synthesis and the Genetic Code

59. Which nucleic acid(s) is(are) involved in **(a)** the process referred to as transcription and **(b)** the process referred to as translation?

60. Explain the role of **(a)** mRNA and **(b)** tRNA in protein synthesis.

61. A portion of the code for a certain gene has the base sequence 5'-ATGAGCGACTTTGCGGGATTA-3'. What is the base sequence of the complementary strand of DNA?

62. What is the sequence of the mRNA that would be produced during transcription from the segment of DNA shown in Problem 61?

63. If the sequence of bases in an mRNA molecule is 3'-UCCGAU-5', what was the sequence of the DNA template?

64. What anticodon on tRNA would pair with each of the following mRNA codons?
a. 5'-UUU-3'   **b.** 5'-CAU-3'
c. 5'-AGC-3'   **d.** 5'-CCG-3'

65. What codon on mRNA would pair with each of the following tRNA anticodons?
a. 5'-UUG-3'   **b.** 5'-GAA-3'
c. 5'-UCC-3'

66. What codon on mRNA would pair with each of the following tRNA anticodons?
a. UCC   **b.** CAC
c. 5'-CAC-3'

67. Use Table 5 to identify the amino acids carried by each tRNA molecule in Problem 65.

68. Use Table 5 to determine the amino-acid sequence produced from the mRNA sequence 5'-AUGAGCGACUUUGCGGGAUUA-3'.

ADDITIONAL PROBLEMS

69. Human insulin molecules are made up of two chains with the following sequences.

Chain A: G-I-V-E-Q-C-C-T-S-I-C-S-L-Y-Q-L-E-N-Y-C-N

Chain B: F-V-N-Q-H-L-C-G-D-H-L-V-E-A-L-Y-L-V-C-G-E-R-G-F-F-Y-T-P-K-T

Chain A has a loop formed by a disulfide linkage between the sixth and eleventh amino acids (designated A-6 to A-11) and is joined to chain B by two disulfide linkages (A-7 to B-7 and A-20 to B-19). What level of protein structure is described by **(a)** the chain sequence of one-letter abbreviations and **(b)** the description of the loop and chain linkages?

70. Synthetic polymers can be formed from amino-acid units of a single kind. Write the formula for a segment of **(a)** polyglycine and **(b)** polyserine. Show at least four repeating units of each.

71. Identify the base in the structure in **(a)** Problem 53 and **(b)** Problem 54 as a purine or a pyrimidine.

72. Answer the following questions for the molecule shown.

a. Is the base a purine or a pyrimidine?
b. Would the compound be incorporated in DNA or in RNA?

73. Answer the questions posed in Problem 72 for the following compound.

74. Use Table 5 to determine the amino acid specified by the DNA triplet 5′-CTC-3′. What amino acid is specified if a mutation changes the DNA triplet to 5′-CTT-3′? To 5′-CTA-3′? to 5′-CAC-3′?

75. Many laundry detergents have enzymes to aid removal of stains of biological origin, such as those from food or blood. The enzyme subtilisin, produced by *Bacillus subtilis*, is one of these. The natural enzyme was not very effective because it was largely deactivated by the harsh detergent environment. A genetically modified form, in which the base sequence 5′-ACCAGCAUGGCG-3′ is replaced by 5′-ACCAGCGCGGCG-3′, is much more effective because it is more stable. What is the amino-acid sequence specified by the bases in this segment in **(a)** the original enzyme and **(b)** the genetically modified enzyme? You may consult Table 5.

76. In the novel *Jurassic Park* by Michael Crichton, the cloned dinosaurs were genetically engineered so as to be unable to survive outside the island park because they were unable to synthesize the amino acid lysine.

This was supposed to make the dinosaurs dependent on their makers to feed them a source of lysine. Examine Table 3, and suggest a reason why this genetic engineering would not keep the dinosaurs from surviving elsewhere.

77. With what mRNA codon would the tRNA in the diagram form a codon–anticodon pair?

78. Write the abbreviated versions of the following structural formula using **(a)** the three-letter abbreviations and **(b)** the one-letter abbreviations.

79. What solvent is typically used for biochemical reactions?

80. What types of molecules are used to store energy in biological systems?
a. hydrocarbons
b. carbohydrates and lipids
c. water and carbon dioxide

81. Which is an example of a way to produce a renewable fuel using biochemical processes or products?
a. turn carbohydrates into fuels
b. use bacteria to convert carbohydrates or CO_2 into biofuels
c. engineer microbes to make gasoline
d. all of the above

82. Which of the following is NOT an advantage of using biochemical methods compared to traditional chemical synthesis?
a. Water is often used as a solvent.
b. Separation of products is difficult.
c. Reaction conditions are mild.
d. Reactions are usually catalytic.

COLLABORATIVE GROUP PROJECTS

Prepare a PowerPoint, poster, or other presentation (as directed by your instructor) to share with the class.

1. Prepare a brief report on (**a**) a carbohydrate such as fructose, glycogen, lactose, maltose, sucrose, or starch or (**b**) a lipid such as beef tallow, corn oil, lard, oleic acid, or palmitic acid. List principal sources and uses of the material.

2. Prepare a brief report on enzyme action, including a comparision of the induced-fit model of action with the older lock-and-key model.

3. Prepare a brief report on one of the following products of genetic engineering. List some advantages and disadvantages of the product.
   a. golden rice
   b. herbicide-resistant transgenic soybeans
   c. transgenic cotton that produces Bt toxin
   d. transgenic tobacco that produces human serum albumin
   e. transgenic tomatoes that have improved resistance to viruses
   f. transgenic *E. coli* that produce human interleukin-2, a protein that stimulates the production of T-lymphocytes that play a role in fighting selected cancers

4. Genetic testing carries both promise and peril, and its use is an important topic in bioethics today. After some online research, write a brief essay on one of the following—or on a similar question assigned by your instructor.
   a. In what cases might a person not want to be tested for a disease his or her parent had?
   b. When is genetic testing most valuable? What privacy issues must be addressed in this area?
   c. Does testing negative for the breast cancer genes mean that a woman doesn't have to have mammograms?

BRIEF ANSWERS TO SELECTED PROBLEMS

Answers are provided for *all in-chapter exercises*. Brief answers are given for *odd-numbered Review Questions*; more complete answers can be obtained by reviewing the text. Answers are provided for *all odd-numbered Problems and Additional Problems*.

NOTE: For numerical problems, your answer may differ slightly from ours because of rounding and the use of significant figures.

1 Mannose differs from glucose in configuration about C-2 only.
2 A. a. H-P-V-A   b. histidylprolylvalylalanine
   B. a. Thr-Gly-Ala-Ala-Leu   b. T-G-A-A-L
3 A. 3   B. 24
4 A. Sugar: ribose; base: uracil; RNA
   B. Neither; thymine occurs only in DNA, ribose only in RNA.
1. Photosynthesis converts solar energy to carbohydrates, which provide energy to plants and to organisms that eat plants.
3. In every cell; muscles, skin, hair, nails
5. Polyamides
7. If the molar mass of a polypeptide exceeds about 10,000 g, it is called a protein.
9. Hydrogen bonds
11. DNA is a double helix; RNA is a single helix with some loops.
13. A process that produces millions of copies of a specific DNA sequence
15. Step 1: isolation and amplification
    Step 2: gene is spliced into a plasmid
    Step 3: plasmid is inserted into a host cell
    Step 4: plasmid replicates, making copies of itself
17. A carbohydrate that cannot be further hydrolyzed; glucose, fructose, and galactose
19. Glycogen is animal starch. Amylose is a plant starch with glucose units joined in a continuous chain. Amylopectin is a plant starch with branched chains of glucose units.
21. c, d
23. Sucrose and lactose
25. a. glucose   b. glucose
27. Ketone and alcohol (hydroxyl)
29. Aldehyde and alcohol (hydroxyl); in configuration about C-4
31. Structurally, oils have more C-to-C double bonds than fats have. At room temperature, fats are solids, and oils are liquid.
33. saturated: a, d; unsaturated: b, c
35. a. 18   b. 16
    c. 18

37. Liquid oil (right); it is unsaturated.
39. An amino group and a carboxyl group; a zwitterion is a molecule that carries both a positive and a negative charge.
41. lysine and leucine
43. a.

$$H_3N^+-CH-C\underset{O^-}{\overset{O}{\big\langle}}$$
$$|$$
$$CH_3$$

b.

$$H_3N^+-CH-C\underset{O^-}{\overset{O}{\big\langle}}$$
$$|$$
$$CH_2SH$$

45. a. $H_3N^+ CH_2CO-NH\,C\,HCOO^-$
       $|$
       CH_3

    b. $H_3N^+ CH_2CO-NH\,C\,HCOO^-$
       $|\qquad\qquad\qquad |$
       $CH_3\qquad\quad CH_2OH$

47. Aspartylphenylalanine
49. Hydrogen bonds, ionic bonds, disulfide linkages, and dispersion forces
51. DNA: a; RNA: b, c
53. Ribose; uracil
55. a. guanine   b. thymine
    c. cytosine   d. adenine
57. Each strand of the parent DNA double helix remains associated with the newly synthesized DNA strand.
59. a. DNA and mRNA   b. mRNA and tRNA
61. 3'-TACTCGCTGAAACGCCCTAAT-5'
63. 5'-AGGCTA-3'
65. a. 3'-AAC-5'   b. 3'-CUU-5'   c. 3'-AGG-5'
67. a. glutamine   b. phenylalanine   c. glycine
69. a. primary   b. secondary
71. a. pyrimidine   b. pyrimidine
73. a. purine   b. RNA
75. a. ~Thr-Ser-Met-Ala~
    b. ~Thr-Ser-Ala-Ala~
77. 3'-AUG-5' (The sequences must be antiparallel.)
79. Water
81. d

Food

From Chapter 17 of *Chemistry for Changing Times*, Thirteenth Edition. John W. Hill, Terry W. McCreary, Doris K. Kolb.

Alex Jackson/Shutterstock

Learning Objectives

> Identify dietary carbohydrates, and state their function. (1)

> Identify dietary lipids, and state their function. (2)

> List the essential amino acids, and explain why they are essential. (3)

> Describe some protein deficiency diseases and their causes. (3)

> Identify the vitamins and the bulk dietary minerals, and state their functions. (4)

> Describe the effects of starvation, fasting, and malnutrition. (5)

> List some common food additives and their purposes. (6)

> Identify and describe some of the main problems with harmful substances in our food. (7)

> Identify common molecules derived from food sources.

> Distinguish polar molecules from nonpolar molecules and predict which can be extracted with ethanol or supercritical carbon dioxide.

> Describe how green chemistry has made the extraction of natural products, bioactive food components, and essential oils from plants safer and less hazardous.

Anna Kucherova/Shutterstock

Food

Have You Ever Wondered?

1. **The doctor said my father has high triglycerides. What are they?**

2. **Is high blood cholesterol mainly a problem for older people?**

3. **How much fat in the diet is "too much"?**

4. **Are large doses of vitamins beneficial?**

5. **Are some foods really "super foods" or "miracle foods"?**

6. **Should the government prohibit food additives?**

Chris Ryan/Alamy

Molecular Gastronomy

FOOD! From holiday feasts to late-night snacks, many of life's joys involve food. Yet the prime purpose of food is not to give pleasure; it is to sustain life. Food supplies all the molecular building blocks from which our bodies are made and all the energy for our life activities. That energy comes ultimately from the Sun through photosynthesis.

In many places on Earth, some people never have enough food. According to *The Hunger Project*, about 1 billion people (one in seven) are always hungry. Poor nutrition contributes to the deaths of about 5 million children each year. The Hunger Project was started in 1977, when an estimated 15,000,000 people died of hunger each year. Now that estimate is 9,000,000 per year. Three-fourths are children under the age of five. Famine and wars make the news,

The food we eat supplies all the molecular building blocks from which our bodies are made and all the energy for our life activities. Those building blocks include carbohydrates, proteins, and fats. Carbohydrates supply most of our energy. Proteins are broken down into amino acids and reassembled into muscle, skin, hair, and other tissue. Fats, consumed in reasonable amounts, provide long-term storage of energy and some essential nutrients. But there is much more to a proper, healthy diet than an adequate supply of these three nutrients. In this chapter, we'll look at the properties of carbohydrates, proteins, fats, but they cause just 10% of hunger deaths. Most result from chronic malnutrition. Worldwide, hunger and malnutrition are the greatest risk to health. And things may be getting worse. Increasing food prices have triggered food riots in several countries. Millions of additional people have fallen into poverty.

While millions starve, other locales have a surplus. Most of us in the Western world have an overabundance of food and often eat too much. Yet even in the United States, the U.S. Department of Agriculture estimates that 31 million people live in households that experience hunger or the risk of hunger. Nearly 9 million people, including more than 3.2 million children, experience hunger, frequently skipping meals or eating too little. These people often have lower-quality diets or must resort to seeking food from emergency sources.

Many of us also frequently eat the wrong kinds of food. Our diet, often too rich in saturated fats, sugar, and alcohol, has been linked in part to at least five of the ten leading causes of death in the United States: heart disease, cancer, stroke, diabetes, and kidney disease. The U.S. Centers for Disease Control and Prevention (CDC) found that 68% of the adults in the United States are overweight. According to the World Health Organization (WHO), 1.5 billion adults and 43 million children under the age of five worldwide are overweight. This excess weight contributes to poor health, increased risk of diabetes, heart attacks, strokes, and some forms of cancer. It also leads to increased susceptibility to other diseases.

The human body is a collection of chemicals. A chemical analysis of the human body would show that it is about two-thirds water. The body contains several minerals and thousands of other chemicals. Our foods are also made up of chemicals. They enable children to grow, provide people with energy, and supply the chemicals needed for the repair and replacement of body tissues.

In this chapter, we discuss food, what it's made of and the substances added to it—by accident or design. The three main classes of foods are carbohydrates, fats, and proteins. These, too, are chemicals. For proper nutrition, our diet should include balanced proportions of these three foodstuffs, plus water, vitamins, minerals, and fiber.

1 Carbohydrates in the Diet

Learning Objective ❯ Identify dietary carbohydrates, and state their function.

Dietary carbohydrates include sugars and starches. Sugars are mainly monosaccharides and disaccharides; starches are polysaccharides.

Sugars have been used for ages to make food sweeter. Two monosaccharides, *glucose* (or *dextrose*) and *fructose* (fruit sugar), and the disaccharide *sucrose* are the most common dietary sugars (Figure 1). Common table sugar is sucrose, usually obtained from sugar cane or sugar beets. Glucose is the sugar used by the cells of our bodies for energy. Because it is the sugar that circulates in the bloodstream, it is often called **blood sugar**. Fructose is found in honey and in some fruits,

▲ **Figure 1** The main sugars in our diet are sucrose (cane or beet sugar), glucose (corn syrup), and fructose (fruit sugar, often in the form of high-fructose corn syrup).

Q: *What is the molecular formula for glucose? For fructose? How are the two compounds related? How is sucrose related to glucose and fructose?*

Jenny Mie Lau King/Shutterstock

▲ **Figure 2** Infants born with galactosemia can thrive on a milk-free substitute formula.

▲ **Figure 3** Bread, flour, cereals, and pasta are rich in starches.

You can do your own carbohydrate digestion experiment. Chew an unsalted saltine cracker for several minutes, and you will notice a slight sweet taste. Your saliva contains enzymes that begin the digestion process. Explain the sweet taste.

but much of it is made from glucose. Corn syrup, made from starch, is mainly glucose. *High-fructose corn syrup (HFCS)* is made by treating corn syrup with enzymes to convert much of the glucose to fructose. Fructose is sweeter than sucrose or glucose. Foods sweetened to the same degree with fructose have somewhat fewer calories than those sweetened with sucrose.

Since 1968, per capita consumption of sugars in the United States has skyrocketed from 11 kg/year to 71 kg/year, including 33 kg of HFCS. Most sugars are consumed in soft drinks, presweetened cereals, candy, and other highly processed foods with little or no nutritive value besides calories. The sugars in sweetened foods also contribute to tooth decay and obesity.

Digestion and Metabolism of Carbohydrates

Glucose and fructose are absorbed directly into the bloodstream from the digestive tract. Sucrose is hydrolyzed (split by water) during digestion to glucose and fructose.

$$\text{Sucrose} + H_2O \longrightarrow \text{Glucose} + \text{Fructose}$$

The disaccharide lactose occurs in milk. During digestion, it is hydrolyzed to two simpler sugars, glucose and galactose.

$$\text{Lactose} + H_2O \longrightarrow \text{Glucose} + \text{Galactose}$$

Nearly all human babies have the enzyme necessary to accomplish this breakdown, but many adults do not. People who lack the enzyme get digestive upsets from drinking milk, a condition called *lactose intolerance.* When milk is cooked or fermented, the lactose is at least partially hydrolyzed. People with lactose intolerance may be able to enjoy cheese, yogurt, or cooked foods containing milk with little or no discomfort. Lactose-free milk, made by treating milk with an enzyme that hydrolyzes lactose, is available in most grocery stores.

All monosaccharides are converted to glucose during metabolism. Some babies are born with *galactosemia,* a deficiency of the enzyme that catalyzes the conversion of galactose to glucose. For proper nutrition, they must be fed a synthetic formula (Figure 2) in place of milk.

Complex Carbohydrates: Starch and Cellulose

Starch and cellulose are both polymers of glucose, but the connecting links between the glucose units are different. Humans can digest starch, but not cellulose. **Starch,** a polymer of glucose in which the units are joined by alpha linkages, is an important part of any balanced diet (Figure 3). **Cellulose,** a glucose polymer with beta linkages, is an important component of dietary fiber.

When digested, starch is hydrolyzed to glucose, as represented by the following equation:

$$(C_6H_{10}O_5)_n + n\,H_2O \xrightarrow{\text{Carbohydrates}} n\,C_6H_{12}O_6$$
$$\text{Starch} \qquad\qquad\qquad\qquad \text{Glucose}$$

The body then metabolizes the glucose, using it as a source of energy. Glucose is broken down in a complex set of more than 50 chemical reactions that produce carbon dioxide and water, with the release of energy.

$$C_6H_{12}O_6 + 6\,O_2 \longrightarrow 6\,CO_2 + 6\,H_2O + \text{Energy}$$

This net reaction is the reverse of photosynthesis. In this way, animals are able to make use of the energy from the Sun that was captured by plants using the process of photosynthesis.

Carbohydrates, which supply about 4 kcal of energy per gram, are our bodies' preferred fuels. When we eat more than our bodies can use, small amounts of carbohydrates can be stored in the liver and in muscle tissue as **glycogen** (animal starch), a highly branched polymer of α-glucose. Large excesses of carbohydrates are converted to fat for storage. Most health authorities recommend obtaining carbohydrates from a diet rich in whole grains, fruits, vegetables, and legumes (beans). We should minimize our intake of the simple sugars and refined starches found in many prepared foods.

Cellulose is the most abundant carbohydrate. It is present in all plants, forming their cell walls and other structural features. Wood is about 50% cellulose, and cotton is almost pure cellulose. Unlike starch, cellulose cannot be digested by humans and many other animals. We get no caloric value from dietary cellulose because its glucose units are joined by beta linkages, and most animals lack the enzymes needed to break this kind of bond. Certain bacteria that live in the gut of termites and in the digestive tract of grazing animals such as cows produce these enzymes, so that these animals can convert cellulose to glucose. Cellulose does, however, play an important role in human digestion, providing *dietary fiber* that absorbs water and helps move food through the digestive tract (Section 4).

▲ It DOES Matter!

With today's emphasis on low-carbohydrate foods, labels on some diet foods give the mass in grams of carbohydrate that can be readily digested. "Only 1 carb" means that a serving contains 1 g of readily digestible carbohydrate. It is important to read the labels of such foods carefully. They may contain a large amount of fat, including saturated fat. They may also contain relatively large amounts of additives (such as glycerin or xylitol) that are digested as carbohydrate—though much more slowly than sugars or even starches.

Self-Assessment Questions

1. About _____ people in the world are hungry today.
   a. 1 in 4
   b. 1 in 7
   c. 1 in 12
   d. 1 in 20

2. Digestion of lactose produces
   a. galactose and fructose
   b. galactose and glucose
   c. glucose and fructose
   d. only glucose

3. People who have lactose intolerance are deficient in the
   a. enzyme that catalyzes the hydrolysis of lactose to galactose and glucose
   b. enzyme that catalyzes the conversion of galactose to glucose
   c. enzymes that catalyze the oxidation of lactose to CO_2 and H_2O
   d. taste receptors for lactose, leaving a bitter taste

4. Galactosemia is an inherited disease that causes a baby to be deficient in the
   a. enzyme that catalyzes the hydrolysis of lactose to galactose and glucose
   b. enzyme that catalyzes the conversion of galactose to glucose
   c. enzymes that catalyze the oxidation of galactose to CO_2 and H_2O
   d. taste receptors for galactose, leaving a bitter taste

5. The monomer units of starch and cellulose, respectively, are
   a. amino acids and glucose
   b. α-glucose and β-glucose
   c. β-glucose and α-glucose
   d. glucose and fructose

6. Small quantities of carbohydrates can be stored in liver and muscle tissue as
   a. amylose
   b. cellulose
   c. glucose
   d. glycogen

7. Humans cannot digest cellulose because they lack enzymes for the hydrolysis of
   a. α-amino acid linkages
   b. α-glucose linkages
   c. β-glucose linkages
   d. sucrose

Answers: 1, b; 2, b; 3, a; 4, b; 5, b; 6, d; 7, c

2 Fats and Cholesterol

Learning Objective › Identify dietary lipids, and state their function.

Fats—esters of fatty acids and glycerol—are high-energy foods, yielding about 9 kcal of energy per gram. Some fats are "burned" as fuel for our activities. Others are used to build and maintain important constituents of our cells, such as cell membranes. The fat in our diet comes from many sources, some of which are shown in Figure 4.

Digestion and Metabolism of Fats

Dietary fats are mainly *triacylglycerols*, commonly called **triglycerides**. Fats are digested by enzymes called *lipases* and are ultimately broken down into fatty acids and glycerol (Figure 5). Some fat molecules are hydrolyzed to a monoglyceride (*monoacylglycerol*; glycerol combined with only one fatty acid) or a diglyceride (*diacylglycerol*; ester of two fatty acids and glycerol). Once absorbed, these products of

1. The doctor said my father has high triglycerides. What are they? Triglycerides are a type of fat molecule found in the bloodstream. High triglycerides are often the result of a diet high in fats, and they contribute to heart disease.

▲ **Figure 4** Cream, butter, margarine, cooking oils, and foods fried in fat are rich in fats. The average American diet contains too much fat. Americans get 37% of their calories from fat, while the recommendation of the FDA is 20–30% fat calories.

Pearson Education/Eric Schrader

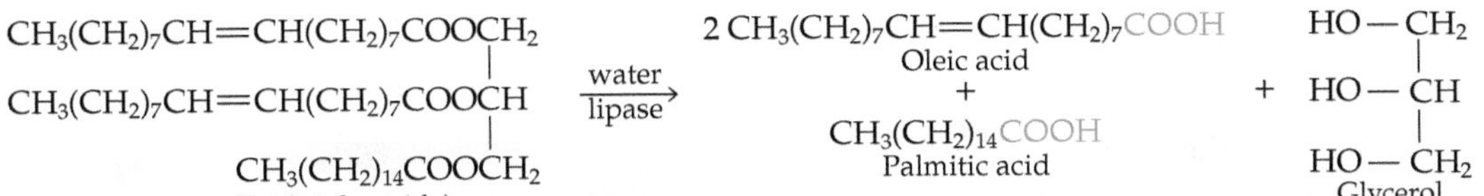

$$CH_3(CH_2)_7CH{=}CH(CH_2)_7COOCH_2$$
$$|$$
$$CH_3(CH_2)_7CH{=}CH(CH_2)_7COOCH \xrightarrow[\text{lipase}]{\text{water}}$$
$$|$$
$$CH_3(CH_2)_{14}COOCH_2$$
Fat (triglyceride)

$$2\;CH_3(CH_2)_7CH{=}CH(CH_2)_7COOH$$
Oleic acid
$$+$$
$$CH_3(CH_2)_{14}COOH$$
Palmitic acid

$$+$$

$$HO{-}CH_2$$
$$|$$
$$HO{-}CH$$
$$|$$
$$HO{-}CH_2$$
Glycerol

▲ **Figure 5** In the digestion of fats, a triglyceride is hydrolyzed to fatty acids and glycerol in a reaction catalyzed by the enzyme lipase.

Q: *What diglyceride is formed by removal of the palmitic acid part of the triglyceride? What monoglyceride is formed by removal of both oleic acid parts?*

fat digestion are reassembled into triglycerides, which are attached to proteins for transportation through the bloodstream.

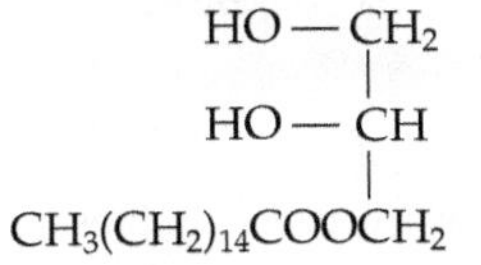

$$HO{-}CH_2$$
$$|$$
$$HO{-}CH$$
$$|$$
$$CH_3(CH_2)_{14}COOCH_2$$

A monoglyceride

$$CH_3(CH_2)_7CH{=}CH(CH_2)_7COOCH_2$$
$$|$$
$$HO{-}CH$$
$$|$$
$$CH_3(CH_2)_{14}COOCH_2$$

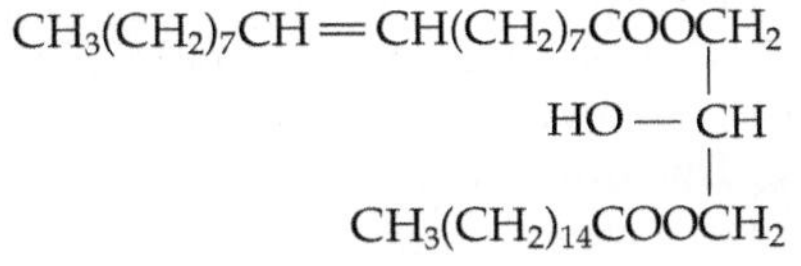

A diglyceride

Fats are stored throughout the body, principally in **adipose tissue**, in locations called **fat depots**. Fat depots around vital organs, such as the heart, kidneys, and spleen, cushion and help prevent injury to these organs. Fat is also stored under the skin, where it helps to insulate against temperature changes.

When fat reserves are called on for energy, fat molecules are hydrolyzed back to glycerol and fatty acids. The glycerol can be burned for energy or converted to glucose. The fatty acids enter a process called the *fatty acid spiral* that removes carbon atoms two at a time. The two-carbon fragments can be used for energy or for the synthesis of new fatty acids.

Fats, Cholesterol, and Human Health

Dietary *saturated fats* and cholesterol have been implicated in *arteriosclerosis* ("hardening of the arteries"). Saturated fats are those containing a large proportion of saturated fatty acids, such as palmitic and stearic acids. Incidence of cardiovascular disease is strongly correlated with diets rich in saturated fats. As the disease develops, deposits form on the inner walls of arteries. Eventually these deposits harden, and the vessels lose their elasticity (Figure 6). Blood clots tend to lodge in the narrowed arteries, leading to a heart attack (if the blocked artery is in heart muscle) or a stroke (if the blockage occurs in an artery that supplies the brain).

The plaque in clogged arteries is rich in cholesterol, a fatlike steroid alcohol found in animal tissues and various foods. Cholesterol is normally synthesized by the liver and is important as a constituent of cell membranes and a precursor to

Martin M. Rotker/Photo Researchers, Inc.   Peter Arnold, Inc./Alamy

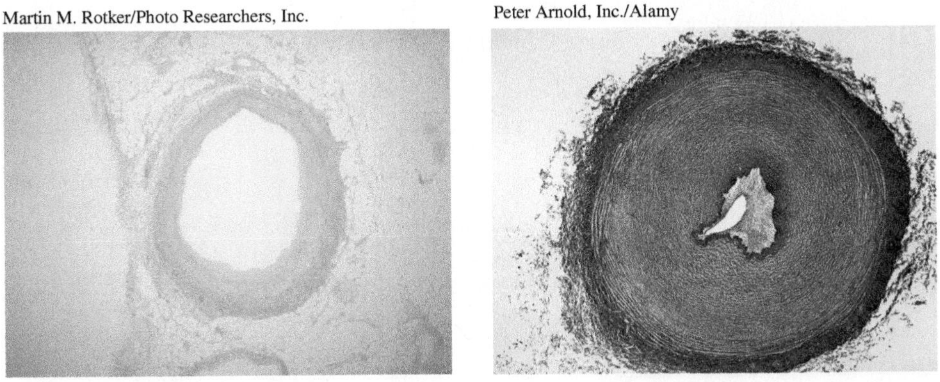

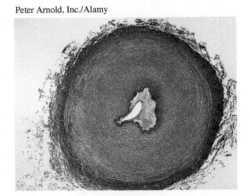

◀ **Figure 6** Photomicrographs of cross sections of a normal artery (left) and a "hardened" artery (right), which shows deposits of plaque that contain cholesterol.

Emulsions

When oil and water are vigorously shaken together, the oil is broken up into tiny, microscopic droplets and dispersed throughout the water, a mixture called an *emulsion*. Unless a third substance has been added, the emulsion usually breaks down rapidly, as the oil droplets recombine and float to the surface of the water.

Emulsions can be stabilized by adding a type of gum, a soap, or a protein that can form a protective coating around the oil droplets and prevent them from coming together. Lecithin in egg yolks keeps mayonnaise from separating, while casein in milk keeps fat droplets suspended. Compounds called *bile salts* keep tiny fat droplets suspended in aqueous media during human digestion. This greatly aids the digestive process. The tiny emulsified droplets provide a much greater surface area on which the water-soluble lipase enzymes can break down the triacylglycerides to glycerol and fatty acids.

▲ Many foods are emulsions. Milk is an emulsion of butterfat in water. The stabilizing agent is a protein called *casein*. Mayonnaise is an emulsion of vegetable oil in water, stabilized by egg yolk.

Pearson Education/Eric Schrader

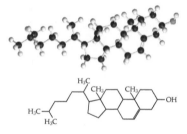

▲ Molecular model and structural formula of cholesterol.

steroid hormones. High blood levels of cholesterol, like those of triglycerides, correlate closely with the risk of cardiovascular disease. Like fats, cholesterol is insoluble in water, as we can determine from its molecular formula ($C_{27}H_{45}OH$) and structure (shown in the margin). Cholesterol is transported in blood by water-soluble proteins. The cholesterol–protein combination is an example of a **lipoprotein**, any of a group of proteins combined with a lipid, such as cholesterol or a triglyceride.

Lipoproteins are usually classified according to their density (Table 1). Very-low-density lipoproteins (VLDLs) serve mainly to transport triglycerides, whereas low-density lipoproteins (LDLs) are the main carriers of cholesterol. LDLs carry cholesterol to the cells for use, and these lipoproteins are the ones that deposit cholesterol in arteries, leading to cardiovascular disease. High-density lipoproteins (HDLs) also carry cholesterol, but they carry it to the liver for processing and excretion. Exercise is thought to increase the levels of HDLs, the lipoproteins sometimes called "good" cholesterol. High levels of LDLs, called "bad" cholesterol, increase the risk of heart attack and stroke. The American Heart Association recommends a maximum of 300 mg/day of cholesterol for the general population and 200 mg/day for people with heart disease or at risk for it.

2. Is high blood cholesterol mainly a problem for older people? The effects of high blood cholesterol are seen mainly in older people because the buildup of plaque in the blood vessels takes time. But those effects are often the result of years of an unhealthy diet and high levels of LDLs. To minimize the long-term effects of high cholesterol, you should consider early preventive measures. Reducing saturated fat in your diet is a good start.

Table 1	Lipoproteins in the Blood			
Class	**Abbreviation**	**Protein (%)**	**Density (g/mL)**	**Main Function**
Very low density	VLDL	5	1.006–1.019	Transport triglycerides
Low density	LDL	25	1.019–1.063	Transport cholesterol to the cells for use
High density	HDL	50	1.063–1.210	Transport cholesterol to the liver for processing and excretion

Fats differ in their effect on blood cholesterol levels. Many nutritionists advise us to use olive oil and canola oil as our major sources of dietary lipids because they contain a high percentage of monounsaturated fatty acids, which have been shown to lower LDL cholesterol. There is also statistical evidence that fish oils can prevent heart disease. For example, Greenlanders who eat a lot of fish have a low risk of heart disease despite a diet that is high in total fat and cholesterol. The probable effective agents are polyunsaturated fatty acids such as eicosapentaenoic acid (EPA) and docosahexaenoic acid (DHA):

$$CH_3(CH_2CH=CH)_5(CH_2)_3COOH$$
EPA

$$CH_3(CH_2CH=CH)_6(CH_2)_2COOH$$
DHA

These fatty acids are known as *omega-3 fatty acids* because they have a carbon-to-carbon double bond that begins at the *third* carbon from the end opposite the COOH group—the *omega* end. Studies have shown that adding omega-3 fatty acids to the diet leads to lower cholesterol and triglyceride levels in the blood.

Fats and oils containing carbon-to-carbon double bonds can undergo hydrogenation, addition of an H_2 molecule to each double bond. Hydrogenation of vegetable oils to produce semisolid fats is an important process in the food industry. The chemistry of this conversion process is identical to the hydrogenation reaction of alkenes.

$$CH_3(CH_2)_7CH=CH(CH_2)_7COOH \xrightarrow[Ni]{H_2} CH_3(CH_2)_7CH_2CH_2(CH_2)_7COOH$$
Oleic acid (monounsaturated) Stearic acid (saturated)

By properly controlling the reaction conditions, inexpensive vegetable oils (cottonseed, corn, and soybean) can be partially hydrogenated to yield soft, spreadable fats suitable for use in margarine or fully hydrogenated to produce harder fats like shortening. The consumer would get much higher unsaturation by using the oils directly, but most people would rather spread margarine than pour oil on their toast.

Concern about the role of saturated fats in raising blood cholesterol and clogging arteries caused many consumers to switch from butter to margarine. However, some of the unsaturated fats that remain after partial hydrogenation of vegetable oils have structures similar to saturated fats. These unsaturated fats raise cholesterol levels and increase the risk of coronary heart disease.

Figure 7 presents molecular models of three types of fatty acids. Most naturally occurring unsaturated fatty acids have a *cis* arrangement about the double bond. For example, oleic acid has the structure given by Figure 7(c). A *cis* arrangement about double-bonded carbon atoms has both hydrogen atoms on the same side of the double bond. During hydrogenation, the arrangement in

▲ It DOES Matter!

Half of the total fat, three-fourths of the saturated fat, and all the cholesterol in a typical human diet come from animal products such as meat, milk, cheese, and eggs. Advertising that a vegetable oil (for example) contains no cholesterol is silly. No vegetable product contains cholesterol.

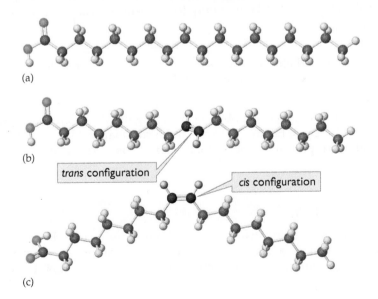

(a)

(b)

trans configuration   *cis* configuration

(c)

◀ **Figure 7** The structures of (a) stearic acid (a saturated fatty acid) and (b) the *trans* isomer of oleic acid (a *trans* unsaturated fatty acid) are similar in shape, and these acids behave similarly in the body; (c) oleic acid (a *cis* unsaturated fatty acid) has a very different shape.

some of the molecules is changed so that the hydrogen atoms of the double-bonded carbon atoms are on opposite sides of the double bond, a *trans* arrangement, shown in Figure 7(b). If we draw a straight line passing through the double-bonded carbon atoms and if the hydrogen atoms on those carbon atoms are on the same side of the line, the molecule represents a *cis* fatty acid. If they are on opposite sides, it is a *trans* fatty acid.

Note in Figures 7(a) and 7(b) that both saturated fatty acids (such as stearic acid) and *trans* fatty acids are more or less straight and can stack neatly like logs. This maximizes the intermolecular attractive forces, making saturated and *trans* fatty acids more likely to be solids than *cis* fatty acids.

On the other hand, *cis* fatty acids [Figure 7(c)] have a bend in their structure, fixed in position by the double bond. They have weaker intermolecular forces and are more likely to be liquids. Because *trans* fatty acids also resemble saturated fatty acids in their tendency to raise blood levels of LDL cholesterol, the FDA requires manufacturers to provide the *trans* fat content of foods on labels.

Many Americans eat too much fat, especially saturated and *trans* fats. Health experts generally advise us to limit our overall intake of fats, and of saturated and *trans* fats in particular. Many health professionals recommend that fats should not exceed 30% of total calories, and no more than one-third of the fat should be saturated fat.

3. How much fat in the diet is "too much"? Not more than about 30% of total daily calories should come from fat, and not more than 10% should come from saturated fat. For a 2000-kcal daily allowance, this means less than 600 kcal from fat and less than 200 kcal from saturated fat.

Example 1   Nutrient Calculations

A single-serving pepperoni pan pizza has 38 g of fat and 780 total calories. (Recall that a food calorie is a kilocalorie.) Estimate the percentage of the total calories from fat.

Solution

First, we calculate the calories from fat. Fat furnishes about 9 kcal/g, so 38 g of fat furnishes

$$38 \text{ g fat} \times \frac{9 \text{ kcal}}{1 \text{ g fat}} = 340 \text{ kcal}$$

Now, we divide the calories from fat by the total calories. Then multiply by 100% to get the percentage (parts per 100).

$$\text{Percentage of calories from fat} = \frac{340 \text{ kcal}}{780 \text{ kcal}} \times 100\% = 44\%$$

This answer is only an estimate for two reasons: The value of 9 kcal/g is approximate, and the 38 g of fat is known only to the nearest gram. A proper answer is about 44%.

■ EXERCISE 1A

A serving of two fried chicken thighs has 51 g of fat and furnishes 720 kcal. What percentage of the total calories comes from fat?

■ EXERCISE 1B

A lunch consists of a regular hamburger with 12 g of fat and 275 kcal, a serving of french fries with 12 g of fat and 240 kcal, and a chocolate milkshake with 9 g of fat and 360 kcal. What percentage of the total calories comes from fat?

Example 2   Fatty Acids

Following are line-angle structures of three fatty acids. Each corner and each end of a line is a carbon atom, and each carbon atom is attached to enough hydrogen atoms to give each carbon atom four bonds. **(a)** Which is a saturated fatty acid? **(b)** Which is a monounsaturated fatty acid? **(c)** Which is an omega-3 fatty acid?

I. 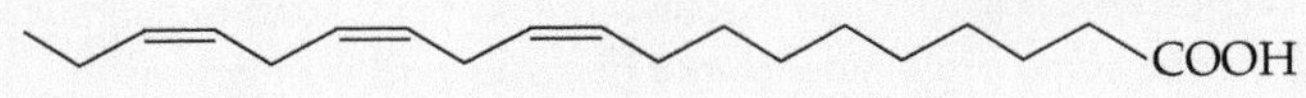 COOH

II. 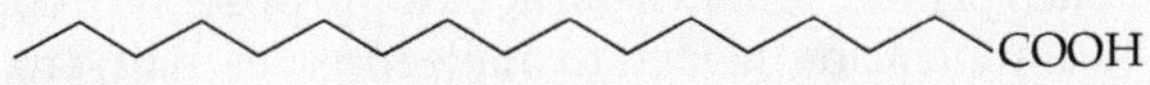 COOH

III. 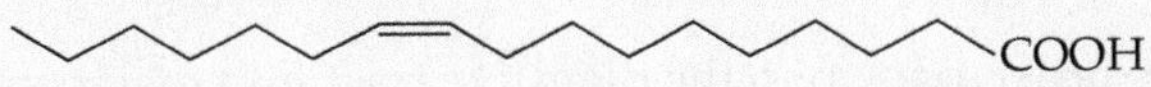 COOH

Solution

a. Fatty acid II has no carbon-to-carbon double bonds; it is a saturated fatty acid.

b. Fatty acid III has one carbon-to-carbon double bond; it is a monounsaturated fatty acid.

c. Fatty acid I has one of its carbon-to-carbon double bonds three carbons removed from the end farthest from the carboxyl group (the omega end); it is an omega-3 fatty acid.

■ EXERCISE 2A
Which of the fatty acids in Example 2 is polyunsaturated?

■ EXERCISE 2B
Is fatty acid III likely to be more similar physiologically to fatty acid II or to fatty acid I? Explain.

Self-Assessment Questions

1. Fats are
   a. esters of glycerol and fatty acids
   b. esters of cholesterol and fatty acids
   c. polymeric steroids
   d. polymers of amino acids

2. Among lipoproteins, LDLs are
   a. bad because they can block arteries
   b. the form that carries cholesterol to the liver for processing and excretion
   c. the good form because they can clear arteries
   d. the kind increased by exercise

Questions 3–5 refer to the following structures.
   a. $CH_3(CH_2)_{16}COOH$
   b. $CH_3(CH_2)_5CH=CH(CH_2)_7COOH$
   c. $CH_3(CH_2)_3(CH_2CH=CH)_2(CH_2)_7COOH$
   d. $CH_3(CH_2CH=CH)_3(CH_2)_7COOH$

3. Which is a saturated fatty acid?
4. Which is polyunsaturated but not an omega-3 fatty acid?
5. Which is polyunsaturated and an omega-3 fatty acid?
6. In shape, *trans* fatty acid molecules resemble
   a. cholesterol
   b. disaccharides
   c. other unsaturated fatty acids
   d. saturated fatty acids

7. According to most health professionals, what percentages of total calories should the total daily intake of fat and of saturated fat, respectively, not exceed?
   a. 30, 15   b. 10, 30   c. 30, 10   d. 60, 20

Answers: 1, a; 2, a; 3, a; 4, c; 5, d; 6, d; 7, c

3 Proteins: Muscle and Much More

Learning Objectives ❯ List the essential amino acids, and explain why they are essential. ❯ Describe some protein deficiency diseases and their causes.

Proteins are polymers of amino acids. A gene carries the blueprint for a specific protein, and each protein serves a particular purpose. We require protein in our diet to provide the amino acids needed to make muscles, hair, enzymes, and many other cellular components vital to life.

Protein Metabolism: Essential Amino Acids

Proteins are broken down in the digestive tract into their component amino acids.

$$\text{Proteins} + n\,H_2O \xrightarrow{\text{Proteases}} \text{Amino acids}$$

From these amino acids, our bodies synthesize proteins for growth and repair of tissues. When a diet contains more protein than is needed for the body's growth

Vegetarian Diets

Green plants trap a small fraction of the energy that reaches them from the Sun. They use some of this energy to convert carbon dioxide, water, and mineral nutrients (including nitrates, phosphates, and sulfates) to proteins. Cattle eat plant protein, digest it, and convert a small portion of it to animal protein. It takes 100 g of protein feed to produce 4.7 g of edible beef or veal protein, an efficiency of only 4.7%. People eat this animal protein, digest it, and reassemble some of the amino acids into human protein.

Some of the energy originally transformed by green plants is lost as heat at every step. If people ate the plant protein directly, one highly inefficient step would be skipped. A vegetarian diet conserves energy. Pork production, at a protein conversion efficiency of 12.1%, and chicken or turkey production (at 18.2%) are more efficient than beef production. Milk production (22.7%) and egg production (23.3%) are still more efficient but do not compare well with eating plant protein directly.

Vegetarians generally are less likely than meat eaters to have high blood pressure. Vegetarian diets that are low in saturated fat can help us avoid or even reverse coronary artery disease. These diets also offer protection from some other diseases. However, although complete proteins can be obtained by eating a carefully selected mixture of vegetable foods, total (*vegan*) vegetarianism can be dangerous, especially for young children. Even when the diet includes a wide variety of plant materials, an all-vegetable diet is usually short in several nutrients, including vitamin B_{12} (a nutrient not found in plants), calcium, iron, riboflavin, and vitamin D (required by children not exposed to sunlight). A modified vegetarian (*lacto-ovo*) diet that includes eggs, milk, and milk products without red meat can provide excellent nutrition.

A variety of traditional dishes supply relatively good protein by combining foods from plant sources, usually a cereal grain with a legume (beans, peas, peanuts, and so on). The grain is deficient in tryptophan and lysine, but it has sufficient methionine. The legume is deficient in methionine, but it has enough tryptophan and lysine. A few such combinations are listed in Table 2. Peanut butter sandwiches are a popular American example of a legume–cereal grain combination.

Table 2 — Traditional Foods That Combine a Cereal Grain with a Legume

Group	Food[a]
Mexican	Corn tortillas and beans
Japanese	Rice and soybean curds (tofu)
English working class	Baked beans on toasted bread
Native American	Corn and beans (succotash)
Western African	Rice and peanuts (ground nuts)
Cajun (Louisiana)	Red beans and rice
Middle Eastern	Hummus and pita bread

[a]Cereal grains are in red, and legumes are in blue.

and repair, the excess protein is used as a source of energy, providing about 4 kcal per gram.

The adult human body can synthesize all but nine of the amino acids needed for making proteins. These nine are called **essential amino acids**—isoleucine, lysine, phenylalanine, tryptophan, leucine, methionine, threonine, arginine, and valine—and must be included in our diet. Each of the essential amino acids is a **limiting reactant** in protein synthesis. When the body is deficient in one of them, it can't make proper proteins.

An *adequate* (or *complete*) *protein* supplies all the essential amino acids in the quantities needed for the growth and repair of body tissues. Most proteins from animal sources contain all the essential amino acids in adequate amounts. Lean meat, milk, fish, eggs, and cheese supply adequate protein. Gelatin, a component of jellied candies and desserts, is one of the few inadequate animal proteins. It contains almost no tryptophan and has only small amounts of threonine, methionine, and isoleucine.

In contrast, most plant proteins are deficient in one or more amino acids. Corn protein has insufficient lysine and tryptophan, and people who subsist chiefly on corn may suffer from malnutrition even though they get adequate calories. Protein from rice is short of lysine and threonine. Wheat protein lacks enough lysine. Even soy protein, one of the best nonanimal proteins, is deficient in the essential amino acid methionine.

The distinction between essential and nonessential amino acids is somewhat ambiguous, because some amino acids can be produced from others. For example, both methionine and cysteine contain sulfur, and although methionine cannot be synthesized from other precursors, cysteine can partially meet the need for methionine. Similarly, tyrosine can partially substitute for phenylalanine. And histidine is essential for infants and children, but it is not essential for healthy adults.

Protein Deficiency in Young and Old

Our daily requirement for protein is about 0.8 g per kilogram of body weight. Diets with inadequate protein are common in some parts of the world. A protein-deficiency disease called *kwashiorkor* (Figure 8) is rare in developed countries but is common during times of famine in parts of Africa where corn is the major food. In the United States, protein deficiency occurs mainly among elderly persons in nursing homes.

Nutrition is especially important during a child's early years. This is readily apparent from the fact that the human brain reaches nearly full size by the age of two. Early protein deficiency leads to both physical and mental retardation.

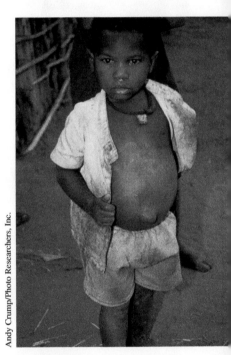

▲ **Figure 8** An extreme lack of proteins and vitamins causes a deficiency disease called *kwashiorkor*. The symptoms include retarded growth, discoloration of skin and hair, bloating, a swollen belly, and mental apathy.

Self-Assessment Questions

1. The numbers of kilocalories in 1 g of carbohydrate, fat, and protein, respectively, are
   a. 4, 7, 4   **b.** 4, 4, 7   **c.** 4, 9, 4   **d.** 4, 12, 6

2. The end products of the hydrolysis of a protein are
   a. amino acids   **b.** fatty acids
   c. monosaccharides   **d.** peptides

3. An essential amino acid is one that
   a. has more calories than other amino acids
   b. is needed in greater quantities than some others
   c. is synthesized in the body
   d. must be included in the diet

4. Which of the following foods furnishes complete protein?
   a. brown rice   **b.** eggs
   c. gelatin with fruit   **d.** tofu

5. The daily protein requirement for an 80-kg male is
   a. 0.8 g   **b.** 48 g   **c.** 64 g   **d.** 100 g

6. One can get complete protein by eating whole wheat bread with
   a. butter   **b.** jelly   **c.** peanut butter   **d.** corn chips

7. Strict vegetarian diets are often deficient in
   a. B vitamins and vitamin C   **b.** magnesium and folic acid
   c. vitamin B_{12} and iron   **d.** vitamin B_{12} and folic acid

Answers: 1, c; 2, a; 3, d; 4, b; 5, c; 6, c; 7, c

4 Minerals, Vitamins, and Other Essentials

Learning Objectives ❯ Identify the vitamins and the bulk dietary minerals, and state their functions.

In addition to the three major foodstuffs—carbohydrates, fats, and proteins—humans require a variety of minerals and vitamins for good nutrition. We also need dietary fiber and adequate water. According to the World Health Organization (WHO), one of every three people in developing countries is affected by mineral and vitamin deficiencies. Let's consider some of the most important minerals and vitamins.

Dietary Minerals

Thirty elements, listed in Table 3, are known to be essential to one or more living organisms. Among these are six structural elements found in organic compounds such as carbohydrates, fats, and proteins. Several inorganic substances, called **dietary minerals**, are vital to life. Minerals represent about 4% of the weight of the human body. Eleven elements that comprise the structural elements and the macro-minerals make up more than 99% of all the atoms in the body. The 19 trace elements include iron, copper, zinc, and 16 others called *ultratrace elements*.

Minerals serve a variety of functions; that of iodine is quite dramatic. According to WHO, 740 million people suffer from iodine deficiency, and 50 million of them have some degree of mental impairment. A small amount of iodine is necessary for proper thyroid function. Greater deficiencies have dire effects, of which goiter is perhaps the best known (Figure 9). Pregnant women deficient in iodine can experience stillbirths or spontaneous abortions or have babies with congenital abnormalities. Iodine is available naturally in seafood, but to guard against iodine deficiency, a small amount of potassium iodide (KI) is often added to table salt. The use of iodized salt has greatly reduced the incidence of goiter.

▲ **Figure 9** A person with goiter. The swollen thyroid gland in the neck results from a dietary deficiency of the trace element iodine.

Table 3	Elements Essential to Life				
Element	**Symbol**	**Form Used**	**Element**	**Symbol**	**Form Used**
Bulk Structural Elements			**Ultratrace Elements**		
Hydrogen	H	Covalent	Manganese	Mn	Mn^{2+}
Carbon	C	Covalent	Molybdenum	Mo	Mo^{2+}
Oxygen	O	Covalent	Chromium	Cr	?
Nitrogen	N	Covalent	Cobalt	Co	Co^{2+}
Phosphorus[a]	P	Covalent	Vanadium	V	?
Sulfur[a]	S	Covalent	Nickel	Ni	Ni^{2+}
			Cadmium	Cd	Cd^{2+}
Macrominerals			Tin	Sn	Sn^{2+}
Sodium	Na	Na^+	Lead	Pb	Pb^{2+}
Potassium	K	K^+	Lithium	Li	Li^+
Calcium	Ca	Ca^{2+}	Fluorine	F	F^-
Magnesium	Mg	Mg^{2+}	Iodine	I	I^-
Chlorine	Cl	Cl^-	Selenium	Se	$SeO_4{}^{2-}$?
Phosphorus[a]	P	$H_2PO_4{}^-$	Silicon	Si	?
Sulfur[a]	S	$SO_4{}^{2-}$	Arsenic	As	?
			Boron	B	H_3BO_3
Trace Elements					
Iron	Fe	Fe^{2+}			
Copper	Cu	Cu^{2+}			
Zinc	Zn	Zn^{2+}			

[a]Note that phosphorus and sulfur each appear twice; they are structural elements and are also components of the macrominerals phosphate and sulfate.

Iron(II) ions (Fe^{2+}) are necessary for proper functioning of the oxygen-transporting compound hemoglobin. Without sufficient iron, the oxygen supply to body tissues is reduced, and anemia, a general weakening of the body, results. According to WHO, more than 30% of people worldwide, but especially in developing countries, suffer from anemia, which is often made worse by malaria and parasitic worm infections. Foods especially rich in iron compounds include red meat and liver. It appears that most adult males need very little dietary iron because iron is retained by the body and lost mainly through bleeding.

Calcium and phosphorus are necessary for the proper development of bones and teeth. Growing children need about 1.5 g of each of these minerals each day, which they can get from milk. The calcium and phosphorus needs of adults are less precisely known but are very real. For example, calcium ions are necessary for the coagulation of blood (to stop bleeding) and for maintenance of the rhythm of the heartbeat. Phosphorus occurs in phosphate units in adenosine triphosphate (ATP), the "energy currency" of the body. Phosphorus is necessary for the body to obtain, store, and use energy from foods. In phosphate units, phosphorus is also an important part of the backbone of the DNA and RNA chains.

Sodium ions and chloride ions make up sodium chloride (salt). In moderate amounts, salt is essential to life. It is important to the exchange of fluids between cells and plasma, for example. However, the presence of salt increases water retention, and a high volume of retained fluids can cause swelling and high blood pressure (hypertension). Most physicians agree that our diets generally contain too much salt. About 65 million people in the United States suffer from hypertension, the leading risk factor for stroke, heart attack, kidney failure, and heart failure. Antihypertensives are among the most widely prescribed drugs in the United States.

Iron, copper, zinc, cobalt, manganese, molybdenum, calcium, and magnesium are *cofactors* essential to the proper functioning of many life-sustaining enzymes. A great deal remains to be learned about the role of inorganic chemicals in our bodies. Bioinorganic chemistry is a flourishing area of research.

The Vitamins: Vital, but Not All Are Amines

Why are British sailors called "limeys"? And what does this term have to do with food? Sailors on long voyages had been plagued since early times by *scurvy*. In 1747, Scottish navy surgeon James Lind showed that this disease could be prevented by including fresh fruit and vegetables in the diet. Fresh fruits that could conveniently be carried on long voyages (there was no refrigeration) were limes, lemons, and oranges. British ships put to sea with barrels of limes aboard, and sailors ate a lime or two every day. That is how they came to be known as "lime eaters," or simply "limeys."

In 1897, the Dutch scientist Christiaan Eijkman showed that polished rice lacked something found in the hull of whole-grain rice. Lack of that substance caused the disease *beriberi*, which was a serious problem in the Dutch East Indies (modern Indonesia) at that time. A British scientist, F. G. Hopkins, found that rats fed a synthetic diet of carbohydrates, fats, proteins, and minerals were unable to sustain healthy growth. Again, something was missing.

In 1912, Casimir Funk, a Polish biochemist, coined the word *vitamine* (from the Latin word *vita*, meaning "life") for these missing factors. Funk thought all these factors contained an amine group. In the United States, the final *e* was dropped after it was found that not all the factors were amines. The generic term became *vitamin*. Eijkman and Hopkins shared the 1929 Nobel Prize in Physiology and Medicine for their discoveries relating to vitamins.

Vitamins are specific organic compounds that are required in the diet (in addition to the usual proteins, fats, carbohydrates, and minerals) to prevent specific diseases. Some vitamins, along with their sources and deficiency symptoms, are listed in Table 4. The role of vitamins in the prevention of deficiency diseases, such as those shown in Figure 10, has been well established.

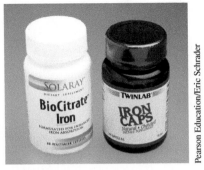

Pearson Education/Eric Schrader

▲ **It DOES Matter!**

Iron is an example of a substance that can be both essential and toxic. The National Institutes of Health recommend a daily intake of 8 mg for adult males and 18 mg for adult females but also point out that a 200-mg dose of iron in children can cause death.

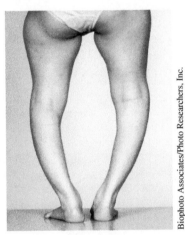

(a)

Biophoto Associates/Photo Researchers, Inc.

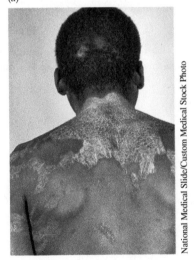

(b)

National Medical Slide/Custom Medical Stock Photo

▲ **Figure 10** (a) Softened bones caused by vitamin D deficiency. (b) Inflammation and abnormal pigmentation characterize pellagra, caused by niacin deficiency.

153

Table 4   Some of the Vitamins

Vitamin[a]	Name	Sources	Deficiency results in
Fat-Soluble Vitamins			
A	Retinol	Fish, liver, eggs, butter, cheese; also (as β-carotene, a vitamin precursor) in carrots and other orange or red vegetables	Blindness in children; night blindness in adults
D_2	Calciferol	Cod liver oil, mushrooms, irradiated ergosterol (milk supplement)	Rickets
E	α-Tocopherol	Wheat germ oil, green vegetables, egg yolks, meat	Sterility, muscular dystrophy
K_1	Phylloquinone	Spinach, other green leafy vegetables	Hemorrhage
Water-Soluble Vitamins			
B_1	Thiamine	Germ of cereal grains, legumes, nuts, milk, and brewer's yeast	Beriberi—polyneuritis resulting in muscle paralysis, enlargement of heart, and ultimately heart failure
B_2	Riboflavin	Milk, red meat, liver, egg white, green vegetables, whole wheat flour (or fortified white flour), and fish	Dermatitis, glossitis (tongue inflammation)
B_3	Niacin	Red meat, liver, collards, turnip greens, yeast, and tomato juice	Pellagra—skin lesions, swollen and discolored tongue, loss of appetite, diarrhea, and various mental disorders (Figure 10)
B_6	Pyridoxine	Eggs, liver, yeast, peas, beans, and milk	Dermatitis, apathy, irritability, and increased susceptibility to infections; convulsions in infants
B_9	Folic acid	Liver, kidney, mushrooms, yeast, and green leafy vegetables	Anemias (folic acid is used to treat megaloblastic anemia, a condition characterized by giant red blood cells); neural tube defects in fetuses of deficient mothers
B_{12}	Cyanocobalamin	Liver, meat, eggs and fish (not found in plants)	Pernicious anemia
C	Ascorbic acid	Citrus fruits, tomatoes, green peppers, broccoli, strawberries	Scurvy

[a]Some vitamins exist in more than one chemical form. We name a common form of each here.

Vitamins do not share a common chemical structure. They can, however, be divided into two broad categories: *fat-soluble vitamins* (A, D, E, and K) and *water-soluble vitamins* (B vitamins and vitamin C). The fat-soluble vitamins incorporate a high proportion of hydrocarbon parts. They contain one or two oxygen atoms but are only slightly polar as a whole.

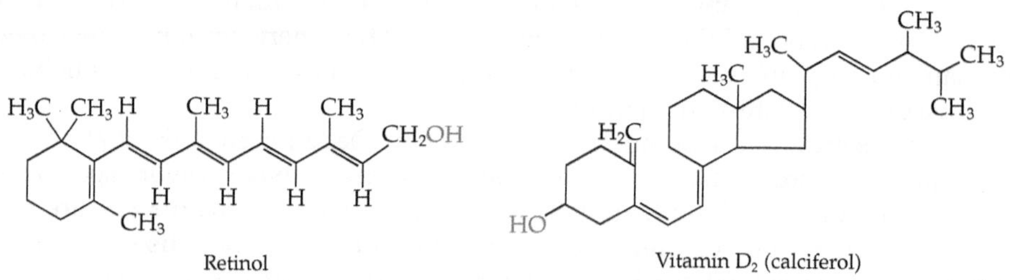

Retinol

Vitamin D_2 (calciferol)

Fat-soluble vitamins

In contrast, a water-soluble vitamin contains a high proportion of the electronegative atoms oxygen and nitrogen, which can form hydrogen bonds to water. Therefore, the molecule as a whole is soluble in water.

Ascorbic acid   Nicotinic acid   Nicotinamide

Water-soluble vitamins (sites for hydrogen bonding in color)

Fat-soluble vitamins dissolve in the fatty tissue of the body, where reserves can be stored for future use. An adult can store several years' supply of vitamin A. If the diet becomes deficient in vitamin A, these reserves are mobilized, and the adult remains free of the deficiency disease for quite a while. However, a small child who has not built up a store of the vitamin soon exhibits deficiency symptoms. WHO estimates that more than 100 million children in developing countries are deficient in vitamin A, and a quarter million to a half million become blind each year. Half the blinded children die within a year.

Because they are efficiently stored in the body, overdoses of fat-soluble vitamins can have adverse effects, although these are rarely encountered. Large excesses of vitamin A cause irritability, dry skin, and a feeling of pressure inside the head. Too much vitamin D can cause pain in the bones, hard deposits in the joints, nausea, diarrhea, and weight loss. Vitamins E and K are also fat soluble, but they are metabolized and excreted. They are not stored to the extent that vitamins A and D are, and excess intake seldom causes problems.

The body has a limited capacity to store water-soluble vitamins. It excretes anything over the amount that can be used immediately. Water-soluble vitamins are needed frequently, every day or so. Some foods lose their vitamin content when they are cooked in water and then drained. The water-soluble vitamins go down the drain with the water.

Other Essentials: Fiber and Water

We need carbohydrates, proteins, fats, minerals, and vitamins in our diets, but some other items are also important. One is *fiber*; another is *water*.

Dietary fiber may be soluble or insoluble. Insoluble fiber is usually cellulose; soluble fiber generally consists of sticky materials called *gums* and *pectins*, often used for gelling, thickening, and stabilizing foods such as jams, jellies, and dairy products such as yogurt. High-fiber diets prevent constipation and are an aid to dieters. Fiber has no calories because the body doesn't absorb it. Therefore, high-fiber foods such as fruits and vegetables are low in fat and often low in calories. Fiber takes up space in the stomach, making us feel full and, therefore, eat less food. Soluble fiber lowers cholesterol levels, perhaps by removing bile acids that digest fat. It may also help control blood sugar by delaying the emptying of the stomach, thus slowing sugar absorption after a meal. This may reduce the amount of insulin needed by a diabetic. These properties make dietary fiber beneficial to people with high blood pressure, diabetes, heart disease, and diverticulitis.

Many of the foods we eat are mainly water. It should come as no surprise that tomatoes are 90% water or that melons, oranges, and grapes are largely water. But water is one of the main ingredients in practically all foods, from roast beef and seafood to potatoes and onions.

In addition to the water we get in our food, we need to drink about 1.0–1.5 L of water each day. We could satisfy this need by drinking plain water, but we often choose other beverages—milk, coffee, tea, and soft drinks. Many people also drink beverages that contain ethanol, made by fermenting grains or fruit juices. Beer is usually made from malted barley, and wine from grape juice. Even these alcoholic beverages are mainly water.

4. Are large doses of vitamins beneficial? Although there is some evidence that large doses of antioxidants such as vitamin C may have beneficial effects, "megadoses" of most vitamins have not generally been shown to have any significant benefit. In fact, some of the fat-soluble vitamins are toxic in large amounts. There are well-documented examples of polar explorers who suffered poisoning from eating the livers of polar bears or seals, which contain extremely high levels of vitamin A.

In 2009, worldwide consumption of beverages included an estimated 328 billion L of tea, 215 billion L of milk, 128 billion L of coffee, 196 billion L of soft drinks, 176 billion L of beer, and 240 billion L of bottled water.

It's a Drug! No, It's a Food! No, It's … a Dietary Supplement!

Almost every day, we see advertisements for products that are claimed to promote rapid weight loss, improve stamina, aid memory, or provide other seemingly miraculous benefits. (There are thousands of such products; see Collaborative Group Project 5 for some examples.) Although these products may appear to act as drugs, many are not classified as such. Legally, they are *dietary supplements*.

The Dietary Supplement Health and Education Act, enacted by the U.S. Congress in 1994, changed the law so that dietary supplements became regulated as foods, not as drugs. Manufacturers are permitted to describe some specific benefits that may be attributed to use of a supplement. However, they must also include a disclaimer, such as: "This statement has not been evaluated by the Food and Drug Administration. This product is not intended to diagnose, treat, cure, or prevent any disease."

Some supplements are simply combinations of various vitamins. Others contain minerals, amino acids, other nutrients, herbs or other plant materials, or extracts of animal or plant origin.

Should you take a particular supplement? Maybe, maybe not. A supplement containing omega-3 oils might well aid in reducing LDL cholesterol. But a tablespoon a day of a special preparation of vitamins and minerals is not likely to reverse the effects of aging, no matter how brightly colored the bottle, or how attractive the person in the advertisement. Perhaps a judicious application of the FLaReS principles (see this chapter's Critical Thinking Exercises) to the manufacturer's claims will provide insight.

Supplement Facts

Serving size 1 Tablet

Amount Per Serving		%DV
Vitamin B-6 (as pyridoxine HCl)......5 mg		250%
Folic Acid..................................400 mcg		250%
Vitamin B-12...........................1000 mcg		16666%

DIRECTIONS: As a dietary supplement, take 1 or 2 tablets daily. Allow tablet to dissolve under tongue. Conforms to USP <2091> for weight.

This statement has not been evaluated by the Food and Drug Administration. This product is not intended to diagnose, treat, cure, or prevent any disease.

▲ Most dietary supplements do not go through the rigorous testing that is required by law for all prescription drugs and over-the-counter drugs.

Self-Assessment Questions

1. About what percentage of our body weight is minerals?
   a. 1%   **b.** 4%   **c.** 10%   **d.** 20%

2. A deficiency of iodine results in
   a. anemia   **b.** goiter   **c.** osteoporosis   **d.** scurvy

3. Iron in red blood cells is part of the
   a. cytochromes   **b.** hemoglobin   **c.** myoglobin   **d.** plasma

4. Iron is swiftly depleted from the body by
   a. blood loss   **b.** energetic exercise
   c. inactivity   **d.** weight loss

5. Most of the calcium and phosphorus in the body is in the
   a. blood   **b.** bones and teeth
   c. liver   **d.** muscle tissue

6. People with high blood pressure are usually told to restrict intake of
   a. Ca^{2+} **b.** Mg^{2+} **c.** Na^+ **d.** $SO_4{}^{2-}$

7. Vitamins are
   a. compounds with a common functional group
   b. most effective when taken as supplements
   c. specific organic compounds required in the diet to prevent diseases
   d. vital (essential) amines

8. The water-soluble vitamins are the B vitamins and vitamin
   a. A   **b.** C   **c.** D   **d.** E

9. Eating foods high in fiber
   a. can cause constipation   **b.** helps build muscle
   c. helps to fill you up   **d.** provides quick energy

10. Soluble dietary fiber
    a. acts in the same way as insoluble fiber
    b. may help lower cholesterol levels
    c. is not affected by food processing
    d. is a good source of trace elements

Answers: 1, b; 2, b; 3, b; 4, a; 5, b; 6, c; 7, c; 8, b; 9, b; 10, b

5 Starvation, Fasting, and Malnutrition

Learning Objective ❯ Describe the effects of starvation, fasting, and malnutrition.

When totally deprived of food, whether voluntarily or involuntarily, the human body suffers **starvation**. Involuntary starvation is a serious problem in much of the world. Although starvation is seldom the sole cause of death, those weakened by malnutrition succumb readily to disease. Even a seemingly minor disease, such as measles, can become life threatening.

Metabolic changes like those that accompany starvation also occur during fasting. During total fasting, the body's glycogen stores are depleted in less than a day and the body calls on its fat reserves. Fat is first taken from around the kidneys and the heart. Then it is removed from other parts of the body, eventually even from the bone marrow.

Increased dependence on stored fats as an energy source leads to *ketosis*, a condition characterized by the appearance of compounds called *ketone bodies* in the blood and urine (Figure 11). Ketosis rapidly develops into *acidosis*; the blood pH drops, and oxygen transport is hindered. Oxygen deprivation leads to depression and lethargy.

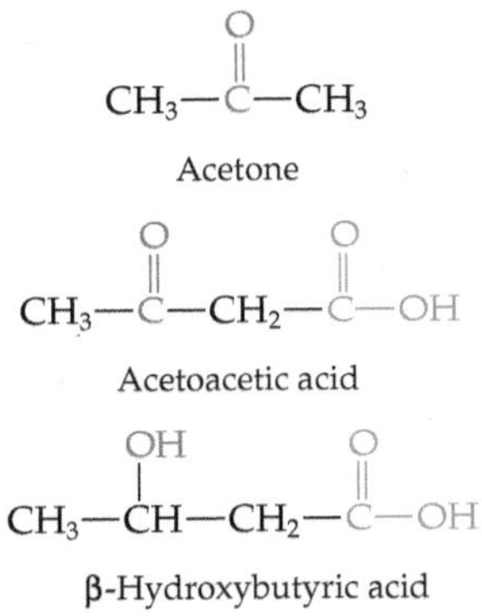

Acidosis is also associated with the insulin-deficiency disease diabetes. Insulin enables the body's cells to take up glucose from the bloodstream. A lack of insulin causes the liver to act as though the cells are starving, and they start burning fat for energy while blood sugar levels rise. This fat metabolism leads to the production of ketone bodies and subsequent acidosis.

In the early stages of a *total* fast, body protein is metabolized at a relatively rapid rate. After several weeks, the rate of protein breakdown slows considerably as the brain adjusts to using the breakdown products of fatty acid metabolism for its energy source. When fat reserves are substantially depleted, the body must again draw heavily on its structural proteins for its energy requirements. The emaciated appearance of a starving individual is due to the depletion of muscle proteins.

Processed Food: Less Nutrition

Malnutrition need not be due to starvation or dieting. It can be the result of eating too much highly processed food.

Whole wheat is an excellent source of vitamin B_1 and other vitamins. To make white flour, the wheat germ and bran are removed from the grain. This greatly increases the storage life of the flour, but the remaining material has few minerals or vitamins and little fiber. We eat the starch and use much of the germ and bran for animal food. Cattle and hogs often get better nutrition than we do. Similarly, polished rice has had most of its protein and minerals removed, and it has almost no vitamins. The disease beriberi became prevalent when polished rice was introduced into Southeast Asia.

When many fruits and vegetables are peeled, they lose most of their vitamins, minerals, and fiber. The peels are often dumped (directly or through a garbage disposal) into a sewage system, where they contribute to water pollution. The heat used to cook food also destroys some vitamins. If water is used in cooking, some of the water-soluble vitamins (vitamin C and B vitamins) and some of the minerals are often drained off and discarded with the water.

▲ **Figure 11** The three ketone bodies produced in fat metabolism.

Q: *Identify the functional groups in each of the compounds. Which ketone body is not a ketone?*

It is estimated that 90% of the food budget of an average family in the United States goes to buy processed foods. A diet of hamburgers, potato chips, and soft drinks is lacking in many essential nutrients. Highly processed convenience foods are making many people in developed nations obese but poorly nourished despite their abundance of food.

Self-Assessment Questions

1. During fasting or starvation, glycogen stores are depleted in about
   a. 1 hour   **b.** 1 day   **c.** 1 week   **d.** 1 month

2. After glycogen stores are depleted, the body draws on its reserves of
   a. amino acids   **b.** fat   **c.** glycogen   **d.** protein

3. When fat reserves have been used up, the body uses for its energy source
   a. adipose tissue   **b.** amino acid reserves
   c. glycogen stores   **d.** structural proteins

4. Which of the following is *not* a ketone body?
   a. CH_3COCH_3 **b.** $CH_3CHOHCH_2COCH_3$
   c. $CH_3CHOHCH_2CHOHCH_3$ **d.** CH_3COCH_2COOH

Answers: 1, b; 2, b; 3, d; 4, c.

5. Are some foods really "super foods" or "miracle foods"? Some foods do provide special benefits. For example, flaxseed has cholesterol-reducing properties, cherries have been found to alleviate symptoms of gout in some people, and cranberries may aid in preventing some urinary tract infections. However, no single food or special combination of foods will magically bring perfect health, especially if the remainder of the diet is unhealthy. A few tablespoons of flaxseed with your breakfast cereal won't offset the adverse effects of a 500-kcal coffee drink laden with sugar and fat.

6 Food Additives

Learning Objective   ❭ List some common food additives and their purposes.

Food labels on processed foods are almost undecipherable. For example, a cake mix box may read "egg whites, vegetable oils, nonfat dry milk, lecithin, mono- and diglycerides, propylene glycol monostearate, xanthan gums, sodium citrate, aluminum sulfate, artificial flavor, iron phosphate, niacin, riboflavin, and irradiated ergosterol."

Ingredients on food labels are listed in decreasing order by weight, but often we can recognize only a few of the ingredients. Just what is in the food we eat? More than 3000 substances appear on a list on the FDA's Web site called "Everything Added to Food in the United States (EAFUS)." We examine some of those here.

Most of the substances listed on a label are **food additives**, substances other than basic foodstuffs that are put into food for various reasons related to production, processing, packaging, or storage. Because food processing removes certain essential substances, some additives are included in prepared food to increase its nutritional value. Other substances are added to enhance color and flavor, to retard spoilage, to provide texture, to sanitize, to bleach, to ripen or prevent ripening, to control moisture levels, or to control foaming. Sugar, salt, and corn syrup are used in the greatest amounts. These three, plus citric acid, baking soda, vegetable colors, mustard, and pepper, make up more than 98% (by weight) of all additives.

Some food additives, such as salt to preserve meat and fish and spices to flavor and preserve foods, have been used since ancient times. Throughout the centuries, other additives were found to be useful. Movement of much of the population from farms to cities increased the necessity for using preservatives. More widespread consumption of convenience foods has also led to greater use of additives.

In the United States, food additives are regulated by the Food and Drug Administration (FDA). The original Food, Drug, and Cosmetic Act was passed by Congress in 1938. Under this act, the FDA had to prove that an additive was unsafe before its use could be prevented. The Food Additives Amendment of 1958 shifted the burden of proof to the food industry. A company that wishes to use a food additive must first furnish proof to the FDA that the additive is safe for the intended use. The FDA can also regulate the quantity of additives that can be used.

6. Should the government prohibit food additives? Many additives provide useful improvements in food. For example, most people find that unsalted bread has little taste. Which soft drink would you prefer if they were all colorless? Canned tomatoes processed without calcium chloride may be soft and mushy.

Table 5 Your Breakfast—As Seen by a Chemist[a]

Chilled Melon

Starches	Anisyl propionate
Sugars	Amyl acetate
Cellulose	Ascorbic acid
Pectin	Vitamin A
Malic acid	Riboflavin
Citric acid	Thiamine
Succinic acid	

Scrambled Eggs

Ovalbumin	Lecithin
Conalbumin	Lipids (fats)
Ovomucoid	Fatty acids
Mucin	Butyric acid
Globulins	Acetic acid
Amino acids	Sodium chloride
Lipovitellin	Lutein
Livetin	Zeazanthin
Cholesterol	Vitamin A

Sugar-Cured Ham

Actomyosin	Adenosine triphosphate (ATP)
Myogen	Glucose

Nucleoproteins	Collagen
Peptides	Elastin
Amino acids	Creatine
Myoglobin	Pyroligneous acid
Lipids (fats)	Sodium chloride
Linoleic acid	Sodium nitrate
Oleic acid	Sodium nitrite
Lecithin	Sodium phosphate
Cholesterol	Sucrose

Coffee

Caffeine	Acetone
Essential oils	Methyl acetate
Methanol	Furan
Acetaldehyde	Diacetyl
Methyl formate	Butanol
Ethanol	Methylfuran
Dimethyl sulfide	Isoprene
Propionaldehyde	Methylbutanol

[a]The chemicals listed are those found normally in the foods. The chemical listings are not necessarily complete.
Source: Manufacturing Chemists Association, Washington, DC.

Some people express concern about the "chemicals in our food," but food itself consists of chemicals. Table 5 shows the chemical composition of a typical breakfast. Many of the chemicals in this breakfast might be harmful in large amounts but are harmless in the trace amounts that occur naturally in foods. Indeed, some make important contributions to delightful flavors and aromas.

Our bodies are also collections of chemicals. If broken down into its elements (Table 6), your body would be worth only a few dollars. It is the unique combination and arrangement of the elements in each human body that make each of us different from everyone else and each individual's worth beyond measure. Since food is chemical and we are chemical, we shouldn't worry about most of the chemicals in our food—perhaps just some specific ones.

Additives That Improve Nutrition

The first nutrient supplement approved by the Bureau of Chemistry (which later became the FDA) of the U.S. Department of Agriculture was potassium iodide (KI), added to table salt in 1924 to reduce the incidence of goiter (recall Figure 9).

Several other chemicals are added to foods to prevent deficiency diseases. Addition of vitamin B_1 (thiamine) to polished rice is essential in the Far East, where beriberi is still a problem. The replacement of the B vitamins thiamine, riboflavin, folic acid, and niacin (which are removed in processing) and the addition of iron, usually ferrous carbonate ($FeCO_3$), to flour are referred to as **enrichment**. Enriched bread or pasta made from this flour still isn't as nutritious as bread or pasta made from whole wheat. It lacks vitamin B_6, pantothenic acid, zinc, magnesium, and fiber, nutrients usually provided by whole-grain flour. Despite these shortcomings, the enrichment of bread, corn meal, and cereals has almost eliminated pellagra, a disease that once plagued the southern United States.

Table 6 Approximate Elemental Analysis of the Human Body

Element	Percent by Weight
Oxygen	65
Carbon	18
Hydrogen	10
Nitrogen	3
Calcium	1.5
Phosphorus	1
Potassium	0.35
Sulfur	0.25
Chlorine	0.15
Sodium	0.15
Magnesium	0.05
Iron	0.004

Trace elements to make 100%

The GRAS List

Some food additives have been used for many years without apparent harmful effects. In 1958, the U.S. Congress established a list of additives *generally recognized as safe* (GRAS). Many of the substances on the **GRAS** list are familiar spices, flavors, and nutrients. Some of the substances placed on the 1958 list have since been removed, including cyclamate sweeteners and some food colors. Some other substances have been added to the original list. About 7000 substances are now given GRAS status.

There were some deficiencies in the original testing procedures. The FDA has since reevaluated several of them based on new research findings—and greater consumer awareness. Improved instruments and better experimental designs have revealed the possibility of harm, though slight, from some additives previously thought safe. Most of the newer experiments involve feeding massive doses of additives to small laboratory animals, and these studies have been criticized for that reason.

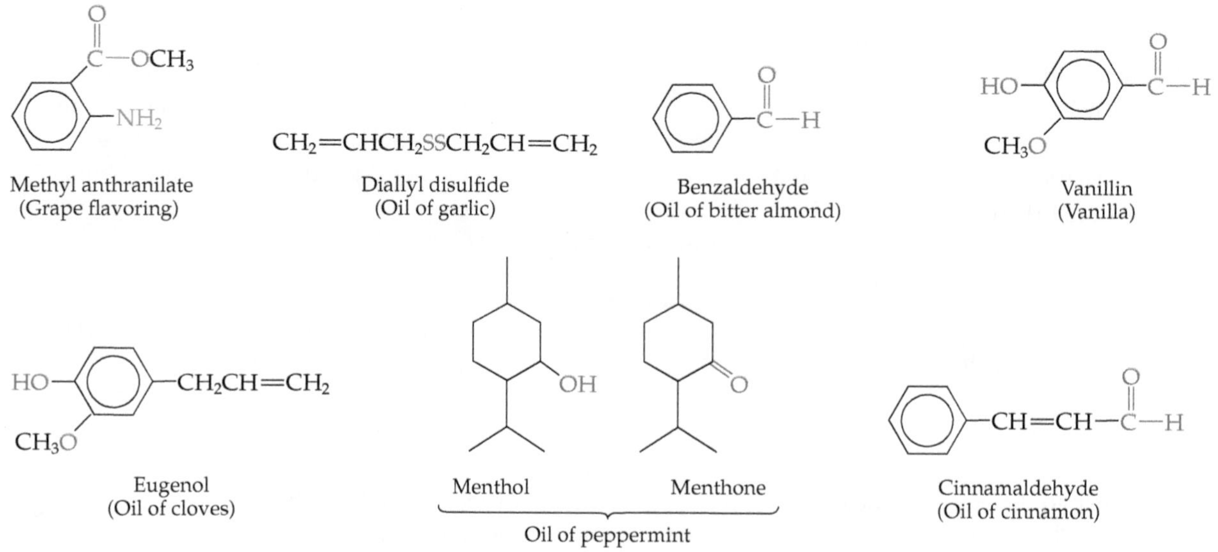

Methyl anthranilate
(Grape flavoring)

Diallyl disulfide
(Oil of garlic)

Benzaldehyde
(Oil of bitter almond)

Vanillin
(Vanilla)

Eugenol
(Oil of cloves)

Menthol

Menthone

Cinnamaldehyde
(Oil of cinnamon)

Oil of peppermint

▲ **Figure 12** Some molecular flavorings.

Q: *Which of the compounds shown here have aldehyde functional groups? Which are phenols? Ethers? Alkenes? Which is an ester? A ketone? An alcohol?*

Vitamin C (ascorbic acid) is frequently added to fruit juices, flavored drinks, and other beverages. Although our diets generally contain enough ascorbic acid to prevent scurvy, some scientists recommend a much larger intake than minimum daily requirements. Vitamin D is added to milk in developed countries, and consumption of fortified milk has led to the almost total elimination of rickets. Similarly, vitamin A, which occurs naturally in butter, is added to margarine so that the substitute more nearly matches butter in nutritional quality.

If we ate a balanced diet of fresh foods, we probably wouldn't need nutritional supplements. But many people choose to eat mainly processed foods and convenience foods. If their usual diet is composed mainly of highly processed foods, people may need the nutrients provided by vitamin and mineral food additives.

Additives That Taste Good

Spice cake, soda pop, gingerbread, sausage, and many other foods depend on spices and other additives for most of their flavor. Cloves, ginger, cinnamon, and nutmeg are examples of natural spices, and basil, marjoram, thyme, and rosemary are widely used herbs. Natural flavors are also extracted from fruits and other plant materials.

Some esters serve as flavors. Other flavor compounds are shown in Figure 12. Chemists can analyze natural flavors and then synthesize components and make mixtures that resemble those flavors. Major components of natural and artificial flavors are often identical. For example, both vanilla extract and imitation vanilla owe

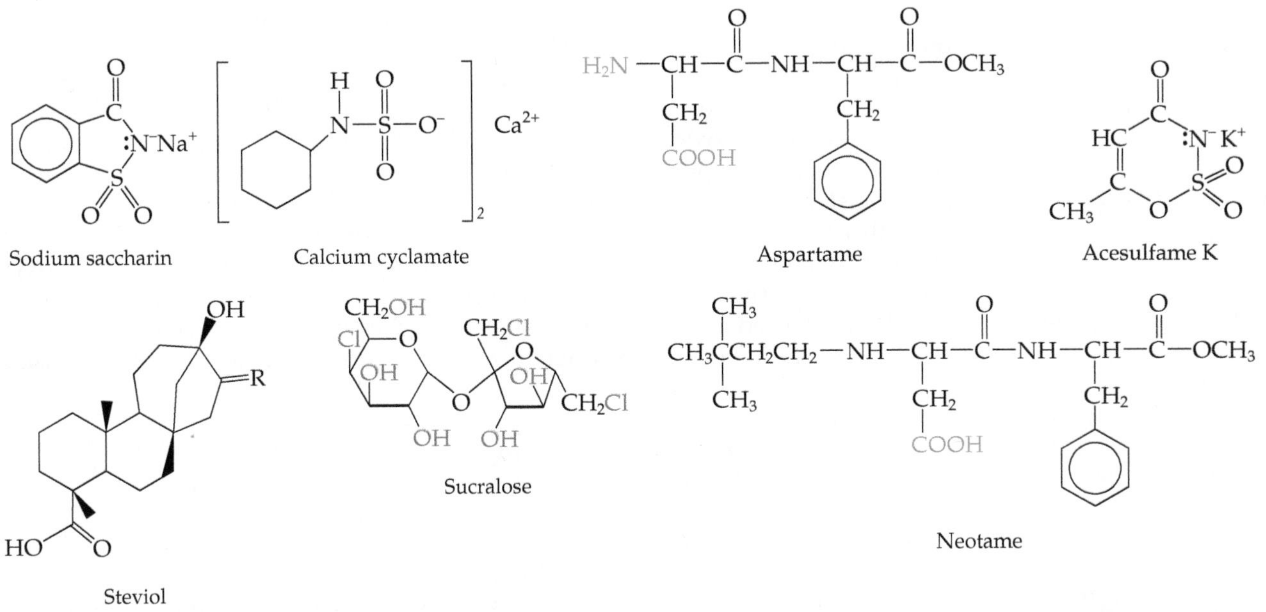

Sodium saccharin   Calcium cyclamate   Aspartame   Acesulfame K

Sucralose

Steviol

Neotame

▲ **Figure 13** Seven artificial sweeteners. Note that sucralose (Splenda®) is a chlorinated derivative of sucrose. It is the only artificial sweetener actually made from sucrose. Steviol is a precursor of the natural sweetener stevia.

their flavor mainly to vanillin. The natural flavor is often more complex because vanilla extract contains a wider variety of chemicals than imitation vanilla does. Flavor additives, whether natural or synthetic, probably present little hazard when used in moderation, and they contribute considerably to our enjoyment of food.

Artificial Sweeteners

Obesity is a major problem in most developed countries. Presumably, people could reduce their intake of calories by replacing sugars with noncaloric sweeteners, but there is little evidence that artificial sweeteners are of value in controlling obesity. People eat more and more sugar; annual per capita consumption in the United States averages 150 lb.

For many years, the major artificial sweeteners were saccharin and cyclamates. Cyclamates were banned in the United States in 1970 after studies showed that they caused cancer in laboratory animals. (Subsequent studies have failed to confirm these findings, but the FDA has not lifted the ban.) In 1977, saccharin was shown to cause bladder cancer in laboratory animals. However, the move by the FDA to ban it was blocked by Congress because at that time saccharin was the only approved artificial sweetener. Its ban would have meant the end of diet soft drinks and other low-calorie products.

There are now five FDA-approved artificial sweeteners (Figure 13). *Aspartame* (the methyl ester of the dipeptide aspartylphenylalanine) was approved in 1981. A closely related compound, called *neotame*, has a 3,3-dimethylbutyl group $CH_3C(CH_3)_2CH_2CH_2$— on the nitrogen atom of the aspartyl unit of the dipeptide. There are anecdotal reports of problems with aspartame, but repeated studies have shown it to be generally safe, except for people with phenylketonuria, an inherited condition in which phenylalanine cannot be metabolized properly. Other artificial sweeteners approved for use in the United States include acesulfame K (Sunette®) and sucralose (Splenda®); these sweeteners can survive the high temperatures of cooking processes, whereas aspartame is broken down by heat. Table 7 compares the sweetness of a variety of substances.

A natural product of note is *stevia*, a South American herb long used as a sweetener by the Guarani Indians of Paraguay. Leaves of this herb (*Stevia rebaudiana*) contain glycosides that provide a sweetness at least 30 times that of sucrose. Stevia, an approved food additive in Japan and South America, is available in the United States as a dietary supplement; it is on the FDA's GRAS list.

Table 7	Relative Sweetness of Some Compounds
Compound	**Relative Sweetness[a]**
Lactose	0.16
Maltose	0.33
Glucose	0.74
Sucrose	1.00
Fructose	1.73
Steviol glycoside	30
Cyclamate	45
Aspartame	180
Acesulfame K	200
Saccharin	300
Sucralose	600
Neotame	13,000

[a]Sweetness is relative to sucrose at a value of 1.

CH₂OH
|
CHOH   CH₂OH
| |
CHOH   CHOH
| |
CHOH   CHOH
| |
CHOH   CHOH
| |
CH₂OH   CH₂OH

Sorbitol   Xylitol

▲ Polyhydroxy alcohols (polyols) are used to sweeten sugar-free products such as chewing gum. These products aid in control of dental caries because the polyols are metabolized slowly if at all in dental plaque.

GraÃ§a Victoria/Shutterstock

What makes a compound sweet? There is little structural similarity among the compounds that taste sweet. Most bear little resemblance to sugars. Sugars are polyhydroxy compounds. Like sugars, many compounds with hydroxyl groups on adjacent carbon atoms are sweet. Ethylene glycol (HOCH₂CH₂OH) is sweet, although it is quite toxic. Glycerol, obtained from the hydrolysis of fats (Section 2), is also sweet and is approved as a food additive. It is used principally as a **humectant** (moistening agent), however, and only incidentally as a sweetener.

Other polyhydroxy alcohols (polyols) used as sweeteners are *sorbitol*, made by the reduction of glucose, and *xylitol*, which has five carbon atoms with a hydroxyl group on each. These compounds occur naturally in foods such as fruits and berries. They are used as sweeteners in sugar-free chewing gums and candies. Unlike sugars, polyols do not cause sudden increases in blood sugar, and thus can be used in moderation by diabetics. Large amounts—more than about 10 g—can cause gastrointestinal distress.

Several thousand sweet-tasting compounds have been discovered. They belong to more than 150 chemical classes. We now know that all the sweet substances act on a single taste receptor. (In contrast, we have more than 30 receptors for bitter substances.) Unlike other taste receptors, the sweet receptor has more than one area that can be activated by various molecules. The different areas have varying affinities for certain molecules. For example, sucralose fits the receptor more tightly than sucrose does, partly because its chlorine atoms carry more negative charge than the oxygen atoms in the OH groups they replace. Neotame fits the receptor so tightly that it keeps the receptor firing repeatedly.

Flavor Enhancers

Some chemical substances, though not particularly flavorful themselves, are used to enhance other flavors. Common table salt (sodium chloride) is a familiar example. In addition to being a necessary nutrient, salt seems to increase sweetness and helps to mask bitterness and sourness.

Another popular flavor enhancer is monosodium glutamate (MSG). MSG is the sodium salt of glutamic acid, one of the 20 amino acids that occur naturally in proteins. It is used in many convenience foods.

CH₃CH₂COOH
Propionic acid

CH₃CH₂COO⁻Na⁺
Sodium propionate

CH₃CH=CHCH=CHCOOH
Sorbic acid

CH₃CH=CHCH=CHCOO⁻K⁺
Potassium sorbate

⬡—COOH
Benzoic acid

⬡—COO⁻Na⁺
Sodium benzoate

$$HOOC-CH_2CH_2CH-\overset{\overset{\displaystyle O}{\|}}{C}-O^-$$
$$^+NH_3$$

Glutamic acid

$$HOOC-CH_2CH_2CH-\overset{\overset{\displaystyle O}{\|}}{C}-O^-Na^+$$
$$NH_2$$

MSG

Although glutamates are found naturally in proteins, there is evidence that huge excesses can be harmful. MSG can numb portions of the brains of laboratory animals. It may also be *teratogenic*, causing birth defects when eaten in large amounts by women who are pregnant.

Additives That Retard Spoilage

Food spoilage can result from the growth of molds, yeasts, or bacteria. Substances that prevent such growth are often called *antimicrobials*, and they include certain carboxylic acids and their salts. Propionic acid and its sodium and calcium salts are used to inhibit molding of bread and cheese. Sorbic acid, benzoic acid, and their salts are also used (Figure 14).

Some inorganic compounds can also be added to inhibit spoilage. Sodium nitrite (NaNO₂) is used to cure meat and to maintain the pink color of smoked hams, frankfurters, and bologna. It also contributes to the tangy flavor of processed meat products. Nitrites are particularly effective as inhibitors of *Clostridium botulinum*, the bacterium that produces botulism poisoning. However, only about 10% of the amount used to keep meat pink is needed to prevent botulism. Nitrites have

▲ **Figure 14** Most spoilage inhibitors are carboxylic acids or salts of carboxylic acids.

been investigated as possible causes of cancer of the stomach. In the presence of the hydrochloric acid (HCl) in the stomach, nitrites are converted to nitrous acid.

$$NaNO_2 + HCl \longrightarrow HNO_2 + NaCl$$

This acid may then react with secondary amines (amines with two alkyl groups on nitrogen) to form *nitroso* compounds.

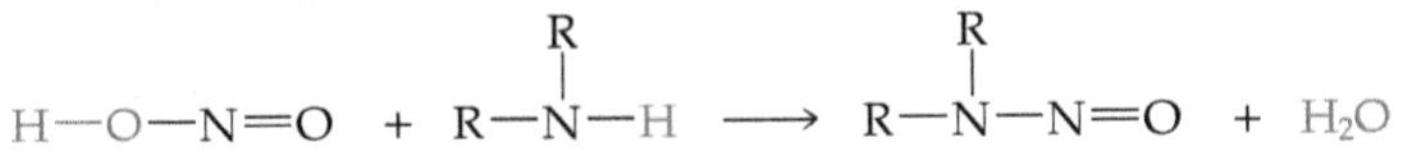

H—O—N=O	+ R—N—H	⟶	R—N—N=O	+ H₂O
Nitrous acid	A secondary amine		A nitroso compound	

The R groups of nitroso compounds can be alkyl groups such as methyl (CH_3—), or ethyl (CH_3CH_2—), or they can be more complex. In any case, these compounds are among the most potent carcinogens known. The rate of stomach cancer is higher in countries where people use prepared meats than in developing nations, where people eat little or no cured meat. However, the incidence of stomach cancer is *decreasing* in the United States, perhaps because ascorbic acid (vitamin C) inhibits the reaction between nitrous acid and amines to form nitrosamines, and many people have orange juice with their breakfast bacon or sausage. Nevertheless, possible problems with nitrites have led the FDA to approve sodium hypophosphite (NaH_2PO_2) as a meat preservative.

Other inorganic food additives include sulfur dioxide and sulfite salts. A gas at room temperature, sulfur dioxide (SO_2) serves as a disinfectant and preservative, particularly for dried fruits such as peaches, apricots, and raisins. It is also used as a bleach to prevent the browning of wines, corn syrup, jellies, dehydrated potatoes, and other foods. Sulfur dioxide seems safe for most people when ingested with food, but it is a powerful irritant when inhaled and is a damaging ingredient of polluted air in some areas. Sulfur dioxide and sulfite salts cause severe allergic reactions in some people. The FDA requires food labels to indicate the presence of these compounds in a food.

One person in a hundred has a strong allergic reaction to sulfur dioxide and related compounds called *sulfiting agents*. Common ones include sodium sulfite (Na_2SO_3), potassium sulfite (K_2SO_3), sodium bisulfite ($NaHSO_3$), potassium bisulfite ($KHSO_3$), sodium metabisulfite ($Na_2S_2O_5$), and potassium metabisulfite ($K_2S_2O_5$).

Antioxidants: BHA and BHT

One class of preservatives is composed of **antioxidants**, which inhibit the chemical spoilage of food that occurs in the presence of oxygen. These substances are added to foods (or their packaging) to prevent fats and oils from forming rancid products that make foods unpalatable. Antioxidants also minimize the destruction of some essential amino acids and vitamins. Packaged foods that contain fats or oils (such as bread, potato chips, sausage, and breakfast cereal) often have antioxidants added. Compounds commonly used as antioxidants include butylated hydroxytoluene (BHT), butylated hydroxyanisole (BHA), propyl gallate, and *tert*-butylhydroquinone (Figure 15).

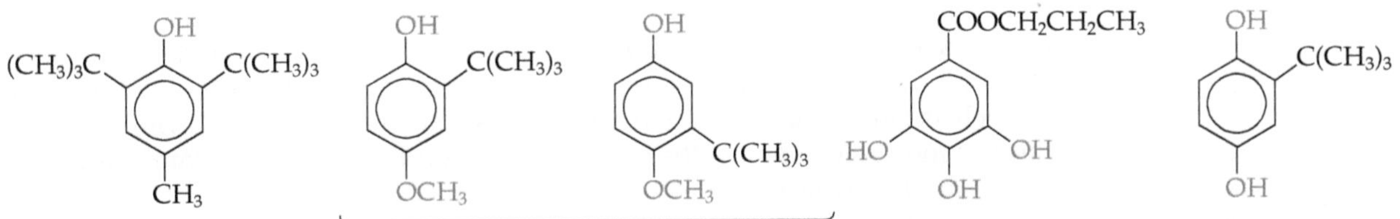

▲ **Figure 15** Four common antioxidants. BHA is a mixture of two isomers.

Fats turn rancid, in part as a result of oxidation, a process that occurs through the formation of molecular fragments called **free radicals**, which have an unpaired electron as a distinguishing feature. Without specifying the structures of radicals, we can summarize the process. First, a fat molecule reacts with oxygen to form a free radical.

$$Fat + O_2 \longrightarrow Free\ radical$$

Q: What functional group is common to all four compounds? What other functional group is present in BHA? In propyl gallate?

The radical then reacts with another fat molecule to form a new free radical that can repeat the process. A reaction such as this, in which intermediates are formed that keep the reaction going, is called a **chain reaction**. One molecule of oxygen can lead to the decomposition of many fat molecules.

To preserve foods containing fats, processors package the products to exclude air. However, it cannot be excluded completely, so chemical antioxidants such as BHT are used to stop the chain reaction by reacting with the free radicals.

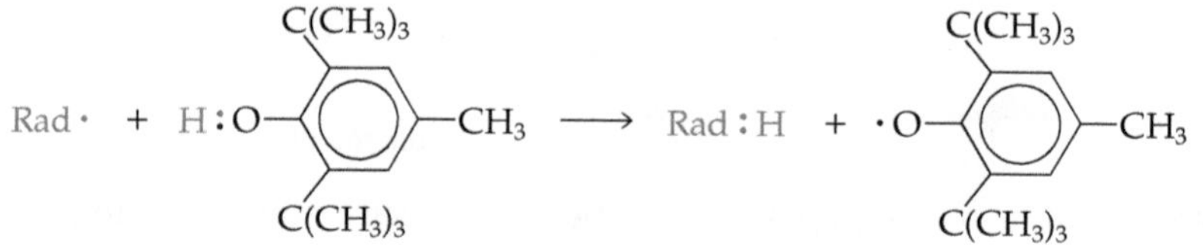

$$Rad\cdot \ + \ H:O-\bigcirc-CH_3 \ \longrightarrow \ Rad:H \ + \ \cdot O-\bigcirc-CH_3$$

BHT

The new radical formed from BHT is rather stable. The unpaired electron doesn't have to stay on the oxygen atom but can move around in the electron cloud of the benzene ring. The BHT radical doesn't react with fat molecules, and the chain is broken.

Why are the butyl groups important? Without them, two phenol molecules would simply couple when exposed to an oxidizing agent.

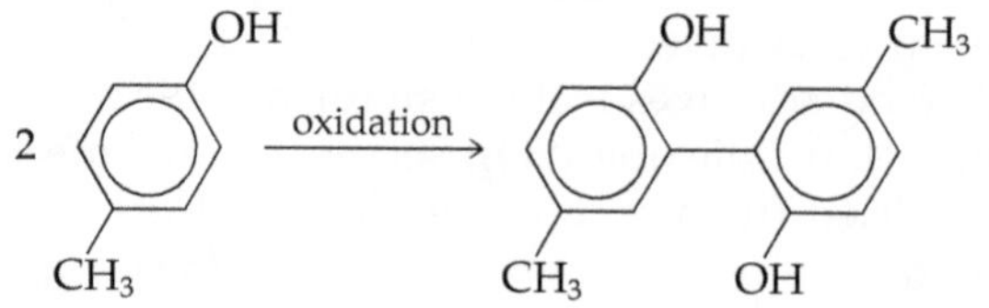

With the bulky butyl groups attached, the rings can't get close enough together for coupling. They are free, then, to trap free radicals formed by the oxidation of fats.

Many food additives have been criticized as being harmful, and BHA and BHT are no exceptions. They have been reported to cause allergic reactions in some people. In one study, pregnant mice fed diets containing 0.5% BHA or BHT gave birth to offspring with brain abnormalities. On the other hand, when relatively large amounts of BHT were fed to rats daily, their life spans were increased by a human equivalent of 20 years. One theory about aging is that it is caused in part by the formation of free radicals. BHT retards this chemical breakdown in cells in the same way that it retards spoilage in foods.

BHA and BHT are synthetic chemicals, but antioxidants such as vitamin E and vitamin C occur naturally. Vitamin E (like BHT) is a phenol, with several substituents on the benzene ring. Presumably, its action as an antioxidant is quite similar to that of BHT. However, one recent study suggests that large doses of vitamin E may also be somewhat harmful.

Color Additives

Some foods are naturally colored. For example, the yellow compound β-carotene (whose structure is shown below) occurs in carrots and is used as a color additive in foods such as butter and margarine. Our bodies convert β-carotene to vitamin A by cutting the molecule in half at the center double bond. Thus, it is a vitamin additive as well as a color additive.

β-Carotene

Too much vitamin A (from liver or supplements) can be toxic, but if too much β-carotene is consumed, the body merely stores it in fat, eventually using or excreting it. Very large amounts of β-carotene have been known to cause the skin to turn orange! The effect is temporary and harmless.

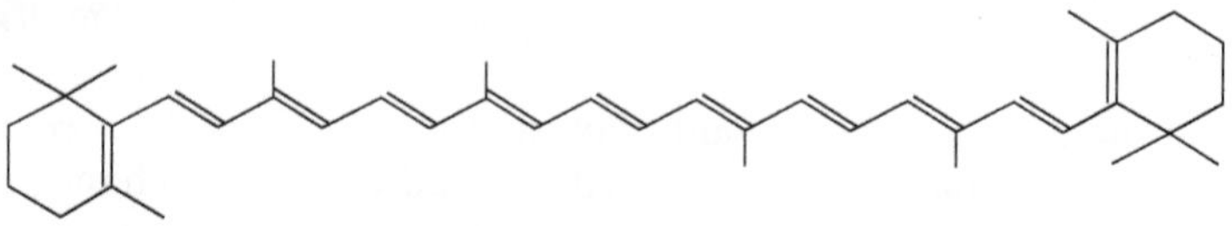

Other natural food colors include beet juice, grape-hull extract, and saffron (from autumn-flowering crocus flowers).

Nanoscience in Foods

Nanoscience and nanotechnology involve the production and use of materials at a nanometer scale—billionths of a meter. The properties of nanomaterials differ from those of larger-scale materials, and nanotechnology has the potential to revolutionize many aspects of food quality and packaging in the future. For example, nanotechnology may be used to develop foods that can adjust in color, flavor, or nutrient content to accommodate each consumer's taste or health condition. Some possible food-related applications of nanoscience include the following:

- **Nano foods.** Several companies are exploring the use of nanotechnology to create drinks containing nanocapsules that can change color and flavor and to make ice cream with nanoparticle emulsions to improve texture. Scientists are also developing novel delivery systems that help protect nutrients and flavors and that improve control of the release of encapsulated compounds.

- **Nano packaging.** Nanomaterials are being developed that will extend food shelf life and change color to signal when the food spoils. Nanoparticles could be used in packaging film to yield a material with greater mechanical strength but lower permeability to oxygen and water. Such film could perhaps remove carbon dioxide or block out gases such as oxygen and ethylene that shorten the shelf life of food.

- **Nano security devices.** Nanosensors are being developed for pathogen and contaminant detection. Single-molecule sensors would detect changes in food quality and thus maintain food safety. Nanodevices are being investigated that would allow the tracking of individual shipments.

Nanotechnology centers around the world are developing an impressive body of research on new possibilities for food production—flavors, nutrition, colors, packaging, and much more. Nanotechnology offers enormous potential benefits to society, but health concerns associated with nanomaterials are surfacing. The same factors that enhance the usefulness of these materials also increase the potential for harm. Some nanoparticles can be absorbed into cells and move throughout the body and brain. Their small size may increase their potential toxicity.

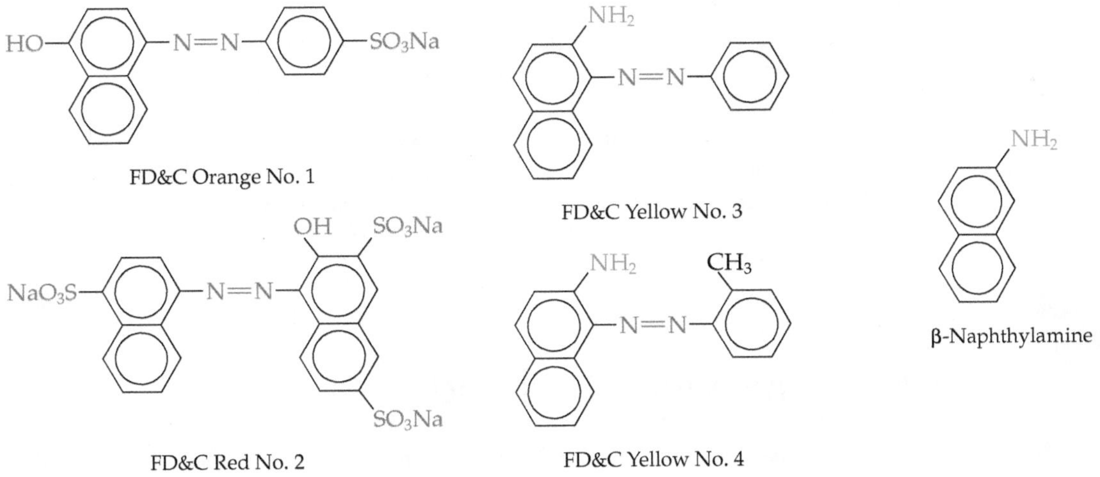

FD&C Orange No. 1

FD&C Yellow No. 3

FD&C Red No. 2

FD&C Yellow No. 4

β-Naphthylamine

▲ **Figure 16** Four synthetic food colorings that have been banned by the FDA (left). Note that the two yellow dyes are related to β-naphthylamine (right), a carcinogen.

We expect many foods to have characteristic colors. To increase the attractiveness and acceptability of its products, the food industry has used synthetic food colors for decades. Since the Food and Drug Act of 1906, the FDA has regulated the use of these chemicals and set limits on their concentrations. But the FDA is not infallible. Some colors once on the approved list were later shown to be harmful and were removed from the list. In 1950, Food, Drug, and Cosmetic (FD&C) Orange No. 1 in pumpkin-colored Halloween candy caused gastrointestinal upsets in several children and was then banned by the FDA.

In following years, other dyes were banned. FD&C Yellow No. 3 and No. 4 were found to contain small amounts of β-naphthylamine, a carcinogen that causes bladder cancer in laboratory animals. Furthermore, they reacted with stomach acids to produce more β-naphthylamine. FD&C Red No. 2 was also shown to be a weak carcinogen in laboratory animals. The structures of these dyes are given in Figure 16.

Food colors, even those that have been banned, present little risk. They have been used for years with apparent safety and are normally used in tiny amounts. Although the risk is low, however, the benefit is largely aesthetic. Any foods that contain artificial colors must say so on the label, so you can avoid them if you want to.

Self-Assessment Questions

1. To use a new food additive, a company must
   a. notify the FDA that it plans to use the additive
   b. pay the FDA to test the additive for safety
   c. provide the FDA with evidence that the additive is safe for the intended use
   d. submit an application to the FDA, but does not have to prove it safe and effective

2. Compared to synthetic flavors, natural flavors
   a. are chemical-free
   b. have different main ingredients
   c. come from the Spice Islands
   d. contain a wider variety of chemicals

3. The flavor enhancer MSG is related to a(n)
   a. amino acid
   b. fatty acid
   c. monosaccharide
   d. polyhydroxy alcohol

4. Calcium propionate is added to bread to
   a. act as an antioxidant
   b. enhance the flavor
   c. inhibit mold growth
   c. replace Ca^{2+} removed in processing

5. The food additive that inhibits formation of botulin toxin is sodium
   a. acetate
   b. ascorbate
   c. benzoate
   d. nitrite

6. Antioxidants
   a. aid in lipid transport
   b. aid in oxygen transport
   c. prevent color fading
   d. trap free radicals

7. Which of the following is an antioxidant used to prevent rancidity?
   a. ascorbic acid
   b. BHT
   c. sodium sulfite
   d. sugar

8. Vitamin C, vitamin E, BHA, BHT, and propyl gallate are
   a. antimicrobial
   b. antioxidants
   c. flavor enhancers
   d. unintentional additives

Answers: 1, c; 2, d; 3, a; 4, c; 5, d; 6, d; 7, b; 8, b

7 Problems with Our Food

Learning Objective > Identify and describe some of the main problems with harmful substances in our food.

People have been trying to deal with poisons in their food for millennia. Early foragers learned—by the painful process of trial and error—that some plants and animals were poisonous. Rhubarb leaves contain toxic oxalic acid. Bruised celery produces *psoralens*, compounds that are powerful mutagens and carcinogens. The Japanese relish a variety of puffer fish that contains deadly poison in its ovaries and liver. Fifty or so Japanese people die each year from improperly prepared puffers.

One of the most toxic substances known is the toxin botulin that is produced by the bacterium *Clostridium botulinum*. This organism grows in improperly canned food. If the food isn't properly sterilized before it is sealed in jars or cans, the microorganism flourishes under anaerobic (without air) conditions. Botulin is so toxic that 1 g of it could kill more than a million people. The point is that a food is not inherently good simply because it is natural. Neither is it necessarily bad because a synthetic chemical substance has been added to it.

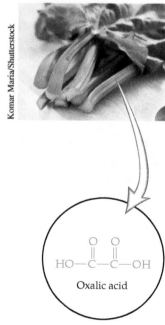

▲ Poisonous oxalic acid is found in rhubarb leaves.

Oxalic acid

GREEN CHEMISTRY

David M. Brown, *Davidson College*

Greener Ways to Isolate Nutrients from Food

The adoption of green chemistry principles has led to dramatic and exciting transformations in the field of molecular gastronomy. At one time, large-scale extractions of natural products, bioactive food components, and essential oils from plants relied on organic solvents, including diethyl ether, methylene chloride, chloroform, carbon tetrachloride, benzene, toluene, and others. Although these substances were once considered acceptable, we now know they are hazardous. Most of them are extremely flammable, highly volatile, carcinogenic, mutagenic, or teratogenic or show some combination of these risks. For these reasons, it is wise to avoid exposure to these hazardous solvents.

As a new generation of chemists evolves and applies the Twelve Principles of Green Chemistry, safer solvents (Principle 5) are being used with increasing frequency. Ethanol and supercritical carbon dioxide are currently the two solvents most widely used to extract natural products, bioactive food components, and essential oils. Ethanol extracts organic molecules of greater polarity. Supercritical carbon dioxide complements that by extracting organic molecules of lesser polarity. Mixtures of ethanol and supercritical carbon dioxide may be used to extract organic molecules of medium polarity. Now we don't have to use the more hazardous solvents.

Further, using more benign solvents such as ethanol and supercritical carbon dioxide instead of more hazardous solvents allows for safer reaction and processing conditions (for instance, flammability is less of a problem, Principle 12). Perhaps the most popular large-scale extraction is that of caffeine from coffee and tea, which was once performed using the carcinogenic and highly volatile solvent methylene chloride, but is now done using safer solvents such as supercritical carbon dioxide or water. The process is now safer and more effective due to green chemistry.

Spurred by the success of the caffeine-extraction process, greener technologies have been extended to the diverse fields of natural products, bioactive food components, and essential oils. It is now common to see bottles of concentrated extracts of dietary supplements, nutraceuticals, phytochemicals, and herbs on the shelves of pharmacies and health food stores as well as in "big-box" retailers. The potential health benefits and exact physiological function at the molecular level of these materials are subjects of research. Shown in the table below are some examples.

Similarly, essential oils from plants are extracted and concentrated from, for example, rosemary, hibiscus, and lavender. These concentrated oils are used as ingredients for fragrances and flavors (perfumes, herbal teas, soft drinks, and candies).

In the extraction of natural products, bioactive food components, and essential oils, green chemistry has played, and will continue to play, a crucial role in the reduction of hazardous solvents and protection of the environment.

Natural Product	Food Sources
Allicin	Garlic
Cyanidin	Dark pigmented berries
Beta-Carotene	Carrots, pumpkin, spinach
Capsaicin	Chili peppers
Epigallocatechin (EGC)	Green tea, pomegranate
Chlorophyll c_1	Algae and green vegetables
Curcumin	Turmeric (a component of curry)
EPA (an omega-3 fatty acid)	Fish
D-Limonene	Oranges, lemons, limes, cherries
Lycopene	Tomatoes, grapefruit, watermelon
Resveratrol	Plums, red grape skins

Botulin toxin (Botox®) is used in minute quantities for producing long-term (lasting for months) paralysis of muscles. Originally intended for the relief of unmanageable muscle spasms, Botox® is now widely used for cosmetic purposes, to paralyze facial muscles to conceal wrinkles. The treatment lasts only 4–6 months.

Carcinogens

There is little chance that we will suffer acute poisoning from approved food additives. But what about cancer? Could all these chemicals in our food increase our risk of developing cancer? The possibility exists, though the risk is low.

Carcinogens occur naturally in food. A charcoal-broiled steak contains 3,4-benzpyrene, a carcinogen also found in cigarette smoke and automobile exhaust fumes. Cinnamon and nutmeg contain *safrole*, a carcinogen that has been banned as a flavoring in root beer.

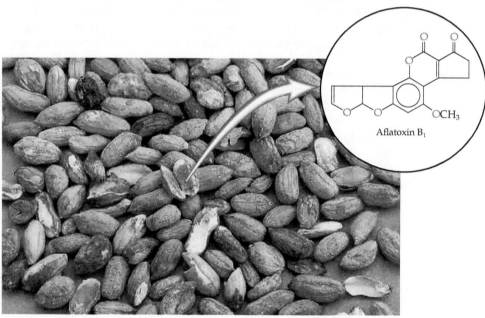

3,4-Benzpyrene   Safrole

Among the most potent carcinogens are **aflatoxins**, compounds produced by molds growing on stored peanuts and grains (Figure 17). Aflatoxin B_1 is estimated to be 10 million times as potent a carcinogen as saccharin, and there is no way to keep it completely out of our food. The FDA sets a limit of 20 ppb for the maximum level of aflatoxins.

▶ **Figure 17** Aflatoxins, toxic and carcinogenic compounds, are produced by molds that grow on peanuts and stored grains.

Aflatoxin B_1

HO/AP Wide World Photos

Scientists estimate that our consumption of natural carcinogens is 10,000 times our consumption of synthetic carcinogens. Should we ban steaks, spices, peanuts, and grains because they contain naturally occurring carcinogens? Probably not. The risk is slight, and more serious risks face us in everyday life. Should we ban additives that have been shown to be carcinogenic? Certainly we should carefully weigh the risks against any benefits the additives might provide.

Food Contaminants

Food contamination can come from many sources and can occur at any step between producer and consumer. Pesticide residues, insect parts, hair from food workers, glass from broken containers, and antibiotics added to animal feeds are examples of contaminants. (See Collaborative Group Project 6.)

Antibiotics in animal feed are a troubling example of food contamination, because they often show up in the meat we eat. Antibiotics are added in low-level dosages to animal feed to promote weight gain. In fact, in 2009, 13.1 million kg of antibiotics were sold for use in animals in the United States. Residues of these antibiotics in meat may result in the sensitization of individuals who eat the meat, thus hastening the development of allergies. Scientists also fear that the use of antibiotics in animal feeds will hasten the process by which bacteria become drug resistant.

Today's food contamination problems are usually biological, not chemical. For example, bacteria such as the O157:H7 strain of *Escherichia coli* (*E. coli*), a fecal contaminant sometimes found in raw meat or dairy products and occasionally in raw fruits and vegetables, can cause serious food poisoning. *E. coli* contamination has been responsible for many costly food recalls in recent years. *Salmonella* contamination of poultry, eggs, unprocessed milk, meat, or water can cause cramping, fever, dehydration, and diarrhea. *Salmonella* is also carried by pet turtles and birds. *Listeria monocytogenes* causes listeriosis, a food-borne illness marked by fever, muscle aches, nausea, and diarrhea.

Viruses such as hepatitis A, which causes a serious contagious disease of the liver, and the Norwalk virus, which causes about 50% of all outbreaks of food-borne gastroenteritis in the United States, can be spread when infected workers handle food products.

Parasites such as the roundworms *Trichinella spiralis*, which causes trichinosis, and *Anisakis simplex*, which causes anisakiasis, are relatively rare problems in developed countries but are fairly common in developing parts of the world. The few cases of trichinosis that occur in the United States result mainly from eating undercooked game meat or pork from home-raised pigs. Trichinosis is characterized by symptoms such as nausea, heartburn, and diarrhea. Anisakiasis results from eating raw or undercooked fish in dishes such as sushi and sashimi (Japan), cod livers (Scandinavia), fermented herrings (Netherlands), or ceviche, a citrus-marinated, raw seafood that is popular in Latin America.

Proper cooking and food handling procedures reduce the chance of contracting most food-borne diseases.

A World without Food Additives

Could we get along without food additives? Some of us could. But food spoilage might drastically reduce the food supply in some parts of an already hungry world, and diseases due to vitamin and mineral deficiencies might increase. Foods might cost more and be less nutritious. Food additives seem to be a necessary part of modern society. Use of some food additives poses potential hazards, but the major problem with our food supply is still contamination by harmful microorganisms, rodents, and insects. Indeed, according to the CDC, about 48 million illnesses and 3000 deaths result each year in the United States from food poisoning caused by bacteria, viruses, and parasites. Few, if any, deaths associated with the use of intentional food additives have been documented.

What should we do about food additives? We should be sure that the FDA is staffed with qualified personnel who can perform adequate testing of proposed food additives. People trained in chemistry are necessary for the control and monitoring of food additives and the detection of contaminants. Research on the analytical techniques necessary for the detection of trace quantities is vital to adequate consumer protection. We should demand laws to prevent the unnecessary and excessive use of pesticides and other agricultural chemicals that might contaminate our food. Above all, we should be alert and informed about these problems that are so vital to our health and well-being.

Self-Assessment Questions

1. Aflatoxins are
   a. antioxidants **b.** carcinogens **c.** on the GRAS list **d.** found only in peanuts

2. About how many people die from food poisoning in the U.S. each year?
   a. 100 **b.** 300 **c.** 3000 **d.** 30,000

3. The major problem with the food supply is contamination by
   a. aflatoxins **b.** chemicals **c.** microorganisms **d.** pesticides

Answers: 1, b; 2, c; 3, c

CRITICAL THINKING EXERCISES

Apply knowledge that you have gained in this chapter and one or more of the FLaReS principles to evaluate the following statements or claims.

1 The author of a new diet book claims that he and many other people have been able to lose a substantial amount of weight by following a diet very low in carbohydrates (from bread, cereals, and pasta) but high in proteins (from meats).

2 An opponent of genetically modified (GM) foods suggests that the outcry against genetic modification occurred because the "public didn't want to eat food with 'genes' in it."

3 A Web site states that a chemical in marijuana, delta 1-tetrahydrocannabinol (delta 1-THC), is a fat-soluble vitamin called "vitamin M." The site claims that vitamin status is justified "because many of the properties of delta 1-THC are similar to those of the fat-soluble vitamins."

4 A Web site states that natural vitamins may be worth the extra cost because those vitamins occur within a family of "things like trace elements, enzymes, cofactors and other unknown factors that help them absorb into the human body and function to their full potential," whereas "synthetic vitamins are usually isolated into that one pure chemical, thereby leaving out some of the additional benefits that nature intended."

5 7-Day Detox is a unique detoxification supplement whose label states that it contains 34 different ingredients intended to flush toxins and fat out of your system.

6 A woman's doctor orders her to follow a strict low-fat diet. She makes a bowl of fat-free popcorn and then sprays it with a "flavor spray." The label of the spray lists the ingredients as canola oil, butter, and lecithin. It also indicates that a serving size of 1 spray (0.5 g) has 5 calories and 0 g of fat. (The FDA allows less than 0.5 g to be rounded to zero.) She sprays the popcorn about 40 times to give it a lot of flavor, pointing out that at zero grams of fat per spray, she is still adhering to the low-fat diet.

SUMMARY

Section 1—The three main classes of substances in foods are carbohydrates, fats, and proteins. We also need vitamins, minerals, fiber, and water in our diets. Carbohydrates include sugars, starches, and cellulose. Glucose, also called blood sugar, is the sugar used directly by cells for energy. Other sugars include fructose, sucrose (table sugar), and lactose. Sucrose and lactose are broken down during digestion. Starch is a polymer of α-glucose, and cellulose is a β-glucose polymer. Human beings can hydrolyze starch to glucose but cannot hydrolyze cellulose, which instead serves as dietary fiber. The liver and muscles store small amounts of carbohydrates as glycogen.

Section 2—Dietary fats are esters called triglycerides, which are broken down by enzymes to form fatty acids and glycerol. Fats are stored in adipose tissue located in fat depots and are hydrolyzed back to glycerol and fatty acids when needed. A lipoprotein is a cholesterol–protein combination transported in the blood. Low-density lipoproteins (LDLs) carry cholesterol to the cells for use and increase the risk of heart disease, while high-density lipoproteins (HDLs) carry it to the liver for excretion. Polyunsaturated fats (mostly from plants), *cis* fatty acids, and omega-3 fatty acids tend to lower LDL levels. Saturated fats (mostly from animals) and *trans* fatty acids made by hydrogenation of polyunsaturated fats have been implicated in cardiovascular disease.

Section 3—Proteins, polymers of amino acids, are broken down to amino acids during digestion. The essential amino acids must be included in the diet. Each essential amino acid is a limiting reactant in protein synthesis; a deficiency leads to an inability to make the proper proteins. Most animal proteins have these essential amino acids; plant proteins usually are deficient and must be combined with other plant proteins for complete nutrition. Protein deficiency is common in developing nations.

Section 4—Dietary minerals are inorganic substances vital to life. Bulk structural elements include carbon, hydrogen, and oxygen. Macrominerals include sodium, potassium, and calcium. We also need trace elements such as iron and ultratrace elements such as manganese, chromium, and vanadium. Minerals serve a variety of functions: Iodine is needed by the thyroid; iron is part of hemoglobin; and calcium and phosphorus are vital to the bones and teeth.

Vitamins are organic compounds that are required in the diet to prevent certain diseases. The B vitamins and vitamin C are water soluble and are needed frequently, whereas vitamins A, D, E, and K are all fat soluble and can be stored.

Dietary fiber may be soluble (gums and pectins) or insoluble (cellulose). It prevents digestion problems such as constipation. Drinking enough water is important, but it need not be plain water. Most drinks are mainly water.

Section 5—Starvation is deprivation of food that causes metabolic changes. The body first depletes its glycogen and then metabolizes fat and muscle tissue. Malnutrition can result from starvation, dieting, or eating too much highly processed food.

Section 6—**Food additives** are substances other than basic foodstuffs that are added to food to aid nutrition, inhibit spoilage, enhance color and flavor, provide texture, and so on. There are thousands of additives. The FDA regulates which additives, and how much of them, can be used.

The list of additives generally recognized as safe is the GRAS list, which is periodically reevaluated. Some additives have been found to be harmful; additives are usually banned if they are shown to cause cancer in laboratory animals.

Enrichment includes the replacement of B vitamins and the addition of iron to flour. Vitamin C is added to many beverages, and vitamin D to milk. Natural herbs and spices, or their synthetic counterparts, add flavor. Artificial sweeteners reduce sugar intake but do not appear to aid in controlling obesity. Glycerol is a sweet-tasting compound that is used primarily as a humectant or moistening agent. Salt and MSG are flavor enhancers.

Propionate, sorbate, and benzoate nitrite salts inhibit spoilage and bacterial growth. Fats may turn rancid partly from formation of free radicals with unpaired electrons. One free radical can cause a chain reaction that leads to decomposition of many fat molecules. BHT and BHA are antioxidants that react with free radicals and prevent rancidity.

Natural food colorings, such as β-carotene, and synthetic food colorings improve the appearance of food.

Section 7—Toxic substances occur naturally in foods, but occasionally are added in the form of pesticide residues or animal feed additives. Charcoal-broiled steak, cinnamon, and nutmeg contain carcinogens. Aflatoxins are produced by molds on peanuts and grain and are potent carcinogens. We may consume about 10,000 times as much of natural carcinogens as synthetic carcinogens. Most food contaminants are not chemicals but rather organisms such as bacteria, viruses, and parasites.

Without food additives, spoilage and disease would be likely to cause serious problems worldwide. Additives continue to be carefully scrutinized and regulated.

Green chemistry Green chemistry has revised extractions of natural products, bioactive food components, and essential oils from plants by substituting less hazardous solvents. For example, in decaffeination of coffee and tea, more benign supercritical carbon dioxide or water has replaced the volatile and carcinogenic solvent methylene chloride. Greener extraction technology is being extended to a large variety of dietary supplements and nutraceuticals derived from plants and other natural products.

Learning Objectives

> Identify dietary carbohydrates, and state their function.	Problems 1, 17–20
> Identify dietary lipids, and state their function.	Problems 2, 21–24, 55, 56
> List the essential amino acids, and explain why they are essential.	Problems 4, 25–27, 29, 30
> Describe some protein deficiency diseases and their causes.	Problem 28
> Identify the vitamins and the bulk dietary minerals, and state their functions.	Problems 3, 5, 11, 31–40, 63
> Describe the effects of starvation, fasting, and malnutrition.	Problem 6
> List some common food additives and their purposes.	Problems 7–9, 12, 13, 15, 16, 41, 42, 44, 46–48, 64, 67
> Identify and describe some of the main problems with harmful substances in our food.	Problems 47, 48
> Identify common molecules derived from food sources.	Problems 69, 71
> Distinguish polar molecules from nonpolar molecules and predict which can be extracted with ethanol or supercritical carbon dioxide.	Problem 70
> Describe how green chemistry has made the extraction of natural products, bioactive food components, and essential oils from plants safer and less hazardous.	Problems 71, 72

REVIEW QUESTIONS

1. What is the role of carbohydrates in the diet?
2. What functions do fats serve?
3. Which vitamins and minerals are organic and which are inorganic?
4. What is the role of proteins in the diet?
5. Is an excess of a water-soluble vitamin or an excess of a fat-soluble vitamin more likely to be dangerous? Why?
6. What is starvation?
7. What is a food additive?
8. What are the two major categories of food additives? Give an example of each.
9. What is MSG?
10. What is botulism? What are aflatoxins?
11. What fat-soluble vitamin serves as an antioxidant?

12. Name three artificial sweeteners. Which are approved for current use in the United States?

13. What is the chemical nature of aspartame?

14. List some contaminants that have been found in foods.

15. List five functions of food additives.

16. What U.S. government agency regulates the use of food additives? What must be done before a company can use a new food additive?

PROBLEMS

Carbohydrates

17. What are the chemical names of the following sugars?
a. blood sugar
b. table sugar
c. fruit sugar

18. What is the main sugar in corn syrup? How is high-fructose corn syrup made?

19. What type of chemical reaction is involved in the digestion of starch?

20. What sugar is formed when starch is digested?

Fats and Cholesterol

21. What type of chemical reaction is involved in the digestion of fats? What products are formed?

22. Where is fat stored in the body?

23. How do animal fats differ from vegetable oils?

24. What is a *trans* fat? How are *trans* fats made?

Proteins

25. What is an adequate protein? List some foods that contain adequate proteins.

26. What is the limiting reactant in any protein synthesis?

27. Which essential amino acids are likely to be lacking in corn? In beans?

28. What is kwashiorkor? What age group in developed countries suffers a similar condition?

29. *Ezekiel* 4:9 describes a bread made from "wheat, and barley, and beans, and lentils, and millet, and spelt . . . ." Would the bread supply complete protein?

30. How do dietary proteins differ from dietary carbohydrates and fats in elemental composition?

Minerals

31. Give a biological function for the dietary mineral or a name to match the biological function.
a. thyroid (regulating metabolism)
b. iron
c. bones and teeth, heartbeat rhythm
d. phosphorus

32. Of the minerals Ca, Cl, Co, Mo, Na, P, and Zn, which is likely to be found in relatively large amounts in the human body? Explain.

Vitamins

33. Classify the following vitamins as water soluble or fat soluble.

Pantothenic acid

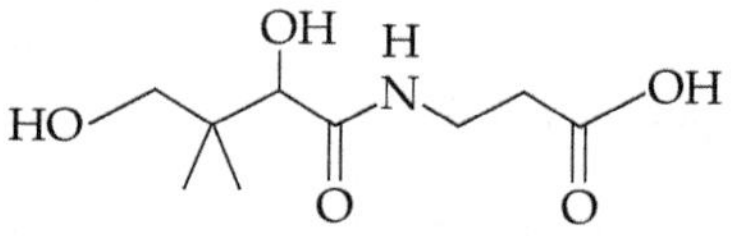

Phylloquinone

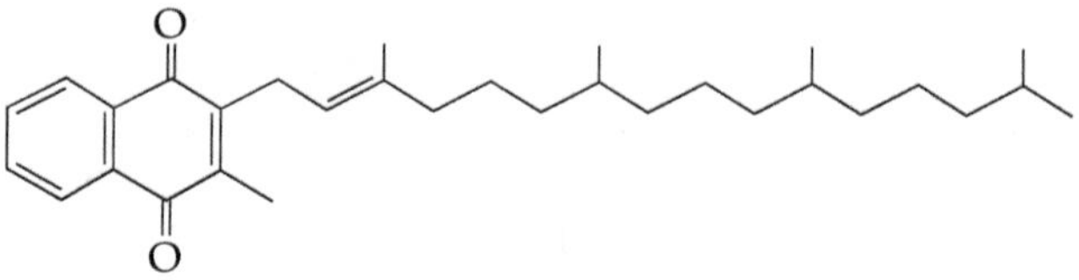

Biotin

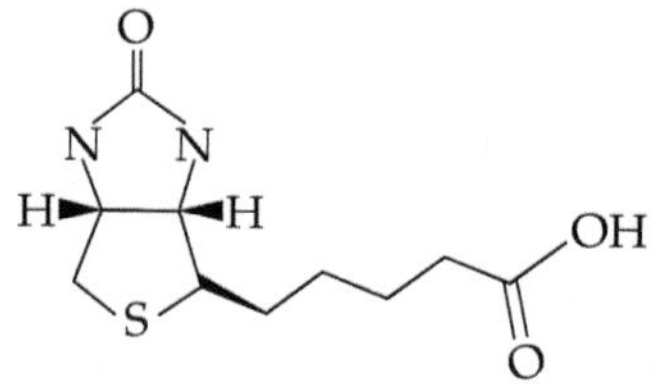

34. Coenzyme Q_{10} (CoQ_{10}; shown below) is claimed by some to have vitamin-like activity: It prevents oxidation of LDLs and may act as an antihypertensive, perhaps reducing the risk of cardiovascular disease. CoQ_{10} belongs to a family of substances called *ubiquinones* and is synthesized in the body. **(a)** Is CoQ_{10} a vitamin? **(b)** Is it fat soluble or water soluble?

CoQ_{10}

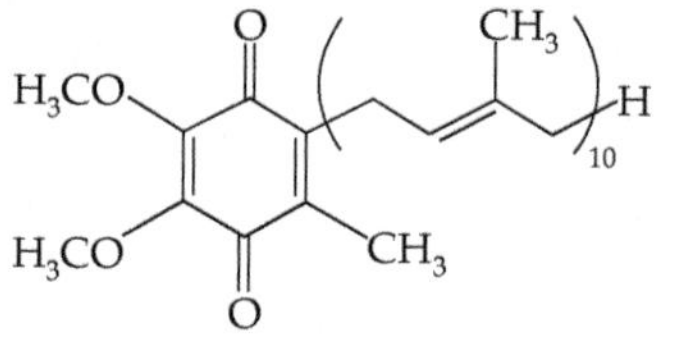

35. Match the compound with its designation as a vitamin.

Compound	Designation
ascorbic acid	vitamin A
calciferol	vitamin B$_{12}$
cyanocobalamin	vitamin C
retinol	vitamin D
tocopherol	vitamin E

36. Which of the following are B vitamins?
a. niacin   **b.** phylloquinone
c. pyridoxine   **d.** calciferol
e. ascorbic acid

37. Name a vitamin that prevents the deficiency disease or a disease that the vitamin prevents.
a. pellagra
b. beriberi
c. cyanocobalamin (vitamin B_{12})

38. Name a vitamin that prevents the deficiency disease or a disease that the vitamin prevents.
a. scurvy   **b.** retinol   **c.** α-tocopherol

39. Identify each of the following vitamins as water soluble or fat soluble.
a. vitamin A   **b.** vitamin B_6
c. vitamin B_{12} **d.** vitamin C
e. vitamin K

40. Identify each of the following vitamins as water soluble or fat soluble.
a. calciferol   **b.** niacin
c. riboflavin   **d.** tocopherol

Food Additives

41. Identify the function of the food additive or name a food additive that has the specified function.
a. $FeCO_3$
b. disinfectant and preservative
c. potassium sorbate

42. Identify the function of the food additive or name a food additive that has the specified function.
a. potassium iodide   **b.** vanillin
c. flavor enhancer   **d.** prevent botulism

43. What is the purpose of each of the following food additives?
a. BHA   **b.** FD&C Yellow No. 5   **c.** saccharin

44. What is the purpose of each of the following food additives?
a. aspartame   **b.** vitamin D
c. sodium hypophosphite

45. Which of the following is true about a dietary supplement labeled "natural"? It is (a) mild acting; (b) without risk of side effects; (c) always safe to use with medications; or (d) none of the above.

46. Propyl gallate is made by esterification of gallic acid, which is obtained by the hydrolysis of tannins from pods of the tara tree. Is propyl gallate a natural antioxidant?

47. What are antioxidants? Name a natural antioxidant and two synthetic antioxidants.

48. What is a chain reaction? What is the action of an antioxidant on a chain reaction?

Calorie and Nutrient Calculations

49. The label on a can of vegetable beef soup indicates that each 1-cup portion supplies 120 kcal and has 8 g of protein, 16 g of carbohydrate, and 3 g of fat. Calculate the percentages of calories that come from carbohydrate, fat, and protein.

50. The label on a can of New-Orleans–style navy beans indicates that each ½-cup serving supplies 130 kcal and has 8 g of protein, 23 g of carbohydrate, and 1.5 g of fat. Calculate the percentages of calories that come from carbohydrate, fat, and protein.

51. A ¼-cup serving of Martha Rose Shulman's asparagus-and-herb lasagna provides 5 g of fat, 6 g of carbohydrate, and 3 g of protein. About how many kilocalories does a serving of lasagna provide? What percentage of the calories comes from fat?

52. A 3-oz grilled lamb chop provides about 170 kcal, 23.5 g protein, and 6 g fat. How much carbohydrate does the lamb provide?

53. An adult female goes on a diet that provides 1200 kcal per day with no more than 25% from fat and no more than 30% of that fat being saturated fat. How much saturated fat, in grams, is permitted in this diet?

54. A very active male teenager needs about 3000 kcal per day. If the guideline of 30% or less of total calories from fat is followed, how much fat, in grams, is permitted?

ADDITIONAL PROBLEMS

55. Omega-6 fatty acids are unsaturated fatty acids in which the double bond closest to the methyl (omega) end of the molecule occurs at the sixth carbon from that end. Which of the following are omega-6 fatty acids? Refer to structures not given here.
a. palmitoleic acid, $CH_3(CH_2)_5CH=CH(CH_2)_7CO_2H$
b. oleic acid
c. linoleic acid
d. linolenic acid
e. arachidonic acid

56. Following are line-angle formulas for two fats. **(a)** Which is a saturated fat and which is a polyunsaturated fat? **(b)** Identify the fatty-acid units in each.

Food

Use the nutritional labels shown below to answer Problems 57–61.

57. What percentage of the energy of whole milk comes from fat?

58. Based on a 2200-kcal diet, what percentage of the maximum daily amount of cholesterol does a cup of whole milk provide?

59. Based on a 2200-kcal diet, what percentage of the maximum daily amount of saturated fat does a cup of whole milk provide?

60. A student drinks 4 cups of fat-free milk in a day and wants to consume 60 g per day of protein. What percentage of that protein is obtained from the milk?

61. What percentage of the calories in fat-free milk comes **(a)** from sugars and **(b)** from protein?

62. Shown below are three substances sold as nutritional supplements. Pangamic acid (I) has not been shown to

be required in the human diet. Dietary deficiency in pangamic acid is not associated with any disease. Carnitine (II) is synthesized in the body from the amino acids lysine and methionine. It is required for the transport of fatty acids from the cellular fluid into the mitochondria during the breakdown of fats. Orotic acid (III) Is manufactured in the body by intestinal microorganisms. For each substance: **(a)** Is it likely to be water soluble or fat soluble? **(b)** Is it a vitamin?

63. Of the vitamins calciferol, riboflavin, retinol, and cyanocobolamin, which are most likely to be needed on a daily basis? Explain.

64. Sodium saccharin and sucralose (Figure 13) are both readily soluble in water, but for somewhat different reasons. Explain.

65. Pioneers in the United States made heavy use of butter, beef tallow, and lard for their long treks across the country. One reason for this was the ready availability of these fats. But even if canola oil, soybean oil, and similar oils had been available, they probably would not have been used much. Suggest a chemical reaction that is related to storage.

66. A diet that includes a lot of meat makes less efficient use of the energy originally captured by plants through photosynthesis than a vegetarian diet does. Explain.

67. When eating a thick canned soup such as beef vegetable soup, you may notice that the liquid in the soup becomes thinner as you eat. Suggest a reason for this phenomenon. (*Hint:* Starches are used as thickeners in some soups.)

68. What structural differences are there between sucrose and sucralose (Figure 13)?

69. Match each natural product with the food(s) in which it can be found.
   a. lycopene   1. algae and green vegetables
   b. resveratrol   2. plums and red grapes
   c. allicin   3. tomatoes, grapefruit, and watermelon
   d. chlorophyll   4. garlic

70. Identify each of the following molecules as polar or nonpolar, and state whether the compound could be extracted efficiently by supercritical carbon dioxide.
   a. cholesterol
   b. sodium chloride
   c. oxalic acid
   d. limonene

71. List the advantages of supercritical carbon dioxide over methylene chloride (CH_2Cl_2) as a solvent for extraction of a substance from food.

72. List the advantages of supercritical carbon dioxide over methylene chloride as a solvent for extraction of a substance from food.

COLLABORATIVE GROUP PROJECTS

Prepare a PowerPoint, poster, or other presentation (as directed by your instructor) to share with the class.

1. The Calorie Control Council lists several fat substitutes. Prepare a brief report on one of them.

2. Prepare a brief report on one of the minerals listed in Table 3. Identify principal dietary sources and uses of the mineral.

3. Prepare a brief report on one of the vitamins listed in Table 4. Identify principal dietary sources and uses of the vitamin.

4. Examine the label on each of the following. Make a list of the food additives in each. Try to determine the function of each additive. Do all the labels provide this information?
   a. a can of soft drink
   b. a can of beer
   c. a box of dried soup mix
   d. a can of soup
   e. a can of fruit drink
   f. a cake mix box

5. Prepare a brief report on one of the following dietary supplements. What is the presumed function of each?
   a. acidophilus
   b. androstenedione
   c. coenzyme Q_{10}
   d. diindolylmethane
   e. glucosamine
   f. L-arginine
   g. St. John's wort
   h. valerian

6. Prepare a brief report on one of the following chemical contaminants found in food in the past. Is the contaminant still found in food today?
   a. acrylamide
   b. bisphenol A
   c. DDT
   d. DES
   e. melamine
   f. perchlorates

BRIEF ANSWERS TO SELECTED PROBLEMS

Answers are provided for *all in-chapter exercises*. Brief answers are given for *odd-numbered Review Questions*; more complete answers can be obtained by reviewing the text. Answers are provided for *all odd-numbered Problems and Additional Problems*.

NOTE: For numerical problems, your answer may differ slightly from ours because of rounding and the use of significant figures.

1 A. About 64%   B. About 34%
2 A. Fatty acid I
   B. Fatty acid I, because fatty acid III is a cis fatty acid and not a trans fatty acid
1. Energy source
3. All vitamins are organic; all minerals are inorganic.
5. Fat soluble; an excess is stored and accumulated; excess water-soluble vitamins are excreted.
7. Substances other than basic foodstuffs that are put into food for various reasons related to production, processing, packaging, or storage
9. Monosodium glutamate, a flavor enhancer
11. α-Tocopherol (vitamin E)
13. The methyl ester of the dipeptide aspartylphenylalanine
15. Add nutritional value, enhance flavor or color, retard spoilage, provide texture, sanitize (and others)
17. a. glucose   b. sucrose
    c. fructose
19. Hydrolysis
21. Hydrolysis; fatty acids, glycerol, mono- and diglycerides
23. Most animal fats are solids; most vegetable oils are liquids; animal fats generally have fewer C-to-C double bonds than vegetable oils.
25. An adequate protein provides all the essential amino acids in sufficient quantities; meat, eggs, milk.
27. Corn: lysine and tryptophan; beans: methionine
29. Yes; it has grains and beans.
31. a. iodine   b. hemoglobin (oxygen transport)
    c. calcium

d. nucleic acids, ATP (obtaining, storing, and using energy from foods), bones, teeth
33. Water soluble: pantothenic acid, biotin; fat soluble: phylloquinone
35. Ascorbic acid, vitamin C; calciferol, vitamin D; cyanocobalamin, vitamin B_{12}; retinol, vitamin A; tocopherol, vitamin E
37. a. niacin (vitamin B_3)
    b. thiamine (vitamin B_1)
    c. pernicious anemia
39. Water soluble: b, c, d; fat soluble: a, e
41. a. improve nutrition   b. SO_2
    c. inhibit spoilage
43. a. antioxidant   b. color
    c. artificial sweetener
45. d
47. Reducing agents, usually free-radical scavengers added to foods to prevent fats and oils from becoming rancid; vitamin E; BHT, and BHA
49. About 53% from carbohydrates; 23% from fat; 27% from protein
51. About 81 kcal; about 56% from fat
53. About 11 g saturated fat
55. c, e
57. About 45%
59. About 23%
61. a. about 60%   b. about 40%
63. Riboflavin and cyanocobalamin; they are water soluble and not easily stored.
65. Double bonds in unsaturated fats are more reactive than single bonds in saturated fats; unsaturated fats and oils would have spoiled more readily than saturated fats.
67. The thick polymeric starch is broken down to smaller, more soluble molecules by enzymes in saliva.
69. a. 3   b. 2   c. 4   d. 1
71. Less toxic; easily removed.

Fitness and Health

Foodpics/Shutterstock

Have You Ever Wondered?

1. **Do large doses or special combinations of vitamins, improve physical fitness?**

2. **Does vitamin C help to cure cancer?**

3. **Which diet pill will help me lose the most weight?**

4. **If I stop exercising, will the muscle I've developed turn to fat?**

Aleksandr Markin/Shutterstock

Learning Objectives

› List the recommendations (sources and percentages) for calories from fats and other sources in the American diet. (1)

› Describe the special dietary requirements of athletes. (1)

› Describe the dietary requirements for vitamins, minerals, and water. (2)

› Explain how weight is lost through diet and exercise. (3)

› Calculate weight loss due to calorie reduction and to exercise. (3)

› Describe several ways to measure fitness. (4)

› Calculate BMI values. (4)

› Differentiate between aerobic exercise and anaerobic exercise, and describe the chemistry that occurs during each. (5)

› Describe how muscles are built and how they work. (5)

› Describe the physiological effects of restorative drugs, stimulant drugs, and anabolic steroids. (6)

› Explain how endorphins, neurotrophins, and tobacco can affect the brain and body. (6)

› Explain how green chemistry principles can help us make transportation choices.

› Describe the relationship between walking or biking and personal health, especially the implications for weight loss.

The Chemistry of Wellness

For much of human history, the main concern of most people was obtaining enough food to stay alive. How the world has changed! Especially in developed countries, people now have scores of labor-saving devices and abundant food. Most people earn their daily bread with little physical exertion. So much food is available, and so little physical effort required to obtain it, that many people eat more than they should and get much less exercise than they need.

Obesity has become a major epidemic. According to the Centers for Disease Control and Prevention (CDC), 68% of American adults are either

Rido/Shutterstock

Exercise and a proper diet as parts of a healthy lifestyle are essential to good health, reducing the risk of diseases of the mind and body. Through chemistry, we gain a better understanding of the effects of diet and exercise on our bodies and minds.

overweight or obese; half of those are considered obese. The International Obesity Task Force estimates that 1.5 billion people worldwide are overweight, with 500 million of those being obese.

How do we stay healthy and physically fit? By some special diet or kind of exercise? In this chapter, we examine nutrition, electrolyte balance, muscle action, drugs, and other topics related to well-being and physical fitness.

1 Calories: Quantity and Quality

Learning Objectives ❯ List the recommendations (sources and percentages) for calories from fats and other sources in the American diet. ❯ Describe the special dietary requirements of athletes.

Although obesity is rampant in the developed world, many people still struggle daily just to obtain enough food to survive. In fact, research shows that undereating is healthier than overeating. Large studies have shown that mice given 40% less food than a control group live longer and have fewer tumors.

Total calorie intake is important, but the distribution of calories is even more important. The *2010 Dietary Guidelines for Americans* from the U.S. Departments of Agriculture (USDA) and Health and Human Services (HHS) include some recommendations, presented as a food plate in Figure 1.

A food plan based on these general recommendations should be tailored to the individual. For the average 2000-calorie-a-day diet, the guidelines suggest

- Enjoy your food, but eat less.
- Avoid oversized portions.
- Make half of your plate fruits and vegetables.
- Whole grains should be at least half of total grains.
- Switch to fat-free or low-fat (1%) milk.
- Compare the sodium content of foods like soup, bread, and frozen meals, and choose the foods with lower amounts.
- Drink water instead of sugary drinks.

The 2000-calorie-per-day diet is an average. You should follow a diet that takes into account your weight, age, and level of activity. Then you should adjust it to include

The Department of Health and Human Services (HHS) and the Department of Agriculture (USDA) jointly publish *Dietary Guidelines for Americans* every 5 years. Find this document on the Internet using the title as key words.

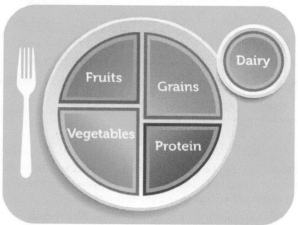

▶ **Figure 1** A daily food guide presented as a plate of food. More detailed recommendations in *Dietary Guidelines for Americans* are based on an individual's age, sex, activity level, and general health.

U.S. Department of Agriculture

fewer calories if you want to lose weight or more calories if you want to gain weight. Calorie intake calculators available on the Internet might be of some help.

A key recommendation for adults is to keep fat intake between 20% and 35% of all calories. Most fats should be made up of polyunsaturated and monounsaturated fatty acids. Only 7–10% of calories should come from saturated fats, and intake of synthetic *trans* fatty acids should be kept to a minimum. Also, the diet should contain less than 300 mg/day of cholesterol.

The "good" fats come from sources such as fish, nuts, and vegetable oils. Olive oil and canola oil are rich in monounsaturated fatty acids, and fish oils contain beneficial omega-3 fatty acids. A study of people living on the Greek island of Crete showed that they had an amazingly low incidence of cardiovascular disease, in spite of their diet, which averaged about 40% fat. This result is thought to be due to the high percentage of olive oil in their diet.

More than half the fats in the typical American diet are animal fats, and 70% of saturated fat comes from animal products. Saturated fats and cholesterol are implicated in artery clogging. They are found in animal products such as butter, lard, red meats, and fast-food hamburgers. We should choose meat, poultry, milk, and milk products that are lean, low in fat, or fat free.

Trans fats, produced when vegetable oils are hydrogenated (for example, to produce margarine), are high in *trans* fatty acids. As the name implies, *trans* fatty acids contain carbon-to-carbon double bonds with the *trans* configuration, so that they behave more like saturated fatty acids. Unless margarine has been specially treated to remove the *trans* fat, it has about the same health effects as butter.

The *percentage* of fat in the American diet has dropped from 40% in 1990 to about 34% today, but the absolute quantity of fat consumed has increased because Americans are eating more total calories. Also, 34% is an average figure; for some people, the percentage is as high as 45%.

A healthy diet can help us avoid disease. Harvard Medical School studies indicate that correct dietary choices, regular exercise, and avoidance of smoking would prevent about 82% of heart attacks, about 70% of strokes, over 90% of Type 2 diabetes, and over 70% of colon cancer. In contrast, the most effective drugs against cholesterol buildup, called *statins*, only reduce heart attacks by about 20–30%.

Nutrition and the Athlete

The recommended ranges for energy nutrients for most people are 20–35% of calories from fat, 45–65% of calories from carbohydrates, and 10–35% of calories from protein. (Each gram of carbohydrate or protein provides about 4 kcal; a gram of fat provides about 9 kcal.) Athletes generally need more calories because they expend more energy than the average sedentary individual. Those extra calories should come mainly from carbohydrates. Foods rich in carbohydrates, especially starches, are the preferred source of energy for the healthy body.

Fatty and protein-rich foods also supply calories, but protein metabolism produces more toxic wastes that tax the liver and kidneys. The pregame steak dinner consumed by some athletes in the past was based on a myth that protein builds muscle. It doesn't. Although athletes do need the **Dietary Reference Intake (DRI)**, quantity of protein (0.8 g protein/kg body weight), with few exceptions, they do not need an excess. DRIs are nutrient-based reference values established by the Food and Nutrition Board of the U.S. National Academy of Sciences for use in planning and assessing diets. They have replaced the Recommended Dietary Allowances (RDAs) that were published since 1941 by the National Academy of Sciences. Protein consumed in amounts greater than that needed for synthesis and repair of tissue only makes an athlete fatter (as a result of excessive calorie intake)—not more muscular.

Muscles are built through exercise, not through eating excess protein. When a muscle contracts against a resistance, an amino acid called *creatine* is released. Creatine stimulates production of the protein myosin, thus building more muscle tissue. If the exercise stops, the muscle begins to shrink after about two days. After about two months without exercise, muscle built through an exercise program is almost completely gone.

$$NH_2-\overset{\displaystyle\parallel}{\underset{\displaystyle NH}{C}}-\overset{}{\underset{\displaystyle CH_3}{N}}-CH_2COOH$$

Creatine

179

Self-Assessment Questions

1. The two major requirements for good health and fitness are
   a. food and entertainment
   b. food and medicine
   c. good nutrition and exercise
   d. nutrition and steroids

2. Which of the following has been shown to extend the life span of mice?
   a. amino acid supplements
   b. low-fat diets
   c. undereating
   d. vitamin supplements

3. The fats most detrimental to health are
   a. all unsaturated fats
   b. monounsaturated fats
   c. polyunsaturated fats
   d. saturated and *trans* fats

4. What is the maximum amount of fat that a diet providing 2200 kcal per day should include?
   a. 22 g
   b. 86 g
   c. 198 g
   d. 220 g

5. What is the maximum amount of saturated fat that a diet providing 2000 kcal per day should include?
   a. 11 g
   b. 22 g
   c. 50 g
   d. 200 g

6. Most of the saturated fats in our diets come from
   a. animal products
   b. cooking oils
   c. candies
   d. vegetables

7. Dietary Reference Intakes (DRIs) are nutrient-based reference values that are
   a. appropriate for undernourished and ill people
   b. guarantees of good health for everyone
   c. useful for planning and assessing diets
   d. minimum daily requirements

8. About how much protein does a 66-kg athlete require per day?
   a. 6.6 g
   b. 8.3 g
   c. 53 g
   d. 2.5 kg

Answers: 1, c; 2, c; 3, d; 4, b; 5, b; 6, a; 7, c; 8, c

2 Vitamins, Minerals, Fluids, and Electrolytes

Learning Objective ❯ Describe the dietary requirements for vitamins, minerals, and water.

Good nutrition requires sufficient carbohydrates, fats, and proteins; proper proportions of essential minerals and vitamins; and adequate water. *Vitamins* are organic substances that the human body needs but cannot manufacture in sufficient quantities. Unlike hormones and enzymes, which the body can synthesize, vitamins must be included in the diet. *Minerals*, inorganic elements that the body needs, must also be present in the diet. Table 1 lists DRIs of vitamins and minerals for young adult women and men. A more complete list for various ages and with a number of qualifications is available from the Food and Nutrition Board.

Many medical professionals say that vitamin and mineral supplements are unnecessary when the diet is well balanced and includes the DRI for each nutrient. However, for those who choose to take such supplements, reasonable doses of vitamins and minerals from tablets and capsules are not likely to cause harm and can be beneficial in some cases. For example, the body has an increased demand for vitamins and minerals during periods of rapid growth, during pregnancy and lactation, and during periods of trauma and recovery from disease. A study of people aged 65 years and older showed that a daily dose of 18 vitamins and minerals seems to strengthen the immune system. The number of infections in the study group was 50% less than that in a control group, which received no supplements.

The DRI values for vitamins and minerals set by the Food and Nutrition Board are quite modest, and they are readily supplied by any well-balanced diet. The DRI values for vitamins are the amounts that will prevent deficiency

Table 1	Dietary Reference Intakes of Vitamins and Minerals for Young Adults	
Nutrient	Females	Males
Vitamins		
Vitamin A	700 μg[a]	900 μg[a]
Vitamin C	75 mg[b]	90 mg[b]
Vitamin D	200 IU[c]	200 IU[c]
Vitamin E	30 IU	30 IU
Thiamine (B$_1$)	1.1 mg	1.2 mg
Riboflavin (B$_2$)	1.1 mg	1.3 mg
Niacin	14 mg	16 mg
Pyridoxine (B$_6$)	1.5 mg	1.7 mg
Cyanocobalamin (B$_{12}$)	3 μg	3 μg
Folacin (folic acid)	400 μg	400 μg
Pantothenic acid	5 mg	5 mg
Biotin	100–200 μg	100–200 μg
Minerals		
Calcium	1200 mg	1200 mg
Phosphorus	700 mg	700 mg
Magnesium	320 mg	420 mg
Iron	15 mg	10 mg
Zinc	12 mg	15 mg
Iodine	150 μg	150 μg
Fluoride	3 mg	4 mg
Selenium	55 μg	70 μg
Potassium	2 g	2 g

[a]To the extent that the vitamin A requirement is met by β-carotene, multiply these by 6.

[b]Smokers should add 35 mg.

[c]IU (for "international unit") is a measure of the biological activity of many vitamins, hormones, and drugs. See also the margin note.

diseases such as beriberi, pellagra, and scurvy. Some scientists believe that *optimum* intakes of some vitamins are somewhat higher than the DRI values. For example, they think that the current DRIs for vitamins C, D, and E are too low. If you eat a well-balanced diet and you are in good health, you probably do not need vitamin supplements. Small doses of vitamins are not toxic; some of the fat-soluble vitamins (A and D) are toxic in large doses, however, so caution is warranted.

Vitamin A is essential for good vision, bone development, and skin maintenance. There is some evidence that it may confer resistance to certain kinds of cancer. This may help to explain the anticancer activity that has been noted for cruciferous vegetables such as broccoli, cauliflower, Brussels sprouts, and cabbage. Most cruciferous vegetables are rich in β-carotene, which is converted to vitamin A in the body.

Vitamin A is a fat-soluble vitamin stored in the fatty tissues of the body and especially in the liver. Large doses can be toxic. The recommended upper limit for intake of vitamin A is 3000 μg/day. Studies in affluent countries have shown that ingesting vitamin A from supplements and in fortified foods at levels even slightly above the DRI leads to an increased risk of bone fractures later in life.

Larger quantities of β-carotene can be taken safely because excess β-carotene is not converted to vitamin A. It may have important functions other than as a precursor of vitamin A. Some nutritionists argue that β-carotene is needed in

1. Do large doses or special combinations of vitamins improve physical fitness? Vitamins should not be thought of as fuel, like food or water or oxygen. Although a daily vitamin tablet may be good insurance for many people, vitamin doses in large excess of the DRIs have not been found to have any special fitness benefit. Nor do special combinations provide improved stamina or strength. In fact, megadoses of some vitamins can have deleterious effects.

▲ Dorothy Crowfoot Hodgkin (1910–1994) used X-rays to determine the structures of several important organic compounds, including vitamin B₁₂, penicillin, and cholesterol.

People with low levels of vitamin C are more likely to develop cataracts and glaucoma, as well as gingivitis and periodontal disease. Some suggest that very large doses of vitamin C may cure or prevent colds, but there is little evidence for this.

2. Does vitamin C help to cure cancer?

A 2008 study by the National Institutes of Health found that *injected* vitamin C does appear to slow brain, ovarian, and pancreatic tumor growth in mice. However, these studies have not yet been extended to human beings. Also, the body precisely regulates the amount of vitamin C in the blood when it is taken orally, so oral doses of the vitamin do not provide these benefits.

An international unit (IU) measures the biological activity of many vitamins, hormones, and drugs. For each substance to which the IU applies, an international agreement specifies the biological effect expected from a dose of 1 IU. The IU is used to measure comparative potency of a substance such as a vitamin because the vitamin may exist in more than one form. For example, 1 IU of vitamin A is the biological equivalent of 0.3 μg retinol or 0.6 μg β-carotene.

quantities greater than those needed to meet the vitamin A requirement. However, a single ½-cup serving of carrots is sufficient to provide the DRI of vitamin A from β-carotene. Consuming foods that contain β-carotene is probably the safest way to obtain the proper quantity of vitamin A.

The B family of vitamins has eight members. Because they are all water soluble, excess intake is excreted in the urine. Little or no toxicity is connected with B vitamins, with the possible exceptions of vitamin B₆ and folic acid, both of which apparently can cause neurological damage in some people if taken in extremely large daily doses. Several B vitamins serve as coenzymes. In addition to preventing the skin lesions of pellagra, niacin (vitamin B₃) offers some relief from arthritis and helps in lowering the blood cholesterol level.

Vitamin B₆ (pyridoxine) has been found to help people with arthritis by shrinking the connective tissue membranes that line the joints. Vitamin B₆ is a coenzyme for more than 100 different enzymes.

Vitamin B₁₂ (cyanocobalamin) is not found in plants, and vegetarians are apt to be deficient in this vitamin. That deficiency can lead to pernicious anemia. The molecular formula of vitamin B₁₂ is $C_{63}H_{88}CoN_{14}O_{14}P$, giving it a molecular mass of 1355.38 u. Its very complicated structure was determined by Dorothy Hodgkin of Oxford University in 1956 using X-ray crystallography, a technique in which an X-ray beam is used to bombard a crystal. The beam is scattered in a definite pattern determined by the crystal structure. No one had ever attempted to establish the structure of a molecule of this size and complexity before. Hodgkin received the 1964 Nobel Prize in Chemistry for this work.

Another B vitamin is folic acid, which is critical in the development of the nervous system of a fetus. Its presence in a pregnant woman's diet prevents spina bifida in her baby. Folic acid also helps prevent cardiovascular disease. An upper limit of 1000 μg has been set; more than that can cause nerve damage.

Vitamin C is ascorbic acid, the component in citrus fruits that combats scurvy. About 60–80 mg daily will prevent scurvy, but vitamin C does more than that. It promotes the healing of wounds, burns, and lesions such as gastric ulcers. It also seems to play an important role in maintaining collagen, the body's major structural protein. Like vitamin E, it is an antioxidant, and these two vitamins, along with β-carotene, are included in many antioxidant formulations. Antioxidants may act as anticarcinogens. About 200 mg of vitamin C per day is probably optimal, and an upper limit of 2000 mg/day has been set.

Vitamin C seems to be essential for efficient functioning of the immune system. *Interferons*, large molecules formed by the action of viruses on their host cells, are agents in the immune system. By producing an interferon, one virus can interfere with the growth of another. An increased level of vitamin C has been shown to increase the body's production of interferons.

Vitamin D is a steroid hormone that protects children against rickets. It promotes the absorption of calcium and phosphorus from foods to produce and maintain healthy bones. Too much vitamin D can lead to excessive calcium and phosphorus absorption, with subsequent formation of calcium deposits in various soft body tissues, including those of the heart. The DRI for vitamin D increases with age, from 200 international units (IU) for adults aged 20–50 to reaching 600 IU for those over 70. The recommended upper limit is 2000 IU.

Vitamin E is a mixture of *tocopherols*, phenols with hydrocarbon side chains. Its antioxidant activity may have value in maintaining the cardiovascular system, and it has been used to treat coronary heart disease, angina, rheumatic heart disease, high blood pressure, arteriosclerosis, varicose veins, and a number of other cardiovascular problems. As an antioxidant, vitamin E can inactivate free radicals. It is generally believed that much of the physiological damage from aging is a result of the production of free radicals. Indeed, vitamin E has been called the "antiaging vitamin." However, studies of these effects are often contradictory and far from conclusive. Vitamin E is also an anticoagulant that has been useful in preventing blood clots after surgery.

Rats deprived of vitamin E become sterile. Vitamin E deficiency can also lead to muscular dystrophy, a disease of the skeletal muscles. A lack of vitamin E can lead to a deficiency in vitamin A. This occurs because vitamin A can be oxidized to an inactive form when vitamin E is not present to act as an antioxidant. Vitamin E also collaborates with vitamin C in protecting blood vessels and other tissues against oxidation. Vitamin E is the fat-soluble antioxidant vitamin, and vitamin C the water-soluble one. Oxidation of unsaturated fatty acids in cell membranes can be prevented or reversed by vitamin E, which is itself oxidized in the process. Vitamin C can then restore vitamin E to its unoxidized form. The upper limit for vitamin E is 800 IU/day or 400 IU/day, depending on side effects. And, according to a study published in October 2011, even 400 IU/day may increase the risk of prostate cancer in men.

LDL cholesterol is oxidized before it is deposited in arteries, and vitamin E prevents the oxidation of cholesterol. Some think this is the mechanism by which vitamin E helps to protect against cardiovascular disease.

Body Fluids and Electrolytes

Another aspect of the relationship of chemistry and nutrition is the balance between fluid intake and electrolyte intake. An **electrolyte** is a substance that conducts electricity when dissolved in water. In the body, electrolytes are ions required by cells to maintain their internal and external electric charge and thus control the flow of water molecules across the cell membrane. The main electrolytes are sodium ions (Na^+), potassium ions (K^+), and chloride ions (Cl^-). Others include calcium ions (Ca^{2+}), magnesium ions (Mg^{2+}), sulfate ions (SO_4^{2-}), hydrogen phosphate ions (HPO_4^{2-}), and bicarbonate ions (HCO_3^-).

Water is an essential nutrient, a fact obvious to anyone who has been deprived of it. Many people seem to prefer to meet the body's need for water by consuming soft drinks, coffee, beer, fruit juice, energy drinks, and other beverages. Some of these beverages actually impair the body's use of the water they contain. Alcoholic drinks promote water loss by blocking the action of *antidiuretic hormone* (*ADH*), also known as *vasopressin*. Caffeine has a diuretic effect on the kidneys, promoting urine formation and consequent water loss.

The best way to replace water lost through respiration, sweat, tears, and urination is to drink water. Unfortunately, thirst is often a *delayed* response to water loss, and it may be masked by such symptoms of dehydration as exhaustion, confusion, headache, and nausea. Sweat is about 99% water, but a liter of sweat typically contains $1.15\,g\,Na^+$, $1.48\,g\,Cl^-$, $0.02\,g\,Ca^{2+}$, $0.23\,g\,K^+$, $0.05\,g\,Mg^{2+}$, and minute amounts of urea, lactic acid, and body oils. Most people consume too much sodium chloride (Na^+ and Cl^-), and only traces of the other electrolytes are lost. Thus, it makes the most sense to replace the water component of lost sweat with plain water.

Commercial beverages such as sports drinks, energy drinks, vitamin waters, protein waters, and fitness waters usually contain one or more ingredients that are more effective as advertising gimmicks than as aids to athletic performance. Sports drinks usually contain sweeteners and electrolytes. Energy drinks usually have sugars and often contain caffeine as a mild stimulant. The ingredients in vitamin waters and protein waters are obvious, but there are far better and less expensive sources of both. Although these drinks are quite popular with both serious and weekend athletes, they are so concentrated (a hazard that can lead to diarrhea) that they are of marginal value except for endurance athletes (Figure 2).

How do you know if you are drinking enough water and are in a proper state of hydration? The urine is a good indicator of hydration. When you are properly hydrated, your urine is clear and almost colorless. When you are dehydrated, your urine gets cloudy or dark because your kidneys are trying to conserve water so as to keep the blood volume from shrinking and to prevent shock.

Dehydration can be quite serious, even deadly. We become thirsty when total body fluid volume decreases by 0.5–1.0%. Beyond that, things get worse

▲ **Figure 2** The best replacement for fluids lost during exercise generally is plain water. Sports drinks help little, except when engaging in endurance activities lasting for 2 hr or more. At that point, carbohydrates in the drinks delay the onset of exhaustion by a few minutes.

Christopher Edwin Nuzzaco/Shutterstock

Improving Athletic Performance through Chemistry

Chemistry has transformed athletic performance in recent decades. New materials have been used to make protective gear such as plastic helmets and foam padding for football, ice hockey, skateboarding, and other sports. Improved equipment has changed the nature of most sports events. Baseball, football, and other sports are quite different when played on artificial turf or under a dome than when played outdoors on grass. Traction changes, the ball bounces differently, and so on. Skateboards of the 1950s consisted of metal roller-skate wheels on a flat wooden board. Today's skateboards have wide urethane wheels, specially shaped composite-construction boards, and shock-absorbing wheel mounts that make incredible stunts almost commonplace. Several decades ago, running shoes had thin leather soles and little or no foot support. Now these shoes have thick, shock-absorbing soles and built-in support for arches and ankles.

A3390 Kay Nietfeld Deutsch Presse Agentur/Newscom

▲ Sometimes technology can be *too* beneficial. Specially designed full-length swimsuits dramatically reduce drag. So many swimming world records were set immediately afterward that the suits were banned in 2010.

Biochemistry has brought a better understanding of the human body and the way it works. Chemistry has helped to provide better nutrition. Today's athletes are bigger, faster, and stronger than their predecessors. More than 30 new world records were set at the 2008 Olympic Games in Beijing.

(Table 2). Muscles tire and cramp. Dizziness and fainting may follow, and brain cells shrink, resulting in mental confusion. Finally, the heat regulatory system fails, causing *heat stroke*, which can be fatal without prompt medical attention.

Table 2	Effects of Varying Degrees of Dehydration
Percentage of Body Weight Lost as Sweat	**Physiological Effect**
2%	Performance impaired
4%	Muscular work capacity declines
5%	Heat exhaustion
7%	Hallucinations
10%	Circulatory collapse and heat stroke

Self-Assessment Questions

1. Which of the following cannot be synthesized by the body and therefore must be included in the diet?
   a. enzymes
   b. hormones
   c. unsaturated fats
   d. vitamins

2. Which of the following is a precursor of vitamin A?
   a. β-carotene
   b. cholesterol
   c. pyridoxine
   d. tryptophan

3. For which of the following are large doses most likely to be harmful?
   a. β-carotene
   b. niacin
   c. vitamin A
   d. vitamin C

4. All B vitamins
   a. are synthetic
   b. are water soluble
   c. have the same functional group
   d. have molecular masses above 1000 u

5. Vitamin C is a(n)
   a. antimetabolite
   c. oxidizing agent
   b. fat-soluble antioxidant
   d. water-soluble antioxidant

6. The major electrolytes in body fluids are
   a. Ca^{2+}, Fe^{2+}, and Cl^-
   c. Na^+, K^+, and Cl^-
   b. Ca^{2+}, Na^+, and $HSO4^-$
   d. Na^+, K^+, and HCO_3^-

7. The best replacement for water lost except in prolonged exercise is
   a. beer   **b.** non-fat milk   **c.** plain water   **d.** soft drinks

8. What is the minimal percentage of body weight lost in fluids that can cause reduced performance?
   a. 2%   **b.** 4%   **c.** 6%   **d.** 10%

Answers: 1, d; 2, a; 3, c; 4, b; 5, d; 6, c; 7, c; 8, a

3 Weight Loss: Diets and Exercise

Learning Objectives ❯ Explain how weight is lost through diet and exercise.
❯ Calculate weight loss due to calorie reduction and to exercise.

With obesity an epidemic and so many people overweight, dieting is a major U.S. industry. It is possible to lose weight through dieting alone, but it isn't easy. One pound of adipose (fatty) tissue stores about 3500 kcal of energy. If you reduce your intake by 100 kcal/day and keep your activity level constant, you will burn off a pound of fat in 35 days. Unfortunately, people are seldom patient enough, and they resort to more stringent diets. To achieve their goals more rapidly, they exclude certain foods and reduce the amounts of others. Such diets can be harmful. Diets with fewer than 1200 kcal/day are likely to be deficient in necessary nutrients, particularly in B vitamins and iron. Further, dieting slows down metabolism. Weight lost through dieting is quickly regained when the dieter resumes old eating habits.

Example 1   Weight Loss through Dieting

If you ordinarily expend 2000 kcal/day and you go on a diet limited to 1500 kcal/day, about how long will it take to lose 1.0 lb of fat?

Solution
You will use 2000 − 1500 = 500 kcal/day more than you consume. There are about 3500 kcal in 1.0 lb of fat, so it will take

$$3500 \text{ kcal} \times \frac{1 \text{ day}}{500 \text{ kcal}} = 7 \text{ days}$$

Keep in mind, however, that your weight loss will not be all fat. You will probably lose more than 1 lb, but it will be mostly water with some protein and a little glycogen.

■ EXERCISE 1A
A person who expends 1800 kcal/day goes on a diet limited to 1200 kcal/day without a change in activities. Estimate how much fat she will lose if she stays on this diet for 3 weeks.

■ EXERCISE 1B
A person who expends 2200 kcal/day goes on a diet limited to 1800 kcal/day and adds exercise activities that use 220 kcal/day. Estimate how much fat he will lose if he stays on this program for 6 weeks.

Biochemistry of Hunger

Scientists are just beginning to understand the complex biochemistry of hunger mechanisms. Several molecules that regulate body weight have been identified. Some determine whether we want to eat now or stop eating. Others control long-term fat balance. Much of what we now know is disappointing for people who want to lose weight: The hunger mechanisms protect against weight loss and favor weight gain.

Two peptide hormones, known as *ghrelin* and *peptide YY (PYY)*, are produced by the digestive tract and are linked to short-term eating behaviors. Ghrelin, a modified peptide, is an appetite stimulant produced by the stomach. PYY acts as an appetite suppressant. Studies at Imperial College, London, found that people ate about 30% less after they were given a dose of PYY. The research also found that obese people had lower natural levels of PYY, which may explain why these people feel hungrier and overeat.

The hormone insulin and a substance called *leptin*, which is produced by fat cells, determine longer-term weight balance. When insulin levels go up, glucose levels go down, and we experience hunger. Conversely, when glucose levels are high, the activity of brain cells sensitive to glucose is lessened, and we feel satiated.

Leptin, a protein consisting of 146 amino-acid units, is produced by fat cells. It causes weight loss in mice by decreasing their appetite and increasing their metabolic rates. Levels of leptin tell the hypothalamus (a regulatory center in the brain) how much fat is in the body. Humans also produce leptin, and scientists hoped it would be the route to a cure for the ever-growing obesity problem. That hope is largely unrealized. Only a few cases of severe human obesity, caused by defects in leptin production, have been helped by leptin treatment. As it turns out, most obese humans have *higher* than normal blood levels of leptin and are resistant to its actions. Leptin's main role seems to be to protect against weight loss in times of scarcity rather than against weight gain in times of plentiful food.

Other substances involved in weight control include *cholecystokinin (CCK)*, a peptide formed in the intestine that signals that we have eaten enough food and a class of compounds called *melanocortins*, which act on the brain to regulate food intake.

It remains to be seen whether this new knowledge about the body's weight-control systems will pay off in better obesity treatments. A complication is that many social factors are also involved in eating behavior. Some people are motivated by environmental cues to eat. A family gathering, the sight or smell of food, and a stressful situation can all trigger the hunger mechanism.

Crash Diets: Quick = Quack

Any weight-loss program that promises a loss of more than a pound or two a week is likely to be dangerous quackery. Most quick-weight-loss diets depend on factors other than fat metabolism to hook prospective customers. The diets often include a **diuretic**, such as caffeine, to increase the output of urine. Weight loss is water loss, and that weight is regained when the body is rehydrated.

Other quick-weight-loss diets depend on depleting the body's stores of glycogen. On a low-carbohydrate diet, the body draws on its glycogen reserves, depleting them in about 24 hours. Recall that glycogen is a polymer of glucose. Glycogen molecules have lots of hydroxyl ($-$OH) groups that can form hydrogen bonds to water molecules. We can store at most about 1 lb of glycogen. Each pound of glycogen carries about 3 lb of water held to it by these hydrogen bonds. Depleting the pound of glycogen results in a weight loss of about 4 lb (1 lb glycogen + 3 lb water). No fat is lost, and the weight is quickly regained when the dieter resumes eating carbohydrates.

If your normal energy expenditure is 2400 kcal/day, the most fat you can lose by *total fasting* for a day is 0.69 lb (2400 kcal/day divided by 3500 kcal/lb of adipose tissue). This assumes that your body burns nothing but fat—which does not occur. The brain runs on glucose, and if that glucose isn't supplied in the diet, it is obtained from protein. Any diet that restricts carbohydrate intake results in a loss of

3. Which diet pill will help me lose the most weight? Most of the so-called diet pills on the market are actually classified as *dietary supplements* and have not been demonstrated to aid in weight loss. A few diet aids have limited use, but most of those are prescription drugs. *Orlistat* (Alli®) was approved for over-the-counter sales in 2007. It has been tested and shown to reduce the amount of fat absorbed from food, but it may have unpleasant side effects including diarrhea.

muscle mass as well as fat. When you gain the weight back (as 90% of all dieters do), you gain mostly fat. People who diet without exercising will replace metabolically active tissue (muscle) with inactive fat when they gain back the lost weight. Weight loss becomes harder with each subsequent attempted diet.

Many crash diets are also deficient in minerals such as iron, calcium, and potassium. A deficiency of these minerals can disrupt nerve-impulse transmissions to muscles, which impairs athletic performance. Nerve-impulse transmission to vital organs may also be impaired in cases of severe restriction, and death can result from cardiac arrest.

Exercise for Weight Loss

Studies consistently show that people who exercise regularly live longer. They are sick less often and have fewer signs of depression. They can move faster, and they have stronger bones and muscles. Although there are dozens of good reasons for regular exercise, many people begin exercise programs for one simple reason: They want to lose weight.

People who do not increase their food intake when they begin an exercise program lose weight. Contrary to a common myth, exercise (for up to an hour a day) does not cause an increase in appetite. Most of the weight loss from exercise results from an increase in metabolic rate during the activity, but the increased metabolic rate continues for several hours after completion of the exercise. Exercise helps us maintain both fitness and proper body weight.

Example 2	Weight Loss through Exercise

A 135-lb person doing high-impact aerobics burns about 6.9 kcal/min. How long does a person have to do such exercise to lose 1.0 lb of adipose (fat) tissue?

Solution
One pound of adipose tissue stores 3500 kcal of energy. To burn it at 6.9 kcal/min requires

$$3500 \text{ kcal} \times \frac{1 \text{ min}}{6.9 \text{ kcal}} = 500 \text{ min}$$

It takes about 500 min (more than 8 hr) to burn 1 lb of fat, even doing high-impact aerobics.

■ EXERCISE 2A
Walking a mile uses about 100 kcal. About how far do you have to walk to burn 1.0 lb of fat?

■ EXERCISE 2B
A moderately active person can calculate the calories needed each day to maintain a desired weight by multiplying the desired weight (in pounds) by 15 kcal/lb. How many calories per day does such a person need to maintain a weight of 180 lb?

The most sensible approach to weight loss is to adhere to a balanced low-calorie diet that meets the DRI for essential nutrients and to engage in a reasonable, consistent, individualized exercise program. This approach applies the principles of weight loss by decreasing intake and increasing output.

Weight loss or gain is based on the law of conservation of energy. When we take in more calories than we use up, the excess calories are stored as fat. When we take in fewer calories than we need for our activities, our bodies burn some of the stored fat to make up for the deficit. One pound of adipose tissue requires 200 mi of blood capillaries to serve its cells. Excess fat therefore puts extra strain on the heart.

There is little evidence that commercial weight-loss programs are effective in helping people drop excess pounds and keep them off. Almost no rigorous studies of the programs have been carried out, and U.S. Federal Trade Commission officials say that companies are unwilling to conduct such studies.

4. If I stop exercising, will the muscle I've developed turn to fat? Muscle does not turn into fat, although without regular exercise muscles become flabby and will lose mass.

On a weight-loss diet (without exercise), about 65% of the weight lost is fat and about 11% is protein (muscle tissue). The rest is water and a little glycogen.

Fad Diets

Weight loss diets are often lacking in balanced nutrition and can be harmful to one's health. In the more extreme low-carbohydrate diets, ketosis is deliberately induced, and possible side effects include depression and lethargy. In the early stages of a diet deficient in carbohydrates, the body converts amino acids to glucose that the brain requires. If there are enough adequate proteins in the diet, tissue proteins are spared.

Even low-carbohydrate diets high in adequate proteins are hard on the body, which must rid itself of the nitrogen compounds—ammonia and urea—formed by the breakdown of proteins. This puts an increased stress on the liver, where the waste products are formed, and on the kidneys, where they are excreted.

Contrary to a popular notion, fasting does not "cleanse" the body. Indeed, quite the reverse occurs. A shift to fat metabolism produces ketone bodies, and protein breakdown produces ammonia, urea, and other wastes. You can lose weight by fasting, but the process should be carefully monitored by a physician.

Self-Assessment Questions

1. How many kilocalories of energy are stored in 1.0 lb of adipose tissue?
   a. 454 kcal   b. 1000 kcal   c. 3500 kcal   d. 10,000 kcal

2. To lose 1.0 lb per week, how many more kilocalories must you burn each day than you take in?
   a. 100   b. 300   c. 500   d. 1000

3. Which of the following hormones acts as an appetite stimulant?
   a. ADH   b. ghrelin   c. leptin   d. PYY

4. Blood glucose levels are lowered by the hormone
   a. cholecystokinin   b. glucagon   c. insulin   d. oxytocin

5. Which of the following seems to tell the brain it is time to stop eating?
   a. cholecystokinin (CCK)   b. ghrelin
   c. leptin   d. oxytocin

6. About how much glycogen can the adult body store?
   a. 100 g   b. 1 lb
   c. 4 lb   d. an almost unlimited quantity

7. Crash diets
   a. are a good way to lose weight and keep it off
   b. depend on glycogen depletion for quick weight loss
   c. result in a decrease in the number of fat cells
   d. lead to a depletion of adipose tissue

Answers: 1. c; 2. c; 3. b; 4. c; 5. a; 6. b; 7. b

Everett Collection

▲ It DOES Matter!

In Europe during the Middle Ages—and even later—people accused of crimes were often tried by some kind of ordeal. In trial by water, the innocent sank and the guilty floated. Suspected witches were tied hand to foot and thrown into the water. The guilty floated, were fished out, dried off, and executed. In those days, body density was *really*

4 Measuring Fitness

Learning Objectives   ❯ Describe several ways to measure fitness. ❯ Calculate BMI values.

Measuring fitness is basically the same as measuring fatness. How much fat is enough? The male body requires about 3% body fat, and the average female body needs 10–12%. It is not easy to measure percent body fat accurately. Weight alone does not indicate degree of fitness. A tall 200-lb man may be much more fit than a 160-lb man with a smaller frame. Skinfold calipers are sometimes used, but they are quite inaccurate and measure water retention as well as fat.

One way to estimate body fat is by measuring a person's density. Mass is determined by weighing, and volume is calculated with the help of a dunk tank like the one shown in Figure 3. The difference between a person's weight in air and when submerged in water corresponds to the *mass* of the displaced water. When this mass is divided by the density of water and then corrected for air in the lungs, it gives a reasonable value for the person's volume. Mass divided by volume yields the person's density, although results can vary with the amount of air in the lungs. Fat is less dense (0.903 g/mL) than the water (1.00 g/mL) that makes up most of the body's mass. The higher the proportion of body fat a person has, the lower the density and the more buoyant that person is in water.

A simpler way to estimate degree of fatness is by measuring the waist and the hips. The waist should be measured at the narrowest point and the hips should be measured where the circumference is the largest. The waist measurement should then be divided by the hip measurement. This ratio should be less than 1 for men and should be 0.8 or less for women. (Because the units cancel out, the measurements can be made in inches or centimeters, as long as the same units are used for both.)

Some modern scales provide a measure of body fat content, using *bioelectric impedance analysis*. The person stands on the scale in bare feet, and a small electric current is sent through the body. Fat has greater impedance (resistance to varying current) than does muscle. By measuring the impedance of the body, the percentage of body fat can be calculated based on height and weight. However, there are many other variables, such as bone density, water content, and location of fat. Although such scales are not very accurate, they may be useful for monitoring *changes* in body fat content.

Body Mass Index

Body mass index (BMI) is a commonly used measure of fatness. It is defined as weight (in kilograms) divided by the square of the height (in meters). For a person who is 1.6 m tall and weighs 62 kg, the body mass index is $62/(1.6)^2 = 24$. A BMI below 18.5 indicates that a person is underweight. A BMI from 25 to 29.9 indicates that a person is overweight, and a BMI of 30 or more indicates obesity. When measurements are in pounds and inches, the equation is

$$\text{BMI} = \frac{705 \times \text{body weight (lb)}}{\left[\text{height (in.)}\right]^2}$$

In other words, a person who is 5 ft 10 in. tall (70 in.) and weighs 140 lb has a BMI of

$$\frac{705 \times 140}{70 \times 70} = 20$$

which is within the ideal range.

David Young-Wolff/PhotoEdit

▲ **Figure 3** When submerged in water, a body displaces its own volume of water. The difference between a person's weight in air and when submerged in water corresponds to the *mass* of the displaced water. Because the density of water is 1.00 g/mL, the mass of water displaced (in grams) equals the person's volume (in milliliters).

Q: *What is the volume, in liters, of a person who displaces 48.5 kg of water?*

Example 3   Body Mass Index

What is the BMI for a person who is 6 ft 1 in. tall and weighs 205 lb?

Solution
The person's height is $(6 \times 12) + 1 = 72 + 1 = 73$ in.

$$\text{BMI} = \frac{705 \times 205}{73 \times 73} = 27$$

The body mass index is 27.

GREEN CHEMISTRY

Doris Lewis, *Suffolk University*

Your Fitness Benefits the Planet

How do you get to class each day? Do you walk, bike, drive, or take public transportation? You might be surprised to learn that green chemistry principles can apply to your personal transportation.

According to green chemistry ideals, we should limit our use of the fossil fuels that support most transport, such as gasoline, because they are nonrenewable resources (Principle 7). Further, burning of these materials produces greenhouse gases including CO_2. Principle 3 suggests that use of fossil fuels should be reduced because this process releases harmful substances to the environment, including gases that have been linked to destructive climate change. As shown in the equation, the combustion of 1 mol of octane, a component of gasoline, releases 8 mol of CO_2.

Although the chemical reactions that power your body when you walk or bike produce CO_2, they are based on renewable fuels—the carbohydrates in your food. The reaction of carbohydrates with oxygen powers your body and leads to CO_2 as a byproduct. The plants that produced the carbohydrates you eat incorporated CO_2 from the atmosphere through photosynthesis and thus decreased the amount of this greenhouse gas. Your energy source, therefore, is carbon-neutral because the carbon dioxide that you produce is balanced by the carbon dioxide used up to make the fuel your body uses. Because the plants you consume use the energy of the Sun to power photosynthesis, it is fair to say that you, too, are powered by renewable solar energy. Although the carbon compounds in fossil fuels came originally from plants, those plants died millions of years ago, so their removal of CO_2 does not help our atmosphere today.

Unlike internal combustion engines that burn at high temperatures, your body is able to fuel your motion at the temperature of 98.6 °F, or 37.0 °C. Therefore, walking or biking is consistent with Principle 6, design for energy efficiency. How does your body perform this feat? Its energy reactions involve enzymes, or selective biochemical catalysts, as prescribed by Principle 9.

Walking and biking are healthier not only for the planet but also for you. Studies have shown that an average of two or more walking trips per week results in an yearly projected weight loss of 0.9–1.8 lb—approximately the yearly weight gain of the average American. A 150-lb person walking only 20 min at 4 mi/h burns 114 calories that would be deposited as fat were the same amount of time spent sitting in a car (Section 3). Walking has been shown to provide protection from heart attack, stroke,

and diabetes. It also triggers release of endorphins, the body's stress-relieving and mood-lifting chemicals (Section 6).

Prefer biking to walking? Riding a bicycle instead of driving a car saves an average of $8000 per year, and biking 10 mi per day burns 110,000 kcal a year. This choice can keep off more than 30 lb of fat each year and save a whopping 3500 lb of greenhouse gas emissions. Bike riders have banded together to promote commuting by bike and safer bike routes and to sponsor Bike-to-Work days in many cities. Riding a bike to work can change your entire day. You arrive at work refreshed and less stressed.

Universities in Boston co-sponsor "Hub on Wheels," a city-wide bike ride and festival, aided by student activists in environmental clubs who promote bikes as alternative transportation. What does your college do to encourage biking? How are students and student groups involved? Students at Suffolk University created a YouTube video as a service project to promote biking.

On Earth Day 2010, the U.S. Department of Transportation released a study that recommends improved biking and walking transport networks as a way of reducing greenhouse emissions. Simply making it easier to walk or bike would reduce greenhouse gases by 0.2–0.6% by 2030, at a relatively low cost (less than $200 per ton of CO_2). Since walking or biking is less expensive than other modes of transportation, there would be a net overall savings. Green chemistry can improve your health and the planet's health, while saving us money.

▲ Bicycling to work or school is an all-win proposition. Even an elaborate bicycle is much less expensive than a car. Bicycling provides healthy exercise, it does not generate pollution, and operating cost is nil.

■ **EXERCISE 3A**
What is the BMI for a person who is 5.0 ft tall and weighs 120 lb?

■ **EXERCISE 3B**
What is the maximum weight, in pounds, that a person who is 5 ft 10 in. tall can maintain and have a BMI that does not exceed 25.0?

V_{O_2} max: A Measure of Fitness

As we increase exercise intensity, our uptake of oxygen must also increase. For example, the faster we run, the more oxygen we need to sustain the pace. However, the body reaches a point at which it simply cannot increase the amount of oxygen it consumes even if the intensity of exercise increases. The V_{O_2} max is the maximum amount (in milliliters per kilogram of body weight) of oxygen that a person can use in 1 minute.

V_{O_2} max is therefore a measure of fitness. The higher the V_{O_2} max, the greater is an athlete's fitness. A person with a high V_{O_2} max can exercise more intensely than those who are less fit. The V_{O_2} max can be increased by working out at an intensity that raises the heart rate to 65–85% of its maximum for at least 20 minutes three to five times a week. Limitations on V_{O_2} max include the ability of muscle cells to use oxygen in metabolizing fuels and the ability of the cardiovascular system and lungs to transport oxygen to the muscles.

Direct testing of V_{O_2} max requires expensive equipment, including a gas analyzer to measure O_2 taken in and exhaled. Percent V_{O_2} max can be estimated indirectly from percent maximum heart rate (%MHR), where MHR is the highest number of beats the heart makes in a minute of exercising.

$$\%MHR = (0.64 \times \%V_{O_2} max) + 37$$

The relationship holds quite well for both males and females of all ages and activity levels. For example, 80% MHR corresponds to a $\%V_{O_2}$ max of

$$80 = (0.64 \times \%V_{O_2} max) + 37$$

$$\%V_{O_2} max = 67$$

Equations for determining MHR values and tables for evaluating fitness levels can be found in exercise physiology textbooks and on the Internet (see Collaborative Group Project 2).

▲ **It DOES Matter!**
Extreme-endurance athletes, such as triathletes and ultramarathoners, may need a bit more protein than the DRI. However, nearly all Americans eat 50% more protein than they need, so even these athletes seldom need protein supplements. Weightlifters and bodybuilders need no extra protein.

Self-Assessment Questions

1. Body mass index (BMI) is calculated as
   a. percentage of body fat × waist circumference (in.)
   b. (height ÷ weight) × 100
   c. [705 × weight (lb)] ÷ [height (in.)]
   d. weight (kg) ÷ [height (m)]^2

2. A person with a BMI of 35 is
   a. obese
   b. overweight but not obese
   c. quite fit
   d. underweight

3. The maximum amount of oxygen used in a minute of exercise is the
   a. aerobic threshold
   b. lactate threshold
   c. oxygen debt
   d. V_{O_2} max

Answers: 1, d; 2, a; 3, d

5 Some Muscular Chemistry

Learning Objectives   ❯ Differentiate between aerobic exercise and anaerobic exercise, and describe the chemistry that occurs during each. ❯ Describe how muscles are built and how they work.

The human body has about 600 muscles. Exercise makes these muscles larger, more flexible, and more efficient in their use of oxygen. Exercise strengthens the heart because the heart is an organ comprised mainly of muscle. With regular exercise, resting pulse and blood pressure usually decline. A person who exercises regularly is able to do more physical work with less strain. Exercise is an art, but it is also increasingly a science—a science in which chemistry plays a vital role.

Energy for Muscle Contraction: ATP

When cells metabolize glucose or fatty acids, only part of the chemical energy in these substances is converted to heat. Some of the energy is stored in the high-energy phosphate bonds of adenosine triphosphate (ATP) molecules.

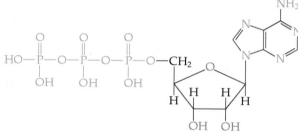

Adenosine triphosphate

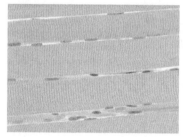

Actin   Myosin

Extended muscle fibers

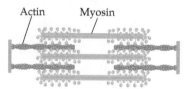

Resting fibers

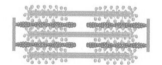

Partially contracted fibers
(b)

▲ **Figure 4** Skeletal muscle tissue has a banded, or *striated*, appearance, shown here in a micrograph at 180× magnification (a). The diagram of the actomyosin complex in muscle (b) shows extended muscle fibers (top), resting fibers (middle), and partially contracted fibers (bottom).

Stimulation of muscles causes them to contract. This contraction is *work*, and it requires energy that the muscles get from the molecules of ATP. The energy stored in ATP powers the physical movement of muscle tissue. Two proteins, actin and myosin, play important roles in this process. Together they form a loose complex called *actomyosin*, the contractile protein that makes up muscles (Figure 4).

When ATP is added to actomyosin in the laboratory, the protein fibers contract. Myosins turn the chemical energy of ATP into motion. Myosin molecules "walk" along the actin filaments. It takes about 2×10^{12} myosin molecules acting in unison in the arm to lift a 40-g spoonful of sugar. Not only does myosin serve as part of the structural complex in muscles, it also acts as an enzyme for the removal of a phosphate group from ATP. Thus, it is directly involved in liberating the energy required for muscle contraction.

In a resting person, muscle activity (including that of the heart muscle) accounts for only about 15–30% of the body's energy requirements. Other activities, such as cell repair, transmission of nerve impulses, and maintenance of body temperature, account for the remaining energy needs. During intense physical activity, the energy requirements of muscle may be more than 200 times the resting level.

Aerobic Exercise: Plenty of Oxygen

The ATP in muscle tissue is sufficient for activities lasting for at most a few seconds. Fortunately, muscles have a more extensive energy supply in the form of glycogen, a starchlike form of dietary carbohydrate that has been ingested, digested to glucose, absorbed, and stored.

When muscle contraction begins, glycogen is converted to pyruvic acid by muscle cells, in a series of steps.

$$(C_6H_{10}O_5)_n \longrightarrow 2n \; CH_3\overset{O}{\overset{\|}{C}}-\overset{O}{\overset{\|}{C}}OH$$

Glycogen   Pyruvic acid

◀ **Figure 5** Aerobic exercise is performed at a pace that allows us to get enough oxygen to our muscle cells to oxidize pyruvic acid to carbon dioxide and water. Aerobic dance is a popular form of aerobic exercise.

Because acids in biological systems are usually ionized at the pH of cellular fluids, biochemists usually refer to them by the names of their anions. For example, lactic acid becomes lactate, and pyruvic acid becomes pyruvate.

Then, if sufficient oxygen is readily available, the pyruvic acid is oxidized to carbon dioxide and water in another series of steps.

$$2\,CH_3\overset{O}{\underset{\|}{C}}-\overset{O}{\underset{\|}{C}}OH + 5\,O_2 \longrightarrow 6\,CO_2 + 4\,H_2O$$

Muscle contractions that occur under these circumstances—that is, in the presence of oxygen—constitute **aerobic exercise** (Figure 5).

Anaerobic Exercise and Oxygen Debt

When sufficient oxygen is not available, pyruvic acid is reduced to lactic acid.

$$CH_3COCOOH + [2\,H] \longrightarrow CH_3CHOHCOOH$$

[2 H] represents hydrogen atoms from one of several biochemical reducing agents.

If **anaerobic exercise** (muscle activity with insufficient oxygen) persists, an excess of lactic acid builds up in the muscle cells. This lactic acid ionizes, forming lactate ions and hydronium ions.

$$CH_3CHOHCOOH + H_2O \longrightarrow CH_3CHOHCOO^- + H_3O^+$$

Muscle fatigue correlates well with lactate levels, which were long thought to be its cause. However, studies have shown that muscle tiredness is related to calcium ion flow. Ordinarily, muscle contractions are managed by the ebb and flow of Ca^{2+} ions. As muscles grow tired, tiny channels in muscle cells start leaking Ca^{2+}, which weakens contractions. At the same time, the leaked Ca^{2+} ions stimulate an enzyme that breaks down muscle fibers, further contributing to the muscle fatigue. Levels of several other products of muscle metabolism, including phosphocreatine (the phosphorylated form of creatine), ATP, and ions such as Na^+, K^+, and $H_2PO_4^-$, change during fatigue. These changes may also contribute to muscle tiredness.

$$H_2O_3PNH-\underset{\underset{NH}{\|}}{C}-\underset{\underset{CH_3}{|}}{N}-CH_2COOH$$

Phosphocreatine

▲ **Figure 6** After a race, the metabolism that fueled the effort continues. The athlete gulps air to repay her oxygen debt.

Well-trained athletes can continue for a while after muscle fatigue sets in, but most people quit. At this point, the **oxygen debt** starts to be repaid (Figure 6). After exercise ends, the cells' demand for oxygen decreases, making more oxygen available to oxidize the lactic acid resulting from anaerobic metabolism back to pyruvic acid. This acid is then converted to carbon dioxide, water, and energy.

Most athletes emphasize one type of exercise (anaerobic or aerobic) over the other. For example, an athlete training for a 60-m dash does mainly anaerobic exercising, but one planning to run a 10-km race does mainly aerobic exercising. Sprinting and weightlifting are largely anaerobic activities. A marathon run (42 km) is largely aerobic. During a marathon, athletes must set a pace to run for more than 2 hours. Their muscle cells depend on slow, steady aerobic conversion of carbohydrates to energy. During anaerobic activities, however, muscle cells use almost no oxygen. Rather, they depend on the quick energy provided by anaerobic metabolism.

After glycogen stores are depleted, muscle cells can switch over to fat metabolism. Fats are the main source of energy for sustained activity of low or moderate intensity, such as the last part of a marathon run.

Muscle Fibers: Twitch Kind Do You Have?

Muscles are tools with which we do work. The quality and type of muscle fibers that an athlete has affect his or her athletic performance, just as the quality of machinery influences how work is done. For example, we can remove snow from a driveway in more than one way. We can do it in 10 min with a snow-blower, or we can spend 50 min shoveling. Muscles are classified according to the speed and effort required to accomplish this work. The two classes of muscle fibers (Figure 7) are **fast-twitch fibers** (which are stronger and larger and most suited for anaerobic activity) and **slow-twitch fibers** (which are best for aerobic work). Table 3 lists some characteristics of these two types of muscle fibers.

▶ **Figure 7** Slow-twitch muscle fibers have more mitochondria (elongated violet dots) than fast-twitch fibers do.

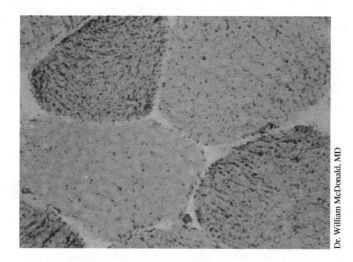

Dr. William McDonald, MD

Myoglobin is a red, heme-containing protein in muscle that stores oxygen (similar to the way hemoglobin stores and transports oxygen in the blood).

Table 3	A Comparison of Two Types of Muscle Fibers	
Characteristic	**Type I**	**Type IIB**[a]
Category	Slow twitch	Fast twitch
Color	Red	White
Respiratory capacity	High	Low
Myoglobin level	High	Low
Catalytic activity of actomyosin	Low	High
Capacity for glycogen use	Low	High

[a]There is a type IIA fiber (not considered here) that resembles type I in some respects and type IIB in others.

Type I (slow-twitch) fibers are called on during activity of light or moderate intensity. The respiratory capacity of these fibers is high, which means that they can provide a large amount of energy via aerobic pathways. The myoglobin level is also high. Aerobic oxidation requires oxygen, and muscle tissue rich in slow-twitch fibers is supplied with high levels of oxygen.

Type I muscle fibers have a low capacity to use glycogen and thus are not geared to anaerobic generation of energy. Their action does not require the hydrolysis of glycogen. The catalytic activity of the actomyosin complex is low. Remember that actomyosin not only is the structural unit in muscle that undergoes contraction but also is responsible for catalyzing the hydrolysis of ATP to provide energy for the contraction. Low catalytic activity means that the energy is parceled out more slowly. Slow energy output is not good if you want to lift 200 kg, but it is great for a 15-km run.

Type IIB (fast-twitch) fibers have characteristics opposite those of type I fibers. Low respiratory capacity and low myoglobin levels do not bode well for aerobic oxidation. A high capacity for glycogen use and a high catalytic activity of actomyosin allow tissue rich in fast-twitch fibers to generate ATP rapidly and also to hydrolyze this ATP rapidly during intense muscle activity. Thus, this type of muscle tissue has the capacity to do short bursts of vigorous work but fatigues rather quickly. A period of recovery, during which lactic acid is cleared from the muscle, is required between the brief periods of activity.

▲ **Figure 8** The New York City Marathon attracts more than 30,000 runners each year.

Q: *What is the predominant muscle type in the elite runners in this race? Do their muscles have high or low aerobic capacity?*

Building Muscles

Endurance exercise increases myoglobin levels in skeletal muscles. The increased myoglobin provides faster oxygen transport and increased respiratory capacity (Figure 8), and these changes usually are apparent within 2 weeks. Endurance training does not necessarily increase the size of muscles.

If you want larger muscles, try weightlifting. Weight training (Figure 9) develops fast-twitch muscle fibers. These fibers increase in size and strength with repeated anaerobic exercise. Weight training does *not* increase respiratory capacity.

Muscle-fiber type seems to be inherited. Research shows that world-class marathon runners may possess as high as 80–90% slow-twitch fibers, while championship sprinters may have up to 70% fast-twitch muscle fibers. Some exceptions have been noted, however, and factors such as training and body composition are important in athletics, as are other factors, including nutrition, fluid and electrolyte balance, and drug use or misuse.

▲ **Figure 9** Weightlifting is a popular activity in many gyms and fitness centers.

Q: *What is the predominant muscle type in elite weightlifters? Do their muscles have high or low aerobic capacity?*

Self-Assessment Questions

1. The high-energy compound used directly by muscles when contracting is
   a. an amino acid   **b.** ATP   **c.** a fatty acid   **d.** glucose

2. When muscle contraction begins, glycogen is converted to
   a. creatine   **b.** creatinine   **c.** lactic acid   **d.** pyruvic acid

3. During aerobic exercise, pyruvic acid is converted to
   a. CO_2 and H_2O **b.** glycogen   **c.** lactic acid   **d.** phosphocreatine

4. During anaerobic exercise, pyruvic acid is converted to
   a. CO_2 and H_2O **b.** glycogen   **c.** lactic acid   **d.** phosphocreatine

5. When produced during exercise, which of the following results in oxygen debt?
   a. ATP   **b.** glycogen   **c.** lactic acid   **d.** pyruvic acid

6. Fast-twitch muscle fiber is classified as
   a. type I   **b.** type IIA   **c.** type IIB   **c.** type III

7. The reddish color of slow-twitch muscle fibers is due to the presence of
   a. actomyosin   **b.** creatine   **c.** myoglobin   **d.** pyruvic acid

Answers: 1, b; 2, d; 3, a; 4, c; 5, c; 6, c; 7, c

6 Drugs, Athletic Performance, and the Brain

Learning Objectives ❯ Describe the physiological effects of restorative drugs, stimulant drugs, and anabolic steroids. ❯ Explain how endorphins, neurotrophins, and tobacco can affect the brain and body.

Muscle chemistry and metabolism, aerobic and anaerobic exercise, and nutrition and fluid balance all rely on normal internal processes. It would seem that hard work and proper nutrition are the best answers to improved performance. However, many athletes turn instead to drugs, such as the stimulants amphetamine and cocaine, to improve performance and to anabolic steroids to build muscles.

Like most other people, athletes use drugs to alleviate pain or soreness that results from overuse and to treat injuries. These **restorative drugs** include analgesics (painkillers), such as aspirin and acetaminophen, and anti-inflammatory drugs, such as aspirin, ibuprofen, ketoprofen, and cortisone. Cortisone derivatives are often injected to reduce swelling in damaged joints and tissues. Relief is often transitory, however, and side effects can be severe. Prolonged use of cortisone derivatives can cause fluid retention, hypertension, ulcers, disturbance of the sex-hormone balance, and other problems. Other substances that can be bought over the counter and applied externally include oil of wintergreen (methyl salicylate) and capsaicin (the active ingredient in hot peppers). These substances are usually one ingredient of an ointment or cream. When applied to the skin, they cause a mild burning sensation, thus serving as a counterirritant for sore muscles. Methyl salicylate is also an aspirin derivative and acts as an analgesic.

Stimulant Drugs

Some athletes use *stimulant drugs* to try to improve performance. The caffeine in a strong cup of coffee may be of some benefit. Caffeine triggers the release of fatty acids. Metabolism of these compounds may conserve glycogen, but any such effect is small. Caffeine also increases the heart rate, speeds metabolism, and increases urine output. The latter effect could lead to dehydration.

Other athletes resort to stronger stimulants, including amphetamines and cocaine. These drugs stimulate the central nervous system, increasing alertness, respiration, blood pressure, muscle tension, and heart rate. They also mask symptoms of fatigue and give an athlete a sense of increased stamina.

Anabolic Steroids

Many strenuous athletic performances depend on well-developed muscles. Muscle mass depends on the level of the male hormone *testosterone*. When boys reach puberty, testosterone levels rise, and the boys become more muscular if they exercise. Men generally have larger muscles than women because they have more testosterone.

Testosterone and some of its semisynthetic derivatives are taken by athletes in an attempt to build muscle mass quicker. Steroid hormones used to increase muscle mass are called **anabolic steroids**. These chemicals aid in the building (anabolism) of body proteins and thus of muscle tissue.

There are no reputable controlled studies demonstrating the effectiveness of anabolic steroids. They do seem to work—at least for some people—but the side effects are many. In males, side effects include testicular atrophy and loss of function, impotence, acne, liver damage that may lead to cancer, edema (swelling), elevated cholesterol levels, and growth of breasts.

Anabolic steroids act as male hormones (androgens), making women more masculine. They help women build larger muscles, but they also result in balding, extra body hair, a deep voice, and menstrual irregularities. What price will athletes pay for improved performance?

Drugs, Athletic Performance, and Drug Screening

The use of drugs to increase athletic performance not only is illegal and physically dangerous but also can be psychologically damaging. Stimulant drugs give users a false sense of confidence by affecting their ego, giving the delusion of invincibility. Such a feeling of "greatness" often ends as the competition begins, however, because the stimulant effect is short lived (it lasts for only half an hour to an hour for cocaine). Exhaustion and extreme depression usually follow. More stimulants are needed to combat these "down" feelings, and the user then runs the risk of addiction or overdose.

Because drug use for the enhancement or improvement of performance is illegal, chemists play an important role in sports: screening blood and urine samples for illegal drugs. Using sophisticated instruments, chemists can detect minute amounts of illegal drugs. Drug testing has been used at the Olympic Games since 1968, and it is rapidly becoming standard practice for athletes in college and professional sports.

Drugs are used at great risk of health (and legal!) problems. The use of illegal drugs violates the spirit of fair athletic competition. Let's work toward a world in which events and medals are won by drug-free athletes who are highly motivated, well-nourished, and well-trained.

Exercise and the Brain

Hard, consistent training improves athletic performance. Few drugs help, but athletes' own bodies manufacture a variety of substances that aid performance. Examples are the pain-relieving **endorphins**.

After vigorous activity, athletes have an increased level of endorphins in their blood. Stimulated by exercise, deep sensory nerves release endorphins to block the pain message. Exercise extended over a long period of time, such as distance running, sometimes causes in an athlete many of the same symptoms experienced by opiate users. Athletes get a euphoric high during or after a hard run. Unfortunately, both natural endorphins and their analogs, such as morphine, seem to be addictive. Athletes, especially runners, tend to suffer from withdrawal: They feel bad when they don't get the vigorous exercise of a long, hard run. This can be positive because exercise is important to the maintenance of good health. It can be negative if the person exercises when injured or to the exclusion of family or work obligations. Athletes also seem to develop a tolerance to their own endorphins. They have to run farther and farther to get that euphoric feeling.

Exercise also directly affects the brain by increasing its blood supply and by producing **neurotrophins**, substances that enhance the growth of brain cells. Exercises that involve complex motions, such as dance movements, lead to an increase in the connections between brain cells. Both our muscles and our brains work better when we exercise regularly.

No Smoking

If you want to stay healthy and fit, one thing you certainly should *not* do is use tobacco. Tobacco use and smoking are dangerous addictions that cause a wide variety of diseases, including cancer, heart disease, and emphysema, and often result in death. More than 400,000 children become regular smokers each year. Almost a third will eventually die from smoking.

Cigarette smoking is the chief preventable cause of premature death in the United States. One in five deaths in the United States is smoking related. According to the CDC, cigarette smoking is associated with death from 24 different diseases, including heart disease, stroke, and lung diseases such as cancer, stroke, emphysema, and pneumonia. Smoking causes diseases of the gums and mouth, chronic hoarseness, vocal cord polyps, and premature aging and wrinkling of the skin. Lung cancer is not the only malignancy caused by cigarette smoking. Cancers of the pancreas, bladder, breast, kidney, mouth and throat, stomach, larynx, and cervix are also associated with smoking. In fact, smoking kills more

A study of military veterans, conducted at Harvard University, concluded that smokers are 4.3 times as likely as nonsmokers to develop Alzheimer's disease. Heavy smokers get Alzheimer's 2.3 years sooner, on average, than nonsmokers.

people than AIDS, alcohol, illegal drugs, car accidents, murders, and suicides combined.

We fear cancer, but heart attack and stroke are the major causes of disability and death of smokers. Cigarette smokers have a 70% higher risk of heart attack than nonsmokers. When they are also overweight, with high blood pressure and high cholesterol, their risk is 200% higher. At every age, the death rate is higher among smokers than among nonsmokers.

Women who smoke during pregnancy have more stillborn babies, more premature babies, and more babies who die before they are a month old. Women who take birth control pills and also smoke have an abnormally high risk of stroke. Women who smoke are advised to use some other method of birth control.

One of the gases in cigarette smoke is carbon monoxide, which ties up about 8% of the hemoglobin in the blood. Smokers therefore breathe less efficiently. They work harder to breathe, but less oxygen reaches their cells. It is no wonder that fatigue is a common problem for smokers. More than 4700 chemicals have been identified in cigarette smoke, including many that are quite poisonous and 63 that are known or suspected carcinogens. Some of these are listed in Table 4.

Table 4 Some Potential Carcinogens[a] and Teratogens[b] Identified in Cigarette Smoke

Acetone	Chromium	Hydrazine	Nitropropane
Acrylonitrile	Chrysene	Indeno(1,2,3-c,d)pyrene	Nitrosamines
Aminobiphenyl	Copper	Lead	Nitrosononicotine
Aniline	Crotonaldehyde	Mercury	Polonium-210
Anthracenes	DDT	N-Nitrosoanabasine	Quinoline
Arsenic	Dibenz(a,h)acridine	N-Nitrosodiethanolamine	Styrene
Benz(a)anthracene	Dibenz(a,h)anthracene	N-Nitrosodiethylamine	Titanium
Benzene	Dibenz(a,j)acridine	N-Nitrosodimethylamine	Toluene
Benzo(a)pyrene	Dibenzo(a,l)pyrene	N-Nitrosoethylmethyl-amine	Toluidine
Benzo(b)fluoranthene	Dibenzo(c,g)carbazole		Urethane
Benzo(j)fluoranthene	Dieldrin	N-Nitrosomorpholine	Vinyl chloride
Butadiene	Dimethylhydrazine	N-Nitrosopyrrolidine	
Cadmium	Ethylcarbamate	Naphthylamine	
Carbon monoxide	Formaldehyde	Nickel	

[a]Proven or suspected of causing cancer; in italics.
[b]Proven or suspected of causing birth defects; in green.

In the linings of the lungs are *cilia* (tiny, hairlike processes) that help to sweep out particulate matter breathed into the lungs. In smokers, the tar from cigarette smoke forms a sticky coating that keeps the cilia from moving freely. The reduced action of the cilia may explain the smoker's cough. Pathologists claim that during an autopsy it is usually easy to tell if the body was that of a smoker. Lungs are normally pink. A smoker's lungs are black.

Unfortunately, cigarette smoke also harms nonsmokers. Secondhand smoke contains more than 7000 chemicals, of which hundreds are toxic and about 70 are carcinogens. Secondhand smoke causes an estimated 3000 premature deaths each year in the United States and causes up to 300,000 children to suffer from lower respiratory tract infections. Children of smokers miss twice as much school time because of respiratory infections as do children of nonsmokers.

Efforts to lessen indoor pollution caused by smoking have led many restaurants, bars, and public buildings to be declared nonsmoking areas. About half of the U.S. population now lives under a ban on smoking covering all workplaces, restaurants, and bars. Smoking has never been a smart or a healthy thing to do, but now it isn't even fashionable.

Chemistry of Sports Materials

The athlete's world is shaped by chemicals. The ability to perform reflects biochemistry within the athlete. Chemicals taken by athletes may hinder or enhance their performance. Yet another chemical dimension to the sports world is that chemicals are used to enhance athletic clothing and equipment (Table 5). Athletic clothing depends on chemicals for its shape and protective qualities.

Swimsuits, ski pants, and elastic support clothing stretch because of synthetic fibers. Undergarments made of polypropylene or polyester fibers wick perspiration away from the skin and keep the athlete dry even during vigorous exercise. Outdoor enthusiasts work and play in rain and winds wearing suits made of materials that have billions of tiny holes too small to pass drops of water but that readily pass water vapor. Raindrops falling on the outside are held together by surface tension and run off rather than penetrating the fabric. Water vapor from sweating skin, however, can pass from the warm area inside the suit where vapor concentration is high to the cooler area outside the suit where the vapor concentration is lower. The runner stays relatively dry.

Athletes of all sorts are aided by equipment made of materials developed by the chemical industry. Football, hockey, and baseball players are protected by polycarbonate helmets and protective pads of synthetic foamed rubbers. Brightly dyed nylon uniforms with synthetic colors add to the glamour of amateur and professional teams. Many sports events are played on artificial turf, a carpet of nylon or polypropylene with an underpad of synthetic foamed polymers. Stadiums are protected from the weather by Teflon covers reinforced with glass fibers and held aloft by air pressure.

The dramatic effect of new materials is perhaps best illustrated in pole vaulting (Figure 10). The sport probably originated with the use of wooden poles to vault over streams or other obstacles. It became a sport in the early nineteenth century when the Germans introduced the vertical vault form of competition. The record using a wooden pole was set at 3.48 m in 1887. Bamboo poles were introduced in 1879 and were popular for decades, with the record set at 4.77 m in 1942. Metal poles came into use in the 1950s with records set in 1957 at 4.78 m using an aluminum pole and in 1960 at 4.80 m with a steel pole. Fiberglass poles were introduced in 1952, but it took several years for athletes to learn how to use these highly flexible poles effectively. The first world record using a fiberglass pole was 4.83 m, set in 1961. Carbon fiber, stronger for its weight than glass fiber, was introduced in 1990. Modern poles are constructed from composites of either fiberglass or carbon fiber and fiberglass in several layers. Today, the world-record pole vault is 6.14 m.

From the soles of sports shoes and the wax used on cross-country skis to titanium golf clubs and tennis sweaters that stretch and yet retain their shape, the sports world is thoroughly immersed in chemicals.

▲ **Figure 10** U.S. silver medalist Jennifer Stuczynski Suhr makes an attempt in the women's pole vault final during the Beijing 2008 Olympic Games.

Table 5	Some Sports and Recreational Items Made from Chemicals Derived from Petroleum		
Wet suits	Motorcycle helmets	Darts	Fishing nets
Golf-cart bodies	Dune-buggy bodies	Tents	Hiking boots
Warm-up suits	Checkers	Stadium cushions	Frisbees
Ping-Pong paddles	Chess boards	Foul-weather gear	Fishing boots
Rafts	Shorts	Foot pads	Diving masks
Uniforms	Tennis shoes	Visors	Guitar picks
Track shoes	Paddles	Basketballs	Beach balls
Dominoes	Decoys	Canoes and kayaks	Sunglasses
Windbreakers	Volleyballs	Ice chests	Dog leashes
Sails	Sleeping bags	Life jackets	Dice
Football helmets	Tennis balls	In-line skates	Pole-vaulting poles
Swimsuits	Insect repellents	Artificial turf	Aquariums
Bicycle tires, seats, and handles	Swimming-pool liners	Golf club impact surfaces	

Self-Assessment Questions

1. Which of the following, as used by athletes, is a restorative drug?
   a. aspirin   **b.** caffeine   **c.** creatinine   **d.** testosterone

2. Caffeine is thought to aid endurance athletes by
   a. conserving creatine
   b. conserving stored O_2
   c. stimulating the release of free amino acids
   d. stimulating the release of fatty acids

3. Anabolic steroids
   a. build muscles without exercise   **b.** increase sexual drive
   c. help build larger muscles   **d.** make female athletes more feminine

4. Endorphins are
   a. chemicals produced by the body that are similar to morphine
   b. chemicals produced by the body that carry pain messages
   c. chemicals produced by the body that stimulate muscle growth
   d. synthetic drugs similar to morphine

5. Exercise is thought to help the brain work better by
   a. acting as a stimulant   **b.** increasing aerobic capacity
   c. increasing levels of neurotrophins   **d.** inhibiting production of endorphins

6. The chemical in cigarette smoke that makes breathing less efficient is
   a. CO   **b.** CO_2 **c.** nicotine   **d.** NO

7. About how many chemicals have been identified in cigarette smoke?
   a. 20   **b.** 60   **c.** 360   **d.** 7000

Answers: 1, a; 2, d; 3, c; 4, a; 5, c; 6, a; 7, d

CRITICAL THINKING EXERCISES

Apply knowledge that you have gained in this chapter and one or more of the FLaReS principles to evaluate the following statements or claims.

1. An advertisement in an American sports magazine claims that an amino-acid supplement helps build muscle mass.

2. In the past, Inuit peoples ate an all-meat diet and seemed to thrive. We should eat a meat-only diet for maximum health.

3. The right nutrients from whole foods will keep your memory sharp and your mind agile as you grow older.

4. The various ways by which performance can be improved are called *ergogenic aids*. These include mechanical, physiological, psychological, pharmacological, and nutritional aids. Unfortunately, many of the claims for these aids have not been substantiated by rigorous scientific trials. Here are several claims:
   a. A creatine supplement "makes muscles much less prone to fatigue and the capacity to undertake strenuous exercise is increased."
   b. Sodium bicarbonate reduces the acidity of the blood and "may be able to draw more of the acid produced within the muscle cells out into the blood and thus reduce the level of acidity within the muscle cells themselves. This could delay the onset of fatigue."
   c. Two factors that limit prolonged exercise are depletion of the body's carbohydrate stores and dehydration. Consuming sports drinks containing carbohydrates and electrolytes before, during, and after exercise will help prevent blood glucose levels falling too low, help maintain the body's glycogen stores, and replace electrolytes lost through perspiration.

5. An online advertisement says, "I cut down 47 lbs of stomach fat in a month by obeying this one old rule."

6. An advertisement for a weight-loss pill claims that the substance in the pill "melts fat from your body."

SUMMARY

Section 1—Good health and fitness require a nutritious diet and regular exercise. Today's dietary guidelines emphasize nutrient-dense foods and a balanced eating program. A balanced diet consists largely of fruits, vegetables, whole grains, and dairy products in the proper proportions. Total fats intake should not exceed 35% of calories; saturated fats (mostly of animal origin) should account for less than 10% of calories. Athletes generally need more calories, which should come mostly from carbohydrates—especially starches. Exercise, not extra protein, builds muscle tissue. The Dietary Reference Intakes (DRIs) for protein and other nutrients are established by the U.S. Academy of Sciences for planning and assessing diets.

Section 2—Organic substances (vitamins) and inorganic substances (minerals) that the body cannot produce must be supplied by the diet. Vitamin and mineral supplements may not be necessary with a well-balanced diet, but they do no harm and may be beneficial. Vitamin A is essential for vision and skin maintenance. There are several B vitamins; B_3 and B_6 may help arthritis patients; B_{12} is not found in plants, and a lack can cause anemia. Vitamin C prevents scurvy, promotes healing, is needed for the immune system, and is an antioxidant. Vitamin D promotes absorption of calcium and phosphorus. Vitamin E is an antioxidant and an anticoagulant, and a deficiency of it can lead to muscular dystrophy. An electrolyte is a substance that conducts electricity in a water solution. The main electrolytes in the body are ions of sodium, potassium, chlorine, calcium, and magnesium, as well as sulfate, hydrogen phosphate, and bicarbonate ions. Water is an essential nutrient.

Section 3—Drastic diets are unlikely to be permanently successful, and the weight lost is usually regained. One pound of adipose tissue stores about 3500 kcal of energy. A variety of chemical substances that are produced in the body are regulators of body weight. Quick-weight-loss diets often include a diuretic to increase urine output, which results in temporary weight loss. Low-carbohydrate diets cause quick weight loss by depleting glycogen and water.

Exercise aids in weight loss, because the increase in metabolic rate that it causes continues after it ends. The most sensible approach to weight loss involves a balanced low-calorie diet and a consistent exercise program.

Section 4—The male body requires about 3% body fat; the female body, 10–12%. The percentage of body fat can be estimated by several methods. Density measurement is probably the most accurate. Body mass index (BMI) indicates fatness, and V_{O_2} max is a measure of fitness.

Section 5—Exercise makes muscles larger, more flexible, and more efficient. Energy for muscular work comes from ATP. A protein complex called *actomyosin* contracts when ATP is added to it. ATP provides energy for just a few seconds, after which glycogen is metabolized. If metabolism occurs with plenty of oxygen—during aerobic exercise—CO_2 and H_2O are formed. With insufficient oxygen—during anaerobic exercise—lactic acid is formed and muscle fatigue occurs. When exercise ends, the oxygen debt is repaid; the cells' oxygen demand decreases, and the lactic acid can be oxidized to CO_2 and H_2O. There are two classes of muscle fibers. Fast-twitch fibers are larger and stronger and good for short bursts of vigorous exercise, while slow-twitch fibers are geared for steady exercise of long endurance. Weight training develops fast-twitch muscles but does not increase respiratory capacity. Long-distance running develops slow-twitch muscles and increases respiratory capacity.

Section 6—Athletes sometimes use restorative drugs, such as aspirin, ibuprofen, or cortisone, to alleviate pain and treat injuries. They may use stimulant drugs such as caffeine and cocaine. Anabolic steroids appear to increase muscle mass, but they have many bad effects, including impotence and liver cancer.

The body can manufacture pain-relieving endorphins that may help performance, but it appears that some athletes can become addicted to them. Exercise also directly affects the brain by producing neurotrophins, substances that enhance the growth of brain cells. Smoking reduces athletic performance, causes diseases, and leads to earlier death, and athletes should avoid it. From modern sports clothing and equipment to artificial turf, chemistry has contributed greatly to the world of sports.

Green chemistry Walking or biking instead of driving is not only healthy and enjoyable but follows green chemistry principles. Your body's energy comes from renewable plant carbohydrate sources rather than nonrenewable fossil fuels whose use in most transportation options leads to harmful carbon dioxide buildup in the atmosphere.

Learning Objectives

› List the recommendations (sources and percentages) for calories from fats and other sources in the American diet.	Problems 1,12
› Describe the special dietary requirements of athletes.	Problems 6, 11, 45
› Describe the dietary requirements for vitamins, minerals, and water.	Problems 13–22
› Explain how weight is lost through diet and exercise.	Problems 3, 9, 23, 24, 31, 32, 60
› Calculate weight loss due to calorie reduction and exercise.	Problems 25–30, 58
› Describe several ways to measure fitness.	Problems 7, 56, 59
› Calculate BMI values.	Problems 33, 34, 57, 59, 61
› Differentiate between aerobic exercise and anaerobic exercise, and describe the chemistry that occurs during each.	Problems 38, 39, 41–44

> Describe how muscles are built and how they work.   Problems 35–46, 62

> Describe the physiological effects of restorative drugs, stimulant drugs, and   Problems 10, 47, 48, 51
  anabolic steroids.

> Describe how endorphins, neurotrophins, and tobacco can affect the brain and body.   Problems 31, 32, 49, 50, 53, 54

> Explain how green chemistry principles can help us make transportation choices.   Problems 64, 67

> Describe the relationship between walking or biking and personal health, especially   Problems 65, 66
  the implications for weight loss.

REVIEW QUESTIONS

1. What kinds of foods are the main dietary source of saturated fats?

2. Why are the federal dietary guidelines (Figure 1) not the same for everyone?

3. How might you lose 5 lb in just 1 week? Would it be a useful way to lose weight and keep it off?

4. Do you think it is likely that obesity is inherited?

5. List three ways in which chemistry has had an impact on sports.

6. How do the nutritional needs of an athlete differ from those of a sedentary individual? How is this extra need best met?

7. List two ways to determine percent body fat. Describe a limitation of each method.

8. Why does excess body fat put a strain on the heart?

9. List some problems that result from low-calorie diets.

10. What are the effects of anabolic steroids on females?

PROBLEMS

Nutrition

11. Do athletes need more protein than other people? Explain.

12. What are two good reasons for not going on a high-protein diet?

Vitamins and Minerals

13. What benefit is derived from vitamin B_{12}?

14. In addition to preventing pellagra, what does vitamin B_3 (niacin) do?

15. What kinds of problems are helped by vitamin B_6 (pyridoxine)?

16. What are some of the benefits of vitamin A?

17. What are the benefits of vitamin D? Is taking a daily megadose of vitamin D a good idea?

18. Vitamins C and E are antioxidants. What does this mean?

Electrolytes

19. What is a diuretic? Describe the function of antidiuretic hormone (ADH).

20. How is the appearance of urine related to dehydration?

21. Is thirst a good indicator of dehydration? Are you always thirsty when dehydrated?

22. What are some of the effects of dehydration? What is heat stroke?

Diet and Exercise

23. List two ways in which fad diets can produce quick weight loss. Why is the weight rapidly regained?

24. Why does a diet that restricts carbohydrate intake lead to loss of muscle mass as well as fat?

25. A quarter-pound burger provides 420 kcal of energy. How long would a 130-lb person have to walk to burn those calories if 1 h of walking uses about 210 kcal?

26. One kilogram of fat tissue stores about 7700 kcal of energy. An average person burns about 40 kcal while walking 1 km. If such a person walks 5 km each day, how much fat will be burned in 1 year?

27. The DRI for protein is about 0.8 g/kg body weight. How much protein is required each day by a 253-lb football player?

28. How much protein is required each day by a 110-lb gymnast? (See Problem 27.)

29. A 70-kg man can store about 2000 kcal as glycogen. How far could such a man run on this stored starch if he expends 100 kcal/km while running and the glycogen is his only source of energy?

30. A 70-kg man can store about 100,000 kcal of energy as fat. How far could such a man run on this stored fat if he expends 100 kcal/km while running and the fat is his only source of energy?

31. Describe the role of each of the following substances involved in the control of body weight.
    a. leptin
    b. ghrelin

32. Describe the role of each of the following substances involved in the control of body weight.
    a. cholecystokinin
    b. PYY

Body Mass Index

33. What is the body mass index (BMI) for a 6-ft 9-in. baseball player who weighs 182 lb?

34. What is the BMI for a 5-ft 11-in. football player who weighs 224 lb?

Muscles

35. How many muscles do humans have?

36. What two proteins make up the actomyosin complex?

37. Muscles are made of protein. Does eating more protein result in larger muscles?

38. What is aerobic exercise? What is anaerobic exercise?

39. Which type of metabolism (aerobic or anaerobic) is primarily responsible for providing energy for (a) intense bursts of vigorous activity and (b) prolonged low levels of activity?

40. What are the two functions of the actomyosin protein complex?

41. Explain why high levels of myoglobin are appropriate for muscle tissue geared to aerobic oxidation.

42. Categorize type I and type IIB muscle fibers as suited to aerobic oxidation or to anaerobic use of glycogen.

43. Why does the high catalytic activity of actomyosin in type IIB fibers suggest that these are the muscle fibers engaged in brief, intense physical activity?

44. Which type of muscle fiber is most affected by endurance training exercises? What changes occur in the muscle tissue?

45. Muscle is protein. Does an athlete need extra protein (above the DRI) to build muscles? What is the best way to build muscles?

46. Describe the biochemical process by which muscles are built.

Drugs

47. How are cortisone derivatives used in sports medicine? What are some of the side effects of their use?

48. What are anabolic steroids? List some side effects of the use of anabolic steroids (a) in males and (b) in females.

49. Give a biochemical explanation of the "runner's high."

50. What evidence indicates that long-distance running is addictive? Give a biochemical explanation of addiction to long-distance running.

51. Does cocaine enhance athletic performance? Explain fully. What happens when the effect of cocaine wears off?

52. What is the role of chemists in the control of drug use by athletes?

Smoking and Health

53. What are some of the health problems related to smoking?

54. Why is it important for pregnant women not to smoke?

ADDITIONAL PROBLEMS

55. If you are moderately active and want to maintain a weight of 160 lb, about how many calories do you need each day?

56. An athlete can run a 400-m race in 45 s. Her maximum oxygen intake is 4 L/min, but working muscles at their maximum exertion requires about 0.2 L of oxygen per minute for each kilogram of body weight. If the athlete weighs 50 kg, what oxygen debt will she incur?

57. Fat tissue has a density of about 0.90 g/mL, and lean tissue a density of about 1.1 g/mL. Calculate the density of a person who has a body volume of 80 L and weighs 85 kg. Is the person fat or lean?

58. The British measure body weight by the stone (1 stone = 14 lb). By how many kilocalories would you have to overeat each day to gain 1.0 stone over the course of a year?

59. Following is a table of data used to determine an individual's percentage of body fat. Make a graph of the data.
    a. Estimate the percent body fat for person A, who has a body density of 1.037 g/cm³.
    b. Estimate the percent body fat for person B, who weighs 165 lb in air and 14 lb when submerged in water.
    c. Which person is more likely to be a well-trained athlete?
    d. A 20-year-old male weighs 89.34 kg on land and 5.30 kg underwater. The water has a density of 0.9951 kg/L. The male's residual lung volume is 1.57 L, and his maximum lung volume is 6.51 L. Calculate his body density. Why does a person float in spite of the fact that his or her body density is greater than that of water?

Body Density (g/cm³)	Body Fat (%)
1.010	38.3
1.030	29.5
1.050	21.0
1.070	12.9
1.090	5.07

60. An athlete gains 40 lb after retiring. What is the likely explanation?

61. What is the body mass index (BMI) for (a) the tallest man in medical history, who was 8 ft 11 in. tall and weighed 199 kg, and (b) one of the heaviest men in history, who weighed 486 kg and stood 184 cm tall?

62. Birds use large, well-developed breast muscles for flying. Pheasants can fly at 80 km/h, but only for short distances. Great blue herons can fly at about 35 km/h but can cruise great distances. What kind of fibers predominate in the breast muscles of each?

63. A 100-mL sample of blood contains 15 g of hemoglobin (Hb). Each gram of Hb can combine with 1.34 mL of $O_2(g)$ at body temperature and pressure. How much O_2 is in (a) 100 mL of blood and (b) the approximately 6.0 L of blood in an average adult?

64. Give two examples of green chemistry principles that support healthy choices about transportation.

65. If you weigh 155 lb and bike at a moderate rate of 12–13.9 mi/h, you burn about 45 k cal/mi. If you live 1 mi from campus and commute round trip 80 days per semester, how many pounds lighter will you be at the end of the semester than if you had driven to class?

66. Endorphins are
a. toxic auto emissions   **b.** mood-enhancing chemicals
c. renewable fuels   **d.** biochemical catalysts

67. Carbon dioxide is an undesirable byproduct because
a. it inhibits photosynthesis
b. it creates fossil fuels
c. it leads to conditions for climate change
d. it decreases engine efficiency

COLLABORATIVE GROUP PROJECTS

Prepare a PowerPoint, poster, or other presentation (as directed by your instructor) to share with the class.

1. Popular diets are often based on books, such as the following:

YOU: On a Diet: The Owner's Manual for Waist Management by Michael F. Roizen and Mehmet Oz

The Fat Smash Diet: The Last Diet You'll Ever Need by Ian Smith

The Sonoma Diet: Trimmer Waist, Better Health in Just 10 Days! by Connie Guttersen

The South Beach Diet: The Delicious, Doctor-Designed, Foolproof Plan for Fast and Healthy Weight Loss by Arthur Agatston

The Good Mood Diet: Feel Great While You Lose Weight by Susan M. Kleiner

Search the Internet or print publications such as *Consumer Reports* for characteristics and views of each diet. Prepare a brief report, pro or con, on one of the diets.

2. Equations for determining maximum heart rate (MHR) and tables for evaluating fitness levels can be found in exercise physiology textbooks and online. Use these resources to calculate your V_{O_2} max. How does your fitness level compare with that of your classmates? With that of each of the following athletes: **(a)** endurance runner or bicyclist, 75 mL/kg/min; **(b)** volleyball (female), 50 mL/kg/min; **(c)** football (male), 60–65 mL/kg/min; and **(d)** baseball (male), 50 mL/kg/min?

3. Choose one or more of the chemicals in Table 4. Use a reference such as *The Merck Index* to determine the formula and properties of the substance.

4. Choose one or more of the sports or recreational items in Table 5, and try to determine what synthetic materials are used in it.

5. Only four Nobel Prizes in Chemistry have been awarded to women: Marie Curie (1911), her daughter Irène Joliot-Curie (1935), Dorothy Crowfoot Hodgkin (1964), and Ada E. Yonath (2009). Write a brief essay about Hodgkin or Yonath based on information from the library or the Internet.

6. Search the Internet or sources from the library for information on the various drugs that athletes use to enhance their performance. Use a reference such as *The Merck Index* to determine the formula and function of one or more of these drugs.

BRIEF ANSWERS TO SELECTED PROBLEMS

Answers are provided for *all in-chapter exercises*. Brief answers are given for *odd-numbered Review Questions*; more complete answers can be obtained by reviewing the text. Answers are provided for *all odd-numbered Problems and Additional Problems*.

NOTE: For numerical problems, your answer may differ slightly from ours because of rounding and the use of significant figures.

1	A. 3.6 lb	B. 7.4 lb
2	A. 35 mi	B. 2700 kcal
3	A. 23.5	B. 174 lb

1. Meat and other animal products
3. Deplete glycogen stores and dehydrate yourself; no, it would be mostly water loss.
5. Better understanding of muscle physiology; drugs; improved equipment
7. Skinfold calipers (inaccurate and measure water retention as well as fat); displacement of water (cannot get all of the air out of the lungs)
9. Often deficient in B vitamins, iron, and other nutrients; slows metabolism, making future dieting more difficult and weight gain easier
11. Most do not.
13. Avoid pernicious anemia
15. Arthritis; B_6 is a cofactor for more than 100 enzymes.
17. Promotes absorption of calcium and phosphorus. The upper limit is 2000 IU; more than that can be toxic.
19. Promotes production of urine; ADH acts to retain urine.
21. No. Thirst is often a delayed response.
23. Depletion of glycogen and water loss

25. 2.0 h
27. 92 g
29. 20 km
31. a. Leptin protects against weight loss.
b. Ghrelin is an appetite stimulant.
33. 19.6
35. About 600
37. No
39. a. anaerobic   b. aerobic
41. Store needed oxygen
43. ATP can be generated rapidly and hydrolyzed rapidly.
45. No; the best way to build muscles is by exercise.
47. Anti-inflammatory; fluid retention, hypertension, ulcers, disturbance of sex hormone balance
49. The body releases endorphins that have much the same effect as some narcotics.
51. The athlete might perform better briefly, but fatigue follows quickly.
53. Heart disease; stroke; lung cancer; emphysema; pneumonia; cancers of the pancreas, bladder, breast, kidney, and cervix
55. 2400 kcal
57. 1.06 g/mL; lean
59. a. 26.7%   b. 3.61%   c. Person B   d. 1.077 g/cm³
61. a. 27   b. 144
63. a. 20 mL O_2 b. 1200 mL O_2
65. 2 lb lighter
67. c

Accurate measurements are essential to science. Measurements can be made in a variety of units, but most scientists use the International System of Units (SI). The data they record often has to be converted from one kind of unit to another and otherwise manipulated mathematically. This appendix extends the discussion of metric measurement and reviews some of the mathematics that you may find useful in this course.

1 The International System of Units

The standard SI unit of length is the *meter*. This distance was once defined as 0.0000001 of Earth's quadrant—that is, of the distance from the North Pole to the equator measured along a meridian. The quadrant proved difficult to measure accurately, and today the meter is defined precisely as the distance light travels in a vacuum during 1/299,792,458 of a second.

The SI unit of mass is the *kilogram* (1 kg = 1000 g). It is based on a standard platinum–iridium cylinder kept at the International Bureau of Weights and Measures. The *gram* is a more convenient unit for many chemical operations.

The derived SI unit of volume is the *cubic meter*. The units more frequently employed in chemistry, however, are the *liter* (1 L = 0.001 m^3) and the *milliliter* (1 mL = 0.001 L). Other SI units of length, mass, and volume are derived from these basic units. Table 1 lists some metric units of length, mass, and volume and illustrates the use of prefixes.

2 Exponential (Scientific) Notation

Scientists often use numbers that are inconceivably large or small. For example, light travels at about 300,000,000 m/s. There are 602,200,000,000,000,000,000,000 carbon atoms in 12.01 g of carbon. On the small side, the diameter of an atom is about 0.0000000001 m, and the diameter of an atomic nucleus is about 0.000000000000001 m. Because it is difficult to keep track of the zeros in such numbers, scientists find it convenient to express them in exponential notation.

Table 1	Some Metric Units of Length, Mass, and Volume
Length	
1 kilometer (km)	= 1000 meters (m)
1 meter (m)	= 100 centimeters (cm)
1 centimeter (cm)	= 10 millimeters (mm)
1 millimeter (mm)	= 1000 micrometers (μm)
Mass	
1 kilogram (kg)	= 1000 grams (g)
1 gram (g)	= 1000 milligrams (mg)
1 milligram (mg)	= 1000 micrograms (μg)
Volume	
1 liter (L)	= 1000 milliliters (mL)
1 milliliter (mL)	= 1000 microliters (μL)
1 milliliter (mL)	= 1 cubic centimeter (cm^3)

From *Chemistry for Changing Times*, Thirteenth Edition. John W. Hill, Terry W. McCreary, Doris K. Kolb.

A number is in *exponential notation* when it is written as the product of a coefficient and a power of 10. (Such a number is called *scientific notation* when the coefficient has a value between 1 and 10). Two examples are

$$4.18 \times 10^3 \quad \text{and} \quad 6.57 \times 10^{-4}$$

Expressing numbers in exponential form generally serves two purposes.

1. We can write very large or very small numbers in a minimum of space and with a reduced chance of typographical error.
2. We can convey explicit information about the precision of measurements: The number of significant figures (Section 4) in a measured quantity is stated unambiguously.

In the expression 10^n, n is the exponent of 10, and the number 10 is said to be raised to the *n*th power. If *n* is a *positive quantity*, 10^n has a value *greater than 1*. If *n* is a *negative quantity*, 10^n has a value *less than 1*. We are particularly interested in cases where *n* is an integer. For example,

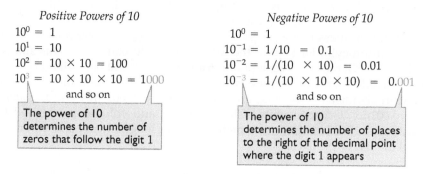

We express 612,000 in scientific notation as follows:

$$612,000 = 6.12 \times 100,000 = 6.12 \times 10^5$$

We express 0.000505 in scientific notation as

$$0.000505 = 5.05 \times 0.0001 = 5.05 \times 10^{-4}$$

We can use a more direct approach to converting numbers to scientific notation.

- Count the number of places a decimal point must be moved to produce a coefficient having a value between 1 and 10.
- The number of places counted then becomes the power of 10.
- The power of 10 is *positive* if the decimal point is moved to the *left*.

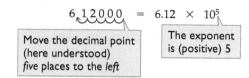

- The power of 10 is *negative* if the decimal point is moved to the *right*.

To convert a number from exponential form to the conventional form, move the decimal point in the opposite direction.

$$3.75 \times 10^6 = 3.750000$$

| The exponent is 6 | Move the decimal point six places to the *right* |

$$7.91 \times 10^{-7} = 0.000000791$$

| The exponent is –7 | Move the decimal point seven places to the *left* |

It is easy to handle exponential numbers on most calculators. A typical procedure is to enter the number, hit the key [EE] or [EXP], and then enter the exponent of 10. The keystrokes required for the number 2.85×10^7 are [2] [.] [8] [5] [EE] [7].

For the number 1.67×10^{-5}, the keystrokes are [1] [.] [6] [7] [EXP] [5] [±]; the last keystroke changes the sign of the exponent. Many calculators can be set to convert all numbers and calculated results to the exponential form, regardless of the form in which the numbers are entered. Most scientific and graphing calculators can also be set to display a fixed number of digits in the results.

Addition and Subtraction

To add or subtract numbers in exponential notation using a scientific or graphing calculator, simply enter the numbers as usual and perform the desired operations. However, to add or subtract numbers *by hand* in exponential notation, it is necessary to express each quantity as the *same power of 10*. In calculations, this approach treats the power of 10 in the same way as a unit—it is simply "carried along." For example, we express each quantity in the following calculation with the power 10^{-3}.

$$(3.22 \times 10^{-3}) + (7.3 \times 10^{-4}) - (4.8 \times 10^{-4}) =$$
$$(3.22 \times 10^{-3}) + (0.73 \times 10^{-3}) - (0.48 \times 10^{-3}) = (3.22 + 0.73 - 0.48) \times 10^{-3}$$
$$= 3.47 \times 10^{-3}$$

Multiplication and Division

To multiply numbers expressed in exponential form by hand, *multiply* all coefficients to obtain the coefficient of the result and *add* all exponents to obtain the power of 10 in the result. Generally, most calculators perform these operations automatically, and no intermediate results need to be recorded.

To divide two numbers in exponential form, *divide* the coefficients to obtain the coefficient of the result and *subtract* the exponent in the denominator from the exponent in the numerator to obtain the power of 10. In the example below, multiplication and division are combined. First, the rule for multiplication is applied to the numerator and to the denominator, and then the rule for division is used.

| | Rewrite in exponential form | |

$$\frac{0.015 \times 0.0088 \times 822}{0.092 \times 0.48} = \frac{(1.5 \times 10^{-2})(8.8 \times 10^{-3})(8.22 \times 10^2)}{(9.2 \times 10^{-2})(4.8 \times 10^{-1})}$$

Apply the rule for multiplication to the numerator and denominator

Apply the rule for division $= \dfrac{1.1 \times 10^{-1}}{4.4 \times 10^{-2}} = 0.25 \times 10^{-1-(-2)} = 0.25 \times 10^1 = 2.5$

Appendix: Review of Measurement and Mathematics

Raising a Number to a Power and Extracting the Root of an Exponential Number

To raise an exponential number to a given power, raise the coefficient to that power and multiply the exponent by that power. For example, we can cube a number (that is, raise it to the *third* power) in the following manner.

Rewrite in exponential form	Cube the coefficient	Multiply the exponent by 3

$$(0.0066)^3 = (6.6 \times 10^{-3})^3 = (6.6)^3 \times 10^{(-3 \times 3)}$$

$$= (2.9 \times 10^2) \times 10^{-9} = 2.9 \times 10^{-7}$$

To extract the root of an exponential number, we raise the number to a fractional power—one-half power for a square root, one-third power for a cube root, and so on. Most calculators have keys designed for extracting square roots and cube roots. Thus, to extract the square root of 1.57×10^5, enter the number 1.57×10^5 into a calculator, and use the $[\sqrt{\ }]$ key.

$$\sqrt{1.57 \times 10^{-5}} = 3.96 \times 10^{-3}$$

Some calculators allow you to extract roots by keying the root in as a fractional exponent. For example, we can take a cube root as follows.

$$(2.75 \times 10^{-9})^{1/3} = 1.40 \times 10^{-3}$$

Self-Assessment Questions

For items 1–4, express the number in scientific notation, and then select the correct answer.

1. 35,400
   a. 3.54×10^{-4} **b.** 35.4×10^{-3} **c.** 3.54×10^4 **d.** 35.4×10^4

2. 43,600,000
   a. 436×10^4 **b.** 43.6×10^{-6} **c.** 4.36×10^7 **d.** 4.36×10^{-7}

3. 0.000000000000312
   a. 3.12×10^{-15} **b.** 3.12×10^{-13} **c.** 3.12×10^{-12} **d.** 3.12×10^{13}

4. 0.000438
   a. 4.38×10^{-3} **b.** 4.38×10^{-4} **c.** 4.38×10^4 **d.** 4.38×10^6

For items 5–6, express the number in decimal (ordinary) notation, and then select the correct answer.

5. 7.1×10^4
   a. 0.00071   **b.** 0.000071   **c.** 71,000   **d.** 710,000

6. 2.83×10^{-4}
   a. 0.000283   **b.** 0.00283   **c.** 2830   **d.** 28,300

For items 7–14, perform the indicated operation, and then select the correct answer.

7. $(3.0 \times 10^4) \times (2.1 \times 10^5) = ?$
   a. 5.1×10^9 **b.** 6.3×10^1 **c.** 6.3×10^9 **d.** 6.3×10^{20}

8. $(6.27 \times 10^{-5}) \times (4.12 \times 10^{-12}) = ?$
   a. 2.58×10^{-17} **b.** 2.58×10^{-16}
   c. 2.58×10^{-59} **d.** 2.58×10^{59}

9. $\dfrac{4.33 \times 10^{-7}}{7.61 \times 10^{22}} = ?$
   a. 5.69×10^{-30} **b.** 5.69×10^{-15}
   c. 5.69×10^{15} **d.** 5.69×10^{30}

10. $\dfrac{9.37 \times 10^9}{3.79 \times 10^{27}} = ?$
    a. 2.47×10^{-36} **b.** 2.47×10^{-35}
    c. 2.47×10^{-18} **d.** 2.47×10^{36}

11. $\dfrac{2.21 \times 10^5}{9.80 \times 10^{-7}} = \text{?}$

   a. 2.26×10^{-12} **b.** 2.26×10^{-11}
   c. 2.26×10^{11} **d.** 4.43×10^{12}

12. $\dfrac{4.60 \times 10^{-12}}{2.17 \times 10^3} = \text{?}$

   a. 2.12×10^{-15} **b.** 2.12×10^{-14}
   c. 2.12×10^{14} **d.** 2.12×10^{15}

13. $(2.19 \times 10^{-6})^2 = \text{?}$

   a. 4.80×10^{-12} **b.** 4.80×10^{-6}
   c. 4.80×10^6 **d.** 4.80×10^{12}

14. $\sqrt{1.74 \times 10^{-7}} = \text{?}$

   a. 1.32×10^{-7} **b.** 4.17×10^{-7}
   c. 4.17×10^{-4} **d.** 1.32×10^{-4}

Answers: 1, c; 2, c; 3, b; 4, b; 5, c; 6, c; 7, c; 8, b; 9, a; 10, c; 11, c; 12, a; 13, a; 14, c

3 Unit Conversions

Because we live in a world in which almost all countries except the United States use metric measurements, we sometimes need to convert between common and metric units. Suppose that an American applies for a job in another country and the job application asks for her height in centimeters. She knows that her height is 66.0 in. Her height is the same, whether we express it in inches, feet, centimeters, or millimeters. Thus, when we measure something in one unit and then convert it to another, we must not change the measured quantity in any fundamental way. We can use equivalencies (given here to three significant figures; Section 4) such as those in Table 2 to derive conversion factors.

In mathematics, multiplying a quantity by 1 does not change its value. We can therefore use a factor equivalent to 1 to convert between inches and centimeters. We find our factor in the definition of the inch in Table 2.

$$1 \text{ in.} = 2.54 \text{ cm}$$

A variety of conversion calculators are available on the Internet. Use the key words *conversion calculator*.

Table 2	Some Conversions between Common and Metric Units
Length	
1 mile (mi) = 1.61 kilometers (km)	
1 yard (yd) = 0.914 meter (m)	
1 inch (in.) = 2.54 centimeters (cm)[a]	
Mass	
1 pound (lb) = 454 grams (g)	
1 ounce (oz) = 28.4 grams (g)	
1 pound (lb) = 0.454 kilogram (kg)	
Volume	
1 U.S. quart (qt) = 0.946 liter (L)	
1 U.S. pint (pt) = 0.473 liter (L)	
1 fluid ounce (fl oz) = 29.6 milliliters (mL)	
1 gallon (gal) = 3.78 liters (L)	

[a]This conversion is exact. The other conversions are available with more significant digits if needed; see any edition of the *CRC Handbook of Chemistry and Physics*.

Notice that if we divide both sides of this equation by 1 in., we obtain a ratio of quantities that is equal to 1.

$$1 = \frac{1 \text{ in.}}{1 \text{ in.}} = \frac{2.54 \text{ cm}}{1 \text{ in.}}$$

If we divide both sides of the equation by 2.54 cm, we also obtain a ratio of quantities that is equal to 1.

$$\frac{1 \text{ in.}}{2.54 \text{ cm}} = \frac{2.54 \text{ cm}}{2.54 \text{ cm}} = 1$$

The two ratios, one shown in red and the other in blue, are conversion factors. A *conversion factor* is a ratio of terms, equivalent to the number 1, used to change the unit in which a quantity is expressed. We call this process the *unit conversion method* of problem solving. Because we set up calculations by examining the *dimensions* associated with the given quantity, those associated with the desired result, and those needed in the conversion factors, the process is sometimes called *dimensional analysis*.

What happens when we multiply a known quantity by a conversion factor? The original unit cancels out and is replaced by the desired unit. Thus, our general approach to using conversion factors is

Desired quantity and unit = given quantity and unit × conversion factors

Now let's return to the question about the woman's height, a measured quantity of 66.0 in. To get an answer in centimeters, we must use the appropriate conversion factor (in blue). Note that the desired unit (cm) is in the numerator and the unit to be replaced (in.) is in the denominator. Thus, we can cancel the unit in. so that only the unit cm remains.

$$66.0 \text{ in.} \times \frac{2.54 \text{ cm}}{1 \text{ in.}} = 168 \text{ cm (rounded off from 167.64)}$$

You can see why the other conversion factor (in red) won't work. No units cancel. Instead, we get a nonsensical unit.

$$66.0 \text{ in.} \times \frac{1 \text{ in.}}{2.54 \text{ cm}} = \frac{26.0 \text{ in.}^2}{\text{cm}}$$

Following are some examples and exercises to give you some practice in this method of problem solving.

Example 1   Unit Conversions

a. Convert 0.742 kg to grams.
b. Convert 0.615 lb to ounces.
c. Convert 135 lb to kilograms.

Solution

a. This is a conversion from one metric unit to another. We simply use our knowledge of prefixes to convert from kilograms to grams.

We start here	This converts kg to g	Our answer: the number and the unit

$$0.742 \text{ kg} \times \frac{1000 \text{ g}}{1 \text{ kg}} = 742 \text{ g}$$

b. This is a conversion from one common unit to another. Here we use the fact that 1 lb = 16 oz to convert from pounds to ounces. Then we proceed as in part (a), arranging the conversion factor to cancel the unit lb.

$$0.615 \text{ lb} \times \frac{16 \text{ oz}}{1 \text{ lb}} = 9.84 \text{ oz}$$

c. This is a conversion from a common unit to a metric unit. We need data from Table 2 to convert from pounds to kilograms. Then we proceed as in part (b), arranging the conversion factor to cancel the unit lb.

$$135 \text{ lb} \times \frac{0.454 \text{ kg}}{1 \text{ lb}} = 61.3 \text{ kg}$$

(Our answers have the proper number of significant figures. If you do not understand significant figures and wish to do so, they are discussed in Section 4. This text uses three significant figures for most calculations.)

■ EXERCISE 1

a. Convert 16.3 mg to grams.
b. Convert 24.5 oz to pounds.
c. Convert 12.5 fl oz to milliliters.

Quite often, to get the desired unit, we must use more than one conversion factor. We can do so by arranging all the necessary conversion factors in a single setup that yields the final answer in the desired unit.

Example 2   Unit Conversions

What is the length, in millimeters, of a 3.25-ft piece of tubing?

Solution
No relationship between feet and millimeters is given in Table 2, and so we need more than one conversion factor. We can think of the problem as a series of three conversions.

1. Use the fact that 1 ft = 12 in. to convert from feet to inches.
2. Use data from Table 2 to convert from inches to centimeters.
3. Use our knowledge of prefixes to convert from centimeters to millimeters.

We could solve this problem in three distinct steps by making one conversion in each step, but it is just as easy to combine three conversion factors into a single setup. Then we proceed as indicated below.

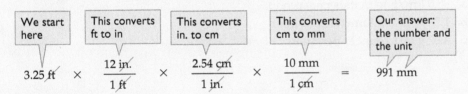

■ EXERCISE 2
Carry out the following conversions.
a. 90.3 mm to meters
b. 729.9 ft to kilometers
c. 1.17 gal to fluid ounces

Sometimes we need to convert two or more units in the measured quantity. We can do this by arranging all the necessary conversion factors in a single setup so that the starting units cancel and the conversions yield the final answer in the desired units.

Example 3   Unit Conversions

A saline solution has 1.00 lb of salt in 1.00 gal of solution. Calculate the concentration in grams per liter of solution.

Solution

First, let's identify the measured quantities. They can be expressed in the form of a ratio of mass of salt in pounds to a volume in gallons.

$$\frac{1.00\text{ lb (salt)}}{1.00\text{ gal (solution)}}$$

This ratio must be converted to one expressed in grams per liter. We must convert from pounds to grams in the numerator and from gallons to liters in the denominator. The following set of equivalent values from Table 2 can be used to formulate conversion factors.

$$1\text{ lb} = 454\text{ g} \qquad 1\text{ gal} = 3.78\text{ L}$$

We start here | To convert lb to g in numerator | To convert gal to L in denominator | Our answer: the number and the unit

$$\frac{1.00\ \cancel{\text{lb}}}{1.00\ \cancel{\text{gal}}} \times \frac{454\text{ g}}{1\ \cancel{\text{lb}}} \times \frac{1\ \cancel{\text{gal}}}{3.78\text{ L}} = 120\text{ g/L}$$

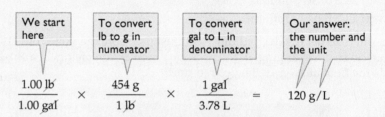

Note that we could also do the conversions in the numerator and denominator separately and then divide the numerator by the denominator.

$$\text{Numerator:}\quad 1.00\ \cancel{\text{lb}} \times \frac{454\text{ g}}{1\ \cancel{\text{lb}}} = 454\text{ g}$$

$$\text{Denominator:}\quad 1.00\ \cancel{\text{gal}} \times \frac{3.78\text{ L}}{1\ \cancel{\text{gal}}} = 3.78\text{ L}$$

$$\text{Division:}\quad \frac{454\text{ g}}{3.78\text{ L}} = 120\text{ g/L}$$

Both methods give the same answer to three significant figures.

■ EXERCISE 3

Carry out the following conversions.

a. 88.0 km/h to meters per second
b. 1.22 ft/s to kilometers per hour
c. 4.07 g/L to ounces per quart

Self-Assessment Questions

For items 1–5, perform the indicated conversion, and then select the correct answer. You may need data from Table 2 for some of the items.

1. 645 μs to seconds
   a. 6.45×10^{-6} s **b.** 6.45×10^{-4} s **c.** 6.45×10^{-2} s **d.** 6.45×10^{8} s
2. 1445 oz to grams
   a. 50.9 g **b.** 90.3 g **c.** 144.5 g **d.** 4.10×10^4 g
3. 1.24×10^5 mm to feet
   a. 10.3 ft **b.** 103 ft **c.** 407 ft **d.** 4.88×10^3 ft
4. 12.0 fl oz to milliliters
   a. 0.405 mL **b.** 240 mL **c.** 355 mL **d.** 3.55×10^5 mL
5. 343 m/s to miles per hour
   a. 0.0592 mi/h **b.** 12.8 mi/h **c.** 767 mi/h **d.** 1220 mi/h

Answers: 1, b; 2, d; 3, c; 4, c; 5, c

4 Precision, Accuracy, and Significant Figures

Counting can give exact numbers. For example, we can count exactly 24 students in a room. Measurements, on the other hand, are subject to error. One source of error is the measuring instruments themselves. For example, an incorrectly calibrated thermometer may consistently yield a result that is 0.2 °C too low. Other errors may result from the experimenter's lack of skill or care in using measuring instruments. But even the most careful measurement will have some uncertainty associated with it. For example, a meter stick can be used to measure to the nearest millimeter or so. But there is no way for a meter stick to give a measurement that is correct to the nearest 0.001 mm.

Precision and Accuracy

Suppose that five students were asked to measure a person's height using a meter stick marked off in millimeters. The five measurements are recorded in Table 3. The *precision* of a set of measurements refers to how closely individual measurements agree with one another. We say that the precision is good if each of the measurements is close to the average or poor if there is a wide deviation from the average value.

Table 3	Five Measurements of a Person's Height
Student	Height (m)
1	1.827
2	1.824
3	1.826
4	1.828
5	1.829
Average	1.827

How would you describe the precision of the data in Table 3? Examine the individual data, note the average value, and determine how much the individual data differ from the average. Because the maximum deviation from the average value is 0.003 m, the precision is quite good.

The *accuracy* of a set of measurements refers to the closeness of the average of the set to the "correct," or most probable, value. Measurements of high precision are more likely to be accurate than are those of poor precision, but even highly precise measurements are sometimes inaccurate. For example, what if the meter sticks used to obtain the data in Table 3 were actually 1005 mm long but still had 1000-mm markings? The accuracy of the measurements would be rather poor, even though the precision would remain good.

Sampling Errors

No matter how accurate an analysis, it will not mean much unless it is performed on valid, representative samples. Consider determining the level of glucose in the blood of a patient. High glucose levels are associated with diabetes, a debilitating disease. Results vary, depending on several factors such as the time of day and what and when the person last ate. Glucose levels are much higher soon after a meal high in sugars. They also depend on other factors, such as stress. Medical doctors usually take blood for analysis after a night of fasting. These fasting glucose levels tend to be more reliable, but physicians often repeat the analysis when high or otherwise suspicious results are obtained. Therefore, there is no one true value for the level of glucose in a person's blood. Repeated samplings provide an average level. Similar

(a) Low accuracy   (b) Low accuracy
   Low precision   High precision

(c) High accuracy   (d) High accuracy
   Low precision   High precision

▲ Comparing precision and accuracy: a dartboard analogy. (a) The darts are both scattered (low precision) and off-center (low accuracy). (b) The darts are in a tight cluster (high precision) but still off-center (low accuracy). (c) The darts are somewhat scattered (low precision) but evenly distributed about the center (high accuracy). (d) The darts are in a tight cluster (high precision) and well centered (high accuracy).

results from several measurements give much more confidence in the findings. For example, a diagnosis of diabetes is usually based on two consecutive fasting blood glucose levels above 120 mg/dL.

Significant Figures

Look again at Table 3. Notice that the five measurements of height agree in the first three digits (1.82); they differ only in the fourth digit. We say that the fourth digit is uncertain. All digits known with certainty, plus the first uncertain one, are called *significant figures*. The precision of a measurement is reflected in the number of significant figures—the more significant figures, the more precise the measurement. The measurements in Table 3 have four significant figures. In other words, we are quite sure that the person's height is between 1.82 m and 1.83 m. Our best estimate of the average value, including the uncertain digit, is 1.827 m.

The number 1.827 has four digits; we say it has four significant figures. In any properly reported measurement, all nonzero digits are significant. Zeros, however, may or may not be significant because they can be used in two ways: as a part of the measured value or to position a decimal point.

- Zeros between two other significant digits are significant. *Examples*: 4807 (four significant figures); 70.004 (five).
- The lone zero preceding a decimal point is there for aesthetic purposes; it is not significant. *Example*: 0.352 (three significant figures).
- Zeros that precede the first nonzero digit are also not significant. *Examples*: 0.000819 (three significant figures); 0.03307 (four).
- Zeros at the end of a number are significant if they are to the right of the decimal point. *Examples*: 0.2000 (four significant figures); 0.050120 (five).

We can summarize these four situations with a general rule: When we read a number from left to right, all the digits starting with the first nonzero digit are significant. Numbers without a decimal point that end in zeros are a special case, however.

- Zeros at the end of a number may or may not be significant if the number is written without a decimal point. *Example*: 700. We do not know whether the number 700 was measured to the nearest unit, ten, or hundred. To avoid this confusion, we can use exponential notation (Section 2). In exponential notation, 700 is recorded as 7×10^2 or 7.0×10^2 or 7.00×10^2 to indicate one, two, or three significant figures, respectively. The only significant digits are those in the coefficient, not in the power of 10.

We use significant figures only with measurements—quantities subject to error. The concept does not apply to a quantity that is

1. inherently an integer, such as 3 sides to a triangle or 12 items in a dozen;
2. inherently a fraction, such as the radius of a circle equals $\frac{1}{2}$ of the diameter;
3. obtained by an accurate count, such as 18 students in a class; or
4. a defined quantity, such as 1 km = 1000 m.

In these contexts, the numbers 3, 12, $\frac{1}{2}$, 18, and 1000 can have as many significant figures as we want. More properly, we say that each is an *exact value*.

Example 4   Significant Figures

In everyday life, common units are often used with metric units in parentheses (or vice versa), but significant figures are not always considered. Which of the following has followed proper significant figure usage?

a. A popular science magazine reports: "Peregrine falcons are the world's fastest animals, reaching speeds of up to 200 mi/h (322 km/h)."
b. A urinal is rated at "1.0 gpf (gallons per flush) or 3.8 lpf (liters per flush)."

Solution

a. The quantity "322 km/h" has three significant figures but "200 mi/h" has only one; significant figure rules were not followed.

b. Each quantity has two significant figures; significant figure rules were followed.

■ **EXERCISE 4**

Which of the following has followed proper significant figure usage?

a. A Web site states: "fats and ethanol have the greatest amount of food energy per mass, 9 and 7 kcal/g (38 and 30 kJ/g) respectively."

b. A set of exercise room weights are rated at "12 lb (26 kg)."

Significant Figures in Calculations: Multiplication and Division

If we measure a sheet of notepaper and find it to be 14.5 cm wide and 21.7 cm long, we can find the area of the paper by multiplying the two quantities. A calculator gives the answer as 314.65. Can we conclude that the area is 314.65 cm²? That is, can we know the area to the nearest hundredth of a square centimeter when we know the width and length only to the nearest tenth of a centimeter? It just doesn't seem reasonable—and it isn't. A calculated quantity can be no more precise than the data used in the calculation, and the reported result should reflect this fact.

A strict application of this principle involves a fairly complicated statistical analysis that we will not attempt here, but we can do a fairly good job by using a practical rule involving significant figures:

> In multiplication and division, the reported result should have no more significant figures than the factor with the fewest significant figures.

In other words, a calculation is only as precise as the least precise measurement that enters into the calculation.

To obtain a numerical answer with the proper number of significant figures often requires that we round off numbers. In rounding, we drop all digits that are not significant and, if necessary, adjust the last reported digit. We use the following rules in rounding.

- If the leftmost digit to be dropped is *4 or less*, drop it and all following digits. *Example*: If we need four significant figures, 69.744 rounds to 69.74, or if we need three significant figures, to 69.7.

- If the leftmost digit to be dropped is *5 or greater*, increase the final retained digit by 1. *Example*: 538.76 rounds to 538.8 if we need four significant figures. Similarly, 74.397 rounds to 74.40 if we need four significant figures or to 74.4 if we need three.

Example 5	Unit Conversions

What is the area, in square centimeters, of a rectangular gauze bandage that is 2.54 cm wide and 12.42 cm long? Use the correct number of significant figures in the answer.

Solution

The area of a rectangle is the product of its length and width. In the result, we can show only as many significant figures as there are in the least precisely stated dimension, the width, which has three significant figures.

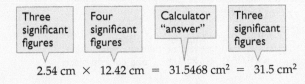

$$2.54 \text{ cm} \times 12.42 \text{ cm} = 31.5468 \text{ cm}^2 = 31.5 \text{ cm}^2$$

We use the rules for rounding off numbers as the basis for dropping the digits 468.

■ **EXERCISE 5**

Calculate the volume, in cubic meters, of a rectangular block of foamed plastic that is 1.827 m long, 1.04 m wide, and 0.064 m thick. Use the correct number of significant figures.

Example 6   **Significant Figures**

For a laboratory experiment, a teacher wants to divide all of a 226.8-g sample of glucose equally among the 18 members of her class. How many grams of glucose should each student receive?

Solution

The number 18 is a counted number, that is, an exact number that is not subject to significant figure rules. The answer should carry four significant figures, the same as in 226.8 g.

$$\frac{226.8\text{ g}}{18\text{ students}} = 12.60\text{ g/student}$$

In this calculation, a calculator displays the result 12.6. We add the digit 0 to emphasize that the result is precise to four significant figures.

■ **EXERCISE 6**

A dozen eggs has a mass of 681 g. What is the average mass of one of the eggs, expressed with the appropriate number of significant figures?

Significant Figures in Calculations: Addition and Subtraction

In addition or subtraction, we are concerned not with the number of significant figures but with the number of digits to the right of the decimal point. When we add or subtract quantities with varying numbers of digits to the right of the decimal point, we need to note the one with the fewest such digits. The result should contain the same number of digits to the right of its decimal point. For example, if you are adding several masses and one of them is measured only to the nearest gram, the total mass cannot be stated to the nearest milligram no matter how precise the other measurements are.

We apply this idea in Example 7. Note that in a calculation involving several steps, we need round off only the final result.

Example 7   **Significant Figures**

Perform the following calculation and round off the answer to the correct number of significant figures.

$$2.146\text{ g} + 72.1\text{ g} - 9.1434\text{ g}$$

Solution

In this calculation, we add two numbers and subtract a third from the sum of the first two.

$$
\begin{array}{ll}
2.146\text{ g} & \text{three decimal places} \\
+\ 72.1\text{ g} & \text{one decimal place} \\
\hline
74.246\text{ g} & \\
\end{array}
$$

$$
\begin{array}{ll}
-\ 9.1434\text{ g} & \text{four decimal places} \\
\hline
65.1026\text{ g} \ = \ 65.1\text{ g} & \text{one decimal place} \\
\end{array}
$$

Note that we do not round off the intermediate result (74.246). When using a calculator, you generally don't need to write down an intermediate result.

■ EXERCISE 7

Perform the indicated operations and give answers with the proper number of significant figures. Note that in addition and subtraction all terms must be expressed in the same unit.

a. 48.2 m + 3.82 m + 48.4394 m

b. 15.436 L + 5.3 L − 6.24 L − 8.177 L

c. (51.5 m + 2.67 m) × (33.42 m − 0.124 m)

d. $\dfrac{125.1\ g\ -\ 1.22\ g}{52.5\ mL\ +\ 0.63\ mL}$

Self-Assessment Questions

1. A measurement has good precision if it
   a. is close to an accepted standard
   b. is close to similar measurements
   c. has few significant figures
   d. is the only value determined

2. Following is data for the length of a pencil as measured by students X, Y, and Z. The length is known to be 11.54 cm.

	Trial 1	Trial 2	Trial 3
X	11.8	11.1	11.5
Y	11.7	11.2	11.6
Z	11.3	11.4	11.5

   Which of the following best characterizes the data?
   a. Y has the most precise data, X the most accurate
   b. Y has the most precise data, Z the most accurate
   c. Z has the most precise data, X the most accurate
   d. Z has the most precise data, Y the most accurate

3. 725.8055 rounded to three significant figures is
   a. 725.806　　b. 725.81　　c. 725.8　　d. 726

For items 4–6, determine the number of significant figures, and then select the correct answer.

4. 0.0000073
   a. 2　　b. 5　　c. 6　　d. 8

5. 0.04000
   a. 2　　b. 4　　c. 5　　d. 6

6. 80.0040
   a. 2　　b. 4　　c. 5　　d. 6

For items 7–16, perform the indicated calculation, and then select the correct answer, with the proper number of significant figures.

7. 7.20 + 3.013 + 0.04327 = ?
   a. 10.26　　b. 10.256　　c. 10.2563　　d. 10.25627

8. 4.702 − 0.4123 = ?
   a. 4.2897　　b. 4.29　　c. 4.290　　d. 4.30

9. 10.03 + 4.555 = ?
   a. 14　　b. 14.59　　c. 14.6　　d. 15

10. 15.3 − 4.001 = ?
    a. 11　　b. 11.2　　c. 11.299　　d. 11.3

11. 4.602 ÷ 0.0240 = ?
    a. 191　　b. 191.75　　c. 191.8　　d. 192

12. $40.625 \times 0.0028 = ?$
    a. 0.11   b. 0.11375   c. 0.1138   d. 0.114

13. $8.64 \div 0.1216 = ?$
    a. 71.1   b. 71.05   c. 71.0526   d. 71.053

14. $(10.30)(0.186) \div 0.085 = ?$
    a. 23   b. 22.5   c. 22.5388   d. 2.254

15. $(42.5 + 0.459) \div 28.45 = ?$
    a. 1.510   b. 1.5103   c. 1.51   d. 1.510

16. $(7.06 \div 0.084) - (29.6 \times 0.023) = ?$
    a. 83   b. 83.3   c. 83.4   d. 83.369

Answers: 1, b; 2, d; 3, d; 4, a; 5, b; 6, d; 7, a; 8, c; 9, b; 10, d; 11, d; 12, a; 13, a; 14, a; 15, c; 16, a

5 Calculations Involving Temperature and Heat

We sometimes need to make conversions from one temperature scale to another or from one energy unit to another.

Temperature

In everyday life, the following ditty will often suffice to assess the meaning of a Celsius temperature.
THE CELSIUS SCALE
Thirty is hot,
Twenty is pleasing,
Ten is quite cool,
And zero is freezing.

On the Fahrenheit scale, the freezing point of water is 32 °F and the boiling point is 212 °F; on the Celsius scale, the freezing point of water is 0 °C and the boiling point is 100 °C. A 100° temperature interval (100 − 0) on the Celsius scale therefore equals a 180° interval (212 − 32) on the Fahrenheit scale. From these facts, we can derive two equations that relate temperatures on the two scales. One of these requires multiplying the degrees of Celsius temperature by the factor 1.8 (that is, 180/100) to obtain the degrees of Fahrenheit temperature, followed by adding 32 to account for the fact that 0 °C = 32 °F.

$$°F = (1.8 \times °C) + 32$$

In the other equation, we subtract 32 from the Fahrenheit temperature to get the number of degrees Fahrenheit above the freezing point of water. Then this quantity is divided by 1.8.

$$°C = \frac{°F - 32}{1.8}$$

The SI unit of temperature is the kelvin. Recall that to convert from °C to K, we simply add 273.15. And to convert from K to °C, we subtract 273.15.

$$K = °C + 273.15 \qquad \text{and} \qquad °C = K - 273.15$$

Example 8 illustrates a practical situation where conversion between Celsius and Fahrenheit temperatures is necessary.

Example 8   Temperature Conversion

At home, you keep your thermostat set at 68 °F. When traveling, you have a room with a thermostat that uses the Celsius scale. What Celsius temperature will give you the same temperature as at home?

Solution

$$°C = \frac{°F - 32}{1.8} = \frac{68 - 32}{1.8} = 20 °C$$

■ EXERCISE 8

a. Convert 85.0 °C to degrees Fahrenheit.
b. Convert −12.2 °C to degrees Fahrenheit.
c. Convert 355 °F to degrees Celsius.
d. Convert −20.8 °F to degrees Celsius.

Heat

The *joule*. A joule (J) is the work done by a force of 1 newton[*] acting over a distance of 1 meter.

$$1 \text{ cal} = 4.184 \text{ J}$$
$$1 \text{ kcal} = 1000 \text{ cal} = 4184 \text{ J}$$

A calorie (cal) is the amount of heat required to raise the temperature of 1 g of water by 1 °C. (This quantity varies slightly with temperature; a calorie is defined more precisely as the amount of heat required to raise the temperature of 1 g of water from 14.5° to 15.5 °C.)

Some substances gain or lose heat more readily than others (Table 4). The *specific heat* of a substance is the amount of heat required to raise the temperature of 1 g of the substance by 1 °C. The definition of a calorie indicates that the specific heat of water is 1.00 cal/g °C. In SI, the specific heat of water is 4.184 J/g °C. Note that metals all have much lower values of specific heat than does water. This means that a sample of water must absorb much more heat to raise its temperature than a sample of a metal of similar mass does. The metal sample may become red hot after absorbing a quantity of heat that makes the water sample only lukewarm.

We can use the following equation, in which ΔT is the change in temperature (in either °C or K), to calculate the quantity of heat absorbed or released by a system.

$$\text{Heat absorbed or released} = \text{mass} \times \text{specific heat} \times \Delta T$$

Table 4	Specific Heats of Selected Substances	
		Specific Heat
Substance	**cal/g °C**	**J/g °C**
Aluminum (Al)	0.216	0.902
Copper (Cu)	0.0921	0.385
Ethyl alcohol (CH₃CH₂OH)	0.588	2.46
Iron (Fe)	0.106	0.443
Ethylene glycol (HOCH₂CH₂OH)	0.561	2.35
Magnesium (Mg)	0.245	1.025
Mercury (Hg)	0.0332	0.139
Sulfur (S)	0.169	0.706
Water (H₂O)	1.000	4.182

[*]A *newton* (N) is the basic SI unit of force. A newton is the force required to give a 1-kg mass an acceleration of 1 m/s². That is, $1 \text{ N} = 1 \text{ kg m/s}^2$. Therefore, $1 \text{ J} = 1 \text{ N m} = 1 \text{ kg m}^2/\text{s}^2$.

Appendix: Review of Measurement and Mathematics

Example 9   Heat Absorbed

How much heat, in calories, kilocalories, and kilojoules, does it take to raise the temperature of 225 g of water from 25.0 °C to 100.0 °C?

Solution

First, we list the quantities we need for the calculations.

$$\text{Mass of water } = 225 \text{ g}$$
$$\text{Specific heat of water } = 1.00 \text{ cal/(g °C)}$$
$$\text{Temperature change } = (100.0 - 25.0) \text{ °C} = 75.0 \text{ °C}$$

Then we use the equation for the quantity of heat absorbed.

$$\text{Heat absorbed } = \text{mass} \times \text{specific heat} \times \Delta T$$
$$= 225 \text{ g} \times 1.00 \text{ cal/g °C} \times 75.0 \text{ °C}$$
$$= 16{,}900 \text{ cal}$$

We can then convert the unit cal to the units kcal and kJ.

$$16{,}900 \text{ cal} \times \frac{1 \text{ kcal}}{1000 \text{ cal}} = 16.9 \text{ kcal}$$

$$16.9 \text{ kcal} \times \frac{4.184 \text{ kJ}}{1 \text{ kcal}} = 70.7 \text{ kJ}$$

■ **EXERCISE 9**

How much heat, in calories, kilocalories, and kilojoules, is released by 975 g of water as it cools from 100.0 °C to 18.0 °C?

Table 5	Some Conversion Units for Energy	
1 calorie (cal) = 4.184 joules (J) (defined; exact)		
1 British thermal unit (Btu) = 1055 joules (J) = 252 calories (cal)		
1 food Calorie = 1 kilocalorie (kcal) = 1000 calories (cal) = 4184 joules (J)		

Self-Assessment Questions

For items 1–10, perform the indicated conversion, and then select the correct answer.

1. 25 °C to kelvins
   a. −298 K   b. −248 K   c. 248 K   d. 298 K

2. 373 K to degrees Celsius
   a. −73 °C   b. 0 °C   c. 73 °C   d. 100 °C

3. 301 K to degrees Celsius
   a. −72 °C   b. 28 °C   c. 128 °C   d. 374 °C

4. 473 °C to kelvins
   a. 100 K   b. 200 K   c. 300 K   d. 746 K

5. 37.0 °C to degrees Fahrenheit
   a. −20.6 °F   b. −38.3 °F   c. 69.0 °F   d. 98.6 °F

6. 5.50 °F to degrees Celsius
   a. −20.8°C   b. −14.7 °C   c. 3.06 °C   d. 6.31 °C

7. 273 °C to degrees Fahrenheit
   a. 152 °F   b. 491 °F   c. 523 °F   d. 549 °F

8. 98.2 °F to degrees Celsius
   a. 36.8 °C   d. 54.6 °C   c. 72.3 °C   d. 177 °C

9. 2175 °C to degrees Fahrenheit
   a. 1190 °F   **b.** 1208 °F   **c.** 1226 °F   **d.** 3947 °F

10. 25.0 °F to degrees Celsius
    a. −31.6 °C   **b.** −13.9 °C   **c.** −3.89 °C   **d.** 42.8 °C

11. Of each of the following pairs, which is the larger unit: °C or °F? cal or Cal?
    a. °C, cal   **b.** °C, Cal   **c.** °F, cal   **d.** °F, Cal

12. The temperatures, 0 K, 0 °C, and 0 °F, arranged from coldest to hottest, are
    a. 0 °C, 0 °F, 0 K   **b.** 0 °C, 0 K, 0 °F   **c.** 0 °F, 0 °C, 0 K   **d.** 0 K, 0 °F, 0 °C

For items 13–20, perform the indicated conversion, and then select the correct answer. You may need data from Table 5 for some of the items.

13. 0.820 kcal to calories
    a. 0.000820 cal   **b.** 8.20 cal   **c.** 820 cal   **d.** 820,000 cal

14. 65,500 cal to kilocalories
    a. 0.0655 kcal   **b.** 0.655 kcal   **c.** 6.55 kcal   **d.** 65.5 kcal

15. 0.359 kJ to joules
    a. 0.000359 J   **b.** 0.00359 J   **c.** 35.9 J   **d.** 359 J

16. 0.741 kcal to joules
    a. 0.000741 J   **b.** 3.10 J   **c.** 741 J   **d.** 3100 J

17. 8.63 kJ to calories
    a. 2.06 cal   **b.** 20.6 cal   **c.** 86.3 cal   **d.** 2060 cal

18. 1.36 kcal to kilojoules
    a. 1.36 kJ   **b.** 5.69 kJ   **c.** 325 kJ   **d.** 5690 kJ

19. 345 cal to joules
    a. 0.345 J   **b.** 1.44 J   **c.** 82.5 J   **d.** 1440 J

20. 873 kJ to kilocalories
    a. 0.873 kcal   **b.** 209 kcal   **c.** 873 kcal   **d.** 2090 kcal

21. How much heat, in calories, is required to raise the temperature of 50.0 g of water from 20.0 °C to 50.0 °C?
    a. 30.0 kcal   **b.** 50.0 kcal   **c.** 1500 cal   **d.** 2500 kcal

22. How much heat, in kilojoules, is required to raise the temperature of 131 g of iron from 15.0 °C to 95.0 °C?
    a. 0.058 kJ   **b.** 1.11 kJ   **c.** 4.65 kJ   **d.** 4650 kJ

Answers: 1, d; 2, d; 3, b; 4, d; 5, d; 6, b; 7, c; 8, a; 9, d; 10, c; 11, b; 12, d; 13, c; 14, d; 15, d; 16, d; 17, d; 18, b; 19, d; 20, b; 21, b; 22, c

BRIEF ANSWERS TO SELECTED PROBLEMS

Answers are provided for *all in-chapter exercises*. Brief answers are given for *odd-numbered Review Questions*; more complete answers can be obtained by reviewing the text. Answers are provided for *all odd-numbered Problems and Additional Problems*.

NOTE: For numerical problems, your answer may differ slightly from ours because of rounding and the use of significant figures.

1   a. 0.0163 g   b. 1.53 lb
    c. 370 mL
2   a. 0.0903 m   b. 0.2224 km
    c. 150 fl oz

3   a. 24.4 m/s   b. 1.34 km/h
    c. 0.136 oz/qt
4   a. No   b. No
5   0.12 m³
6   56.8 g
7   a. 100.5 m   b. 6.3 L
    c. 1800 m² (1.80 × 10³ m²)   d. 2.33 g/mL
8   a. 185 °F   b. 10.0 °F
    c. 179 °C   d. −29.3 °C
9   80,000 cal; 80.0 kcal; 334 kJ

Glossary

Glossary

absolute zero The lowest possible temperature, 0 K or −273.15 °C or −459.7 °F.

absorb Gather a substance on a surface in a condensed layer.

acid A substance that, when added to water, produces an excess of hydrogen ions; a proton donor.

acid–base indicator A substance that is one color in acid and another color in base.

acidic anhydride A substance, such as a nonmetal oxide, that reacts with water to form an acid.

acid rain Precipitation having a pH less than 5.6.

acquired immune deficiency syndrome (AIDS) A disease caused by a retrovirus (HIV) that weakens the immune system.

activated sludge method A technique for secondary sewage treatment in which the sewage is aerated and some sludge is recycled.

activation energy The minimum quantity of energy that must be available before a chemical reaction can take place.

active site The region on an enzyme or a catalyst where a reaction occurs.

addition polymerization A polymerization reaction in which all the atoms of the monomer molecules are included in the polymer.

addition reaction A reaction in which the single product contains all the atoms of two reactant molecules.

adipose tissue Connective tissue where fat is stored.

advanced treatment Sewage treatment designed to remove phosphates, nitrates, other soluble impurities, and metals and other contaminants; also called tertiary treatment.

aerobic exercise Physical activity in which muscle contractions occur in the presence of oxygen.

aerobic oxidation An oxidation process occurring in the presence of oxygen.

aerosol Particles of 1 μm diameter or less, dispersed in air.

aflatoxins Toxins produced by molds growing on stored peanuts and grains.

Agent Orange A combination of 2,4-D and 2,4,5-T used extensively in Vietnam to remove forest cover and destroy crops that maintained enemy armies.

agonist A molecule that fits and activates a specific receptor.

AIDS See **acquired immune deficiency syndrome**.

alchemy A mixture of chemistry and magic practiced in Europe during the Middle Ages (500 to 1500 c.e.).

alcohol (ROH) An organic compound composed of an alkyl group and a hydroxyl group.

aldehyde (RCHO) An organic compound with a carbonyl group that has a hydrogen atom attached to the carbonyl carbon.

aldose A monosaccharide with an aldehyde functional group.

aliphatic compound A nonaromatic substance. *See* also **aromatic compound**.

alkali metal A metal in group 1A in the customary U.S. arrangement of the periodic table or in group 1 of the IUPAC-recommended table.

alkaline earth metal An element in group 2A in the customary U.S. arrangement of the periodic table or in group 2 of the IUPAC-recommended table.

alkaloid A physiologically active nitrogen-containing organic compound that occurs naturally in a plant.

alkalosis A physiological condition in which the pH of the blood is too high.

alkane A hydrocarbon with only single bonds; a saturated hydrocarbon.

alkene A hydrocarbon containing one or more double bonds.

alkyl group (−R) The group of atoms that results when a hydrogen atom is removed from an alkane.

alkyne A hydrocarbon containing one or more triple bonds.

allergen A substance that triggers an allergic reaction.

allotropes Different forms of the same element in the same physical state.

alloy A mixture of two or more elements, at least one of which is a metal; an alloy has metallic properties.

alpha decay Emission of an alpha particle ($_2^4$He) by a radioactive nucleus.

alpha helix A secondary structure of a protein molecule in which the chains coil around one another in a spiral arrangement.

alpha (α) particle A cluster of two protons and two neutrons; a helium nucleus.

Ames test A laboratory test that screens for mutagens, which are usually also carcinogens.

amide group (−CON−) A functional group in which a carbon is joined to an oxygen atom by a double bond and to a nitrogen atom by a single bond.

amine A nitrogen compound derived from ammonia by replacing one or more hydrogen atoms with alkyl or aromatic group(s).

amino acid An organic compound that contains both an amino group and a carboxyl group; amino acids combine to produce proteins.

amino group (−NH$_2$) A functional group comprised of a nitrogen atom bonded to two hydrogen atoms.

amphetamines Stimulant drugs that are similar in structure to epinephrine and norepinephrine.

amphoteric surfactant A surfactant whose active part bears both a negative charge and a positive charge.

anabolic steroid A drug that aids in the building (anabolism) of body proteins and thus of muscle tissue.

anabolism The building up of molecules through metabolic processes.

anaerobic decay Decomposition in the absence of oxygen.

anaerobic exercise Physical activity that takes place without sufficient oxygen.

analgesic A substance that provides pain relief.

androgen A male sex hormone.

anesthetic A substance that causes loss of feeling or awareness.

anion A negatively charged ion.

anionic surfactant A surfactant whose active part (water-soluble head) bears a negative charge.

anode A positive electrode at which oxidation occurs.

antagonist A molecule that prevents the action of an agonist by blocking its receptor.

antibiotic A soluble substance, produced by a mold or bacterium, which inhibits growth of other microorganisms.

anticarcinogen A substance that inhibits the development of cancer.

anticholinergic A drug that acts on nerves using acetylcholine as a neurotransmitter.

anticoagulant A substance that inhibits the clotting of blood.

anticodon The sequence of three adjacent nucleotides in a tRNA molecule that is complementary to a codon on mRNA.

antihistamine A substance that relieves the symptoms caused by allergens: sneezing, itchy eyes, and runny nose.

anti-inflammatory A substance that inhibits inflammation.

antimetabolite A compound that inhibits the synthesis of DNA and thus slows the growth of cancer cells.

antioxidant A reducing agent that retards damaging oxidation reactions in living cells or reacts with free radicals to prevent rancidity in foods.

antiperspirant A formulation that retards perspiration by constricting the openings of sweat glands.

antipyretic A fever-reducing substance.

apoenzyme The pure protein part of an enzyme.

applied research An investigation aimed at creating a useful product or solving a particular problem.

aqueous solution A solution in which the solvent is water.

arithmetic growth A process in which a constant quantity is added during each period of time.

aromatic compound A compound that has a ring structure and properties like those of benzene.

asbestos A fibrous silicate mineral composed of chains of SIO_4 tetrahedra.

astringent A substance that constricts the openings of sweat glands, thus reducing the amount of perspiration that escapes.

atmosphere The thin blanket of air surrounding Earth.

atmosphere (atm) A unit of pressure equal to 760 mmHg.

atom The smallest characteristic particle of an element.

atomic mass unit (u) The unit of relative atomic masses, equal to $\frac{1}{12}$ the mass of a carbon-12 atom.

atomic number (Z) The number of protons in the nucleus of an atom.

atomic theory A model that explains the law of multiple proportions and the law of constant composition by stating that all elements are composed of atoms.

Avogadro's hypothesis Equal volumes of gases, regardless of their compositions, contain equal numbers of molecules when measured at a given temperature and pressure.

Avogadro's law At a fixed temperature and pressure, the volume of a gas is directly proportional to the amount (number of moles) of gas.

Avogadro's number The number of atoms (6.022×10^{23}) in exactly 12 g of pure carbon-12.

background radiation Constantly occurring radiation from cosmic rays and from natural radioactive isotopes in air, water, soil, and rocks.

base A substance that, when added to water, produces an excess of hydroxide ions; a proton acceptor.

base triplet The sequence of three bases on a tRNA molecule that determine which amino acid it can carry.

basic anhydride A substance, such as a metal oxide, that reacts with water to form a base.

basic research The search for knowledge for its own sake.

battery A series of two or more connected electrochemical cells.

becquerel (Bq) A measure of the rate of radioactive decay; 1 becquerel (Bq) = 1 disintegration/s.

beta decay Emission of a beta particle by a radioactive nucleus.

beta (β) particle An electron emitted by a radioactive nucleus.

beta pleated sheet A secondary protein structure in which arrays of chains form a zigzag sheet.

binary ionic compound A compound consisting of cations of a metal and anions of a nonmetal.

binding energy The energy that holds the nucleons together in an atom's nucleus.

biochemical oxygen demand (BOD) The quantity of oxygen required by microorganisms to remove organic matter from water.

biochemistry The study of the chemistry of living things and life processes.

biomass Dry plant material used as fuel.

bitumen A hydrocarbon mixture obtained from tar sands by heating.

bleach An oxidizing agent used to remove unwanted color from fabric or other material.

blood sugar Glucose, a simple sugar that is circulated in the bloodstream and used directly by cells for energy.

boiling point The temperature at which a substance changes state from a liquid to a gas throughout the bulk of the liquid.

bond See **chemical bond**.

bonding pair A pair of electrons shared by two atoms, forming a chemical bond.

Boyle's law For a given mass of gas at constant temperature, the volume varies inversely with the pressure.

breeder reactor A nuclear reactor that converts nonfissionable isotopes to nuclear fuel.

broad-spectrum antibiotic An antibiotic that is effective against a wide variety of microorganisms.

bronze An alloy of copper and tin.

buffer solution A mixture of a weak acid and its conjugate base or a weak base and its conjugate acid that maintains a nearly constant pH when a small amount of strong acid or strong base is added.

builder Any substance (often a complex phosphate) added to a surfactant to increase its detergency.

calorie (cal) The amount of heat required to raise the temperature of 1 g of water by 1 °C.

carbohydrate A compound consisting of carbon, hydrogen, and oxygen; a starch or sugar.

carbon-14 dating A radioisotopic technique for determining the age of artifacts, based on the half-life of carbon-14.

carbonyl group (C═O) A functional group consisting of a carbon atom joined to an oxygen atom by a double bond.

carboxyl group (—COOH) A carbon atom with a double bond to one oxygen atom and a single bond to a second oxygen atom, which in turn is bonded to a hydrogen atom; the functional group of carboxylic acids.

carboxylic acid (RCOOH) An organic compound that contains the carboxyl functional group.

carcinogen A substance or physical entity that causes the growth of tumors.

catabolism Any metabolic process in which complex compounds are broken down into simpler substances.

catalyst A substance that increases the rate of a chemical reaction without itself being used up.

catalytic converter A device that uses catalysts that oxidize carbon monoxide and hydrocarbons to carbon dioxide and reduce nitrogen oxides to nitrogen gas.

catalytic reforming A process that converts straight-chain alkanes to aromatic hydrocarbons.

cathode A negative electrode at which reduction occurs.

cathode ray A stream of high-speed electrons emitted from a cathode in an evacuated tube.

cation A positively charged ion.

cationic surfactant A surfactant whose active part (water-soluble head) bears a positive charge.

celluloid Cellulose nitrate, a synthetic material derived from natural cellulose by treating it with nitric acid.

cellulose A polymer comprised of glucose units joined by beta linkages.

Celsius scale A temperature scale on which water freezes at 0° and boils at 100°.

cement A complex mixture of calcium and aluminum silicates made from limestone and clay; mixed with water to make concrete.

ceramic A hard, solid product made by heating clay and other minerals to fuse them.

chain reaction A self-sustaining reaction in which one or more products of one event cause one or more new events.

charcoal filtration Filtration of water through charcoal to adsorb organic compounds.

Charles's law For a given mass of gas at constant pressure, the volume varies directly with the absolute temperature.

chelating Tying up metal ions by surrounding them.

chemical bond The force of attraction that holds atoms or ions together in compounds.

chemical change A change in chemical composition.

chemical equation A shorthand representation of a chemical change that uses symbols and formulas instead of words.

chemical property A characteristic of a substance that describes the way in which the substance reacts with another substance to change its composition.

chemical symbol An abbreviation, consisting of one or two letters, that stands for an element.

chemistry The study of matter and the changes it undergoes.

chemotherapy The use of chemicals to control or cure diseases.

chiral carbon A carbon atom that has four different groups attached to it.

coal A solid fossil fuel that is rich in carbon.

codon A sequence of three adjacent nucleotides in an mRNA molecule that specifies one amino acid.

coenzyme An organic molecule (often a vitamin) that combines with an apoenzyme to make a complete, functioning enzyme.

cofactor An ion or molecule that combines with an apoenzyme to make a complete, functioning enzyme.

cologne A diluted perfume.

combined gas law The single relationship that incorporates the simple gas laws.

compound A substance made up of two or more elements combined in a fixed ratio.

concentrated solution A solution that has a relatively large amount of solute per unit volume of solution.

concrete A building material made from cement, sand, gravel, and water.

condensation The reverse of vaporization; a change from the gaseous state to the liquid state.

condensation polymerization A polymerization reaction in which not all the atoms in the starting monomers are incorporated in the polymer because water (or other small) molecules are formed as by-products.

condensed structural formula A chemical formula for an organic compound that omits the bonds joining hydrogens to carbons.

conjugate acid–base pair Two molecules or ions that differ by one proton.

copolymer A polymer formed by the combination of two (or more) different monomers.

core electrons Electrons in any shell of an atom except the outermost shell.

corrosive waste A hazardous waste that requires a special container because it destroys conventional container materials.

cosmetics Substances defined in the 1938 U.S. Food, Drug, and Cosmetic Act as "articles intended to be rubbed, poured, sprinkled or sprayed on, introduced into, or otherwise applied to the human body or any part thereof, for cleaning, beautifying, promoting attractiveness or altering the appearance."

cosmic rays Extremely high-energy radiation from outer space.

covalent bond A bond formed when two atoms share one or more pairs of electrons.

cream An emulsion of tiny water droplets in oil.

critical mass The minimum amount of fissionable material required to achieve a self-sustaining chain reaction.

crystal A solid, regular array of ions.

cyclic hydrocarbon A ring-containing hydrocarbon.

daughter isotope An isotope formed by the radioactive decay of another isotope.

defoliant A substance that causes premature dropping of leaves by plants.

density The amount of mass per unit volume.

deodorant A product that contains perfume to mask body odor; some have a germicide to kill odor-causing bacteria.

deoxyribonucleic acid (DNA) The type of nucleic acid found primarily in the nuclei of cells; contains the sugar deoxyribose.

depilatory A hair remover.

deposition The direct formation of a solid from a gas without passing through the liquid state; the reverse of sublimation.

depressant drug A drug that slows both physical and mental activity.

detergent A cleansing agent, usually a synthetic surfactant.

deuterium An isotope of hydrogen with a proton and a neutron in the nucleus (mass of 2 u).

dextro isomer A "right-handed" isomer.

dietary mineral An inorganic substance required in the diet for proper health and well-being.

Dietary Reference Intakes (DRIs) A set of reference values for nutrients established by the U.S. Academy of Sciences for planning and assessing diets.

dilute solution A solution that has a relatively small amount of solute per unit volume of solution.

dioxins Highly toxic chlorinated cyclic compounds produced by burning wastes containing chlorinated compounds; once found as contaminants in the defoliant 2, 4, 5-T.

dipole A molecule that is polar.

dipole–dipole forces The attractive forces that exist among polar covalent molecules.

disaccharide A sugar that on hydrolysis yields two monosaccharide molecules per molecule of disaccharide.

dispersion forces The momentary, usually weak, attractive forces between molecules resulting from electron motions that create short-lived dipoles.

dissociative anesthetic A substance that causes gross personality disorders, including hallucinations similar to those in near-death experiences.

dissolved oxygen Oxygen dissolved in water; provides a measure of the water's ability to support fish and other aquatic life.

disulfide linkage A covalent linkage between cysteine units through two sulfur atoms.

diuretic A substance that increases the output of urine.

double bond The sharing of two pairs of electrons between two atoms.

doubling time The time it takes a population to double in size.

drug A substance that affects the functioning of living things; used to relieve pain, to treat illness, or to improve health or well-being.

drug abuse The use of a drug for its intoxicating effect.

drug misuse The use of a drug in a manner other than its intended use.

elastomer A polymeric material that returns to its original shape after being stretched.

electrochemical cell A device that produces electricity by means of a chemical reaction.

electrode A carbon rod or a metal strip inserted into an electrochemical cell, at which oxidation or reduction occurs.

electrolysis The process of using electricity to cause chemical change.

electrolyte A compound that conducts an electric current in water solution.

electron The subatomic particle that bears a unit of negative charge.

electron capture (EC) A type of radioactive decay in which a nucleus absorbs an electron from the first or second shell of the atom.

electron configuration The arrangement of an atom's electrons in its energy levels.

electron-dot symbol See Lewis symbol.

electronegativity The attraction of an atom in a molecule for a bonding pair of electrons.

electrostatic precipitator A device that removes particulate matter from smokestack gases by creating an electric charge on the particles, which are then removed by attraction to a surface of opposite charge.

element A substance composed of atoms that have the same number of protons.

emollient An oil or grease used as a skin softener.

emulsion A suspension of submicroscopic particles of fat or oil in water.

enantiomers Isomers that are not superimposable on their mirror image.

end note The fraction of a perfume that has the lowest volatility; composed of large molecules.

endorphins Naturally occurring peptides that bond to the same receptor sites as morphine.

endothermic Absorbing energy from the surroundings.

energy The ability to do work.

energy levels (shells) The specific, quantized values of energy that an electron can have in an atom.

enrichment (of food) Replacement of B vitamins and addition of iron to flour.

enrichment (of an isotope) The process by which the proportion of one isotope of an element is increased relative to those of the others.

entropy A measure of the dispersal of energy among the possible states of a system.

enzyme A biological catalyst.

essential amino acid An amino acid that is not produced in the body and must be included in the diet.

ester (RCOOR') A compound derived from a carboxylic acid and an alcohol; the —OH of the acid is replaced by an —OR group.

estrogen A female sex hormone.

ether (ROR') A molecule with two hydrocarbon groups attached to the same oxygen atom.

eutrophication The excessive growth of algae in a body of water, which causes some of the plants to die because of a lack of light; the water becomes choked with vegetation, depleted of oxygen, and useless as a fish habitat or for recreation.

excited state A state in which an atom has at least one electron that has moved from a lower to a higher energy level.

exothermic Releasing energy (usually heat) to the surroundings.

fast-twitch fibers The stronger, larger muscle fibers that are suited for short bursts of vigorous exercise.

fat An ester formed by the reaction of glycerol with three fatty-acid units; a triglyceride or triacylglycerol.

fat depots Storage places for fats in the body.

fatty acid A carboxylic acid that contains 4 to 20 or more carbon atoms in a chain.

first law of thermodynamics (law of conservation of energy) Energy cannot be created or destroyed, only transformed.

flammable waste A hazardous waste that burns readily on ignition, presenting a fire hazard.

FLaReS An acronym representing four rules used to test a claim: falsifiability, logic, replicability, and sufficiency.

flocculent A substance that causes particles to clump together and settle out.

food additive Any substance other than a basic foodstuff that is added to food to aid nutrition, enhance color or flavor, or provide texture.

formula A representation of a chemical substance in which the component chemical elements are represented by their symbols.

formula mass The sum of the masses of the atoms represented in the formula of a substance, expressed in atomic mass units (u).

fossil fuels Natural fuels derived from once-living plants and animals; especially coal, petroleum, and natural gas.

free radical A highly reactive chemical species that contains an unpaired electron.

freezing The reverse of melting; a change from the liquid to the solid state.

fuel A substance that burns readily with the release of significant energy.

fuel cell A device that produces electricity directly from continuously supplied fuel and oxygen.

functional group An atom or group of atoms that confers characteristic properties to a family of organic compounds.

fundamental particle An electron, proton, or neutron.

gamma decay Emission of a gamma ray ($_0^0\gamma$) by a radioactive nucleus.

gamma (γ) rays Radiation that is emitted by radioactive substances and has higher energy and is more penetrating than X-rays.

gas The state of matter in which the substance takes both the shape and volume of a container that it occupies.

gasoline The fraction of petroleum that consists of hydrocarbons, mainly alkanes, with five to twelve carbons and is used as automotive fuel.

gene The segment of a DNA molecule that contains the information necessary to produce a protein; the smallest unit of hereditary information.

general anesthetic A depressant that acts on the brain to produce unconsciousness and insensitivity to pain.

geometric growth A process in which the rate of growth itself increases during each period of time.

geothermal energy Energy derived from the heat of Earth's interior.

glass A noncrystalline solid material obtained by melting sand with soda, lime, and various other metal oxides.

glass transition temperature (T_g) The temperature above which a polymer is rubbery and tough and below which the polymer is brittle.

global warming An increase in Earth's average temperature.

globular protein A protein whose molecules are folded into compact spherical or ovoid shapes.

glycogen A polymer of glucose with alpha linkages and branched chains; stored in the liver and muscles.

GRAS list A list, established by the U.S. Congress in 1958, of food additives generally recognized as safe.

green chemistry An approach that uses materials and processes that are intended to prevent or reduce pollution at its source.

greenhouse effect The retention of the Sun's heat energy by Earth's atmosphere as a result of excess carbon dioxide and other gases in the atmosphere.

ground state The state of an atom in which all of its electrons are in the lowest possible energy levels.

group The elements in a column in the periodic table; a family of elements.

half-life The length of time required for one-half of the radioactive nuclei in a sample to decay.

hallucinogenic drug A drug that produces visions and sensations that are not part of reality.

halogen An element in group 7A in the customary U.S. arrangement of the periodic table or in group 17 of the IUPAC-recommended table.

hard water Water containing excessive concentrations of ions of calcium, magnesium, and/or iron.

hazardous waste A waste that, when improperly managed, can cause or contribute to death or illness or threaten human health or the environment.

heat Energy transfer that occurs as a result of a temperature difference.

heat of vaporization The amount of heat involved in the evaporation or condensation of a fixed amount of a substance.

heat stroke A failure of the body's heat regulatory system; unless the victim is treated promptly, the rapid rise in body temperature will cause brain damage or death.

herbicide A material used to kill weeds (plants classified as pests).

heterocyclic compound A cyclic compound in which one or more atoms in the ring is not carbon.

homogeneous Completely uniform; a property of a sample that has the same composition in all parts.

homologous series A series of compounds whose adjacent members differ by a fixed unit of structure.

hormone A chemical messenger secreted into the blood by an endocrine gland.

humectant A moistening agent added to food.

hydrocarbon An organic compound that contains only carbon and hydrogen.

hydrogen bomb A bomb based on the nuclear fusion of isotopes of hydrogen.

hydrogen bond A type of intermolecular force in which a hydrogen atom covalently bonded in one molecule is attracted to a nonmetal atom in a neighboring molecule; both the atom to which the hydrogen atom is bonded and the one to which it is attracted are small, highly electronegative atoms, usually N, O, or F.

hydrolysis The reaction of a substance with water; literally, a splitting by water.

hydrophilic Attracted to polar solvents such as water.

hydrophobic Not attracted to water; attracted to oil or grease.

hypoallergenic cosmetics Cosmetics claimed to cause fewer allergic reactions than regular products.

hypothesis A tentative explanation of observations that can be tested by experiment.

ideal gas law The volume of a gas is proportional to the amount of gas and its Kelvin temperature and inversely proportional to its pressure.

induced radioactivity Radioactivity caused by bombarding a stable isotope with elemental particles, forming a radioactive isotope.

industrial smog (sulfurous smog) Polluted air associated with industrial activities, characterized by sulfur oxides and particulate matter.

inorganic chemistry The study of the compounds of all elements other than carbon.

insecticide A substance that is used to kill insects.

iodine number The number of grams of iodine that reacts with 100 g of a fat or oil; an indication of the degree of unsaturation.

ion A charged atom or group of atoms.

ionic bond The chemical bond that results when electrons are transferred from a metal to a nonmetal; the electrostatic attraction between ions of opposite charge.

ionizing radiation Radiation that produces ions as it passes through matter.

isoelectronic Having the same electron configuration.

isomers Compounds that have the same molecular formula but different structures.

isotopes Atoms that have the same number of protons but different numbers of neutrons.

joule (J) The SI unit of energy (1 J = 0.239 cal).

juvenile hormone A hormone that controls the rate of development of young organisms; used to prevent insects from maturing.

kelvin (K) The SI unit of temperature; zero on the Kelvin scale is absolute zero.

keratin The tough, fibrous protein that comprises most of the outermost layer of the epidermis.

kerogen The complex material found in oil shale; has an approximate composition of $(C_6H_8O)_n$, where n is a large number.

ketone (RCOR′) An organic compound with a carbonyl group between two carbon atoms.

ketose A monosaccharide with a ketone functional group.

kilocalorie (kcal) A unit of energy equal to 1000 cal; one food calorie.

kilogram (kg) The SI unit of mass, a quantity equal to about 2.2 lb.

kinetic energy The energy of motion.

kinetic–molecular theory An explanation of the behavior of gases based on the motion and energy of particles.

lanolin A natural wax obtained from sheep's wool.

law of combining volumes The volumes of gaseous reactants and products are in a small whole-number ratio when all measurements are made at the same temperature and pressure.

law of conservation of energy See **first law of thermodynamics.**

law of conservation of mass Matter is neither created nor destroyed during a chemical change.

law of definite proportions A compound always contains the same elements in exactly the same proportions by mass; also called the *law of constant composition.*

law of multiple proportions Elements may combine in different proportions to form more than one compound—for example, CO and CO_2.

LD$_{50}$ The dosage that is lethal to 50% of a population of test animals.

levo isomer A "left-handed" isomer.

Lewis formula A structural formula of a molecule or polyatomic ion that shows the arrangement of atoms, bonds, and lone pairs.

Lewis symbol A symbol consisting of the element's symbol surrounded by dots representing the atom's valence electrons; also referred to as an *electron-dot symbol.*

limiting reactant The reactant that is used up first in a reaction, after which the reaction ceases no matter how much remains of the other reactants.

line-angle formula A representation of a molecule in which the corners and ends of lines are understood to be carbon atoms and each carbon atom is understood to be attached to enough hydrogen atoms to give it four bonds.

line spectrum The pattern of colored lines emitted by an element.

lipid A substance from animal or plant cells that is soluble in solvents of low polarity and insoluble in water.

lipoprotein A protein combined with a lipid, such as a triglyceride or cholesterol.

liquid The state of matter in which the substance assumes the shape of its container, flows readily, and maintains a fairly constant volume.

liter (L) A unit of volume equal to a cubic decimeter.

local anesthetic A substance that renders part of the body insensitive to pain while leaving the patient conscious.

lone pair A pair of unshared electrons in the valence shell of an atom; also called a *nonbonding pair.*

lotion An emulsion of tiny oil droplets dispersed in water.

main group elements The elements in the A groups of the customary U.S. arrangement of the periodic table or in groups 1, 2, and 13–18 of the IUPAC-recommended table.

marijuana A hallucinogenic drug consisting of the leaves, flowers, seeds, and small stems of the *Cannabis* plant.

mass A measure of the quantity of matter.

mass–energy equation Einstein's equation $E = mc^2$ in which E is energy, m is mass, and c is the speed of light.

mass number (A) The sum of the numbers of protons and neutrons in the nucleus of an atom; also called the *nucleon number.*

matter The stuff of which all materials are made; anything that has mass and occupies space.

melanin A brownish-black pigment that determines the color of the skin and hair.

melting point The temperature at which a substance changes from the solid to the liquid state.

messenger RNA (mRNA) The type of RNA that contains the codons for a protein; travels from the nucleus of the cell to a ribosome.

metabolism The set of coordinated chemical reactions that keep the cells of an organism alive.

metalloid An element with properties intermediate between those of metals and those of nonmetals.

metals The elements that are to the left of the heavy, stepped line in the periodic table.

meter (m) The SI unit of length, slightly longer than a yard.

mica A mineral composed of SiO_4 tetrahedra arranged in a two-dimensional, sheetlike array.

micelle A tiny spherical oil droplet in which the hydrocarbon tails of soap molecules are embedded, with their hydrophilic heads lying along the outer surface.

micronutrient A substance needed by a plant or animal in only tiny amounts.

middle note The fraction of a perfume that is intermediate in volatility and is responsible for the lingering aroma after most top-note compounds have vaporized.

mineral (dietary) An inorganic substance required in the diet for good health.

mineral (geological) A naturally occurring inorganic solid with a definite composition.

mixture Matter with a variable composition.

moisturizer A substance that acts to retain moisture in the skin by forming a protective physical barrier.

molarity (M) The concentration of a solution in moles of solute per liter of solution.

molar mass The mass of one mole of a substance expressed in units of grams/mole.

molar volume The volume occupied by 1 mol of a substance (usually a gas) under specified conditions.

mole (mol) The amount of a substance that contains 6.022×10^{23} elementary units (atoms, molecules, or formula units) of the substance.

molecular mass The mass of a molecule of a substance; the sum of the atomic masses as indicated by the molecular formula, expressed in atomic mass units (u).

molecule An electrically neutral unit of two or more atoms joined by covalent bonds; the smallest fundamental unit of a molecular substance.

monomer A substance of relatively low molecular mass; monomer molecules are the building blocks of polymers.

monosaccharide A carbohydrate that cannot be hydrolyzed into simpler sugars.

mousse A foamy hair care product composed of resins and used to hold hair in place.

mutagen Any entity that causes changes in genes without destroying the genetic material.

narcotic A depressant, analgesic drug that induces narcosis (sleep).

natural gas A mixture of gases, mainly methane, found in underground deposits.

natural philosophy Philosophical speculation about nature.

neuron A nerve cell.

neurotransmitter A chemical that carries an impulse across a synapse from one nerve cell to the next.

neurotrophin A substance produced during exercise that promotes the growth of brain cells.

neutralization The combination of H^+ and OH^- to form water or the reaction of an acid and a base to produce a salt and water.

neutron A nuclear particle with a mass of approximately 1 u and no electric charge.

nitrogen cycle The various processes by which nitrogen is cycled among the atmosphere, soil, water, and living organisms.

nitrogen fixation A process that combines nitrogen with one or more other elements.

noble gases Generally unreactive elements that appear in group 8A of the customary U.S. arrangement of the periodic table or in group 18 of the IUPAC-recommended table.

nonbonding pair See **lone pair.**

nonionic surfactant A surfactant whose active part bears no ionic charge.

nonmetals The elements to the right of the heavy, stepped line in the periodic table.

nonpolar covalent bond A covalent bond in which there is equal sharing of the bonding pair of electrons.

nonsteroidal anti-inflammatory drug (NSAID) A type of anti-inflammatory drug that is milder than the more potent steroidal anti-inflammatory drugs such as cortisone and prednisone.

nuclear fission The splitting of an atomic nucleus into two smaller ones.

nuclear fusion The combination of two small atomic nuclei to produce one larger nucleus.

nuclear reactor A power plant that produces electricity using nuclear fission reactions.

nucleic acid A nucleotide polymer, DNA or RNA.

nucleon A proton or a neutron.

nucleon number See **mass number**.

nucleotide A combination of an amine base, a sugar unit, and a phosphate unit; the monomer unit of nucleic acids.

nucleus The tiny core of an atom, composed of protons and neutrons and containing all the positive charge and most of the mass of the atom.

octane rating The comparison of the antiknock quality of a gasoline to that of pure isooctane (with a rating of 100).

octet rule Atoms tend to have eight electrons in the outermost shell.

oil (food) A substance formed from glycerol and fatty acids, which is liquid at room temperature.

oil shale Fossil rock from which oil can be obtained at high cost.

optical brightener A compound that absorbs the invisible ultraviolet component of sunlight and reemits it as visible light at the blue end of the spectrum; added to detergents to make whites "whiter."

orbital A volume of space in an atom that is occupied by one or two electrons.

organic chemistry The study of the compounds of carbon.

organic farming Farming without using synthetic fertilizers or pesticides.

oxidation An increase in oxidation number; combination of an element or compound with oxygen; loss of hydrogen; loss of electrons.

oxidizing agent A substance that causes oxidation and is itself reduced.

oxygen cycle The various processes by which oxygen is cycled among the atmosphere, soil, water, and living organisms.

oxygen debt The demand for oxygen in muscle cells that builds up during anaerobic exercise.

ozone layer The layer of the stratosphere that contains ozone and shields living creatures on Earth from the Sun's ultraviolet radiation.

paint A surface coating that contains a pigment, a binder, and a solvent.

particulate matter (PM) An air pollutant composed of solid and liquid particles whose size is greater than that of a molecule.

peptide bond The amide linkage that joins amino acids in chains of peptides, polypeptides, and proteins.

percent by mass The concentration of a solution, expressed as (mass of solute ÷ mass of solution) × 100%.

percent by volume The concentration of a solution, expressed as (volume of solute ÷ volume of solution) × 100%.

perfume A fragrant mixture of plant extracts and other chemicals dissolved in alcohol.

period A horizontal row of the periodic table.

periodic table A systematic arrangement of the elements in columns and rows; elements in a given column have similar properties.

pesticide A substance that kills some kind of pest (weeds, insects, rodents, and so on).

petroleum A thick liquid mixture of (mostly) hydrocarbons occurring in various geologic deposits.

pH The negative logarithm of the hydronium ion concentration, which indicates the degree of acidity or basicity of a solution.

pharmacology The study of the response of living organisms to drugs.

phenol A compound with an OH group attached to a benzene ring.

pheromone A chemical secreted by an insect or other organism to mark a trail, send out an alarm, or attract a mate.

photochemical smog Smog created by the action of sunlight on hydrocarbons and nitrogen oxides, which come mainly from automobile exhaust.

photon A unit particle of energy.

photosynthesis The chemical process used by green plants to convert solar energy into chemical energy by reducing carbon dioxide and producing glucose.

photovoltaic cell A solar cell; a cell that uses semiconductors to convert sunlight directly to electric energy.

physical change A change in physical state or form.

physical property A quality of a substance that can be demonstrated without changing the composition of the substance.

phytoremediation A method of wastewater treatment that allows plants in a lagoon to remove metals and other contaminates.

placebo effect The phenomenon in which an inactive substance produces results in recipients for psychological reasons.

plasma A state of matter similar to a gas but composed of isolated electrons and nuclei rather than discrete whole atoms or molecules.

plasticizer A substance added to some plastics to make them more flexible and easier to work with.

poison A substance that causes injury, illness, or death of a living organism.

polar covalent bond A covalent bond in which the bonding pair of electrons is shared unequally by the two atoms, giving each atom a partial positive or negative charge.

polar molecule A molecule that has a separation between centers of positive and negative charge; a dipole.

pollutant A chemical that causes undesirable effects by being in the wrong place and/or in the wrong concentration.

polyamide A polymer that has monomer units joined by amide linkages.

polyatomic ion A charged particle consisting of two or more covalently bonded atoms.

polyester A polymer that has monomer units joined by ester linkages.

polymer A molecule with a large molecular mass that is formed of repeating smaller units (monomers).

polymerase chain reaction (PCR) A process that reproduces many copies of a DNA fragment.

polypeptide A polymer of amino acids, usually of lower molecular mass than a protein.

polysaccharide A carbohydrate, such as starch or cellulose, that consists of many monosaccharide units linked together.

polyunsaturated fat A fat containing fatty-acid units that have two or more carbon-to-carbon double bonds.

positron (β^+ or $_{+1}^{\ 0}e$) A positively charged particle with the mass of an electron.

potential energy Energy due to position or composition.

preemergent herbicide A herbicide that is rapidly broken down in the soil and can therefore be used to kill weed plants before crop seedlings emerge.

primary plant nutrients Nitrogen, phosphorus, and potassium.

primary sewage treatment Treatment of wastewater in a holding pond to allow some of the sewage solids to settle out as sludge.

primary structure The amino-acid sequence in a protein.

product A substance produced by a chemical reaction; product formulas follow the arrow in a chemical equation.

progestin A steroid hormone that mimics the action of progesterone.

prostaglandin One of several hormone-like lipids that are derived from the fatty acid arachidonic acid; involved in increased blood pressure, the contractions of smooth muscle, and other physiological processes.

protein An amino acid polymer with a molecular weight exceeding about 10,000 u.

proton (H^+) The hydrogen ion in acid–base chemistry.

proton (nuclear) The unit of positive charge in the nucleus of an atom.

psychotropic drugs Drugs that affect the mind.

purine A heterocyclic amine base with two fused rings, found in nucleic acids.

pyrimidine A heterocyclic amine base with one ring, found in nucleic acids.

quantum A discrete unit of energy; one photon.

quartz A silicate composed of SiO_4 tetrahedra arranged in a three-dimensional array.

quaternary structure An arrangement of protein subunits in a particular pattern.

radiation therapy Use of radioisotopes to destroy cancer cells.

radioactive decay The disintegration of an unstable atomic nucleus with spontaneous emission of radiation.

radioactive fallout Radioactive debris produced by explosion of a nuclear bomb.

radioactivity The spontaneous emission of particles (for example, alpha or beta) or rays (gamma) from unstable atomic nuclei.

radioisotopes Atoms or ions with radioactive nuclei.

reactant A starting material in a chemical change; reactant formulas precede the arrow in a chemical equation.

reactive wastes Hazardous wastes that tend to react spontaneously or to react vigorously with air or water.

Recommended Daily Allowance (RDA) The recommended level of a nutrient necessary for a balanced diet.

reducing agent A substance that causes reduction and is itself oxidized.

reduction A decrease in oxidation number; a gain of electrons; a loss of oxygen; a gain of hydrogen.

replication Copying or duplication; the process by which DNA reproduces itself.

resin A polymeric organic material, usually a sticky solid or semisolid.

restorative drug A drug used to relieve the pain and reduce the inflammation resulting from overuse of muscles.

retrovirus An RNA virus that synthesizes DNA in a host cell.

reverse osmosis A method of pressure filtration through a semipermeable membrane; water flows from an area of high salt concentration to an area of low salt concentration.

ribonucleic acid (RNA) The form of nucleic acid found mainly in the cytoplasm but also present in all other parts of the cell; contains the sugar ribose.

risk–benefit analysis A technique for estimating a desirability quotient by dividing the benefits by the risks.

rule of 72 A mathematical formula that gives the doubling time for a population growing geometrically; 72 divided by the annual rate of growth expressed as a percentage equals the doubling time.

salt An ionic compound produced by the reaction of an acid with a base.

saponins Natural compounds in some plants that produce a soapy lather.

saturated fat A triglyceride composed of a large proportion of saturated fatty acids esterified with glycerol.

saturated hydrocarbon An alkane; a compound of carbon and hydrogen with only single bonds.

science An accumulation of knowledge about nature and the physical world.

scientific law A summary of experimental data; often expressed in the form of a mathematical equation.

scientific model A representation of an invisible process that uses tangible items or pictures.

sebum An oily secretion that protects the skin from moisture loss.

second law of thermodynamics The entropy of the universe increases in any spontaneous process.

secondary plant nutrients Magnesium, calcium, and sulfur.

secondary sewage treatment Passing effluent from primary sewage treatment through gravel and sand filters to aerate the water and remove suspended solids.

secondary structure The arrangement of a protein's polypeptide chains—for example, helix or pleated sheet.

sex attractant A pheromone released by an organism to attract a mate.

shell One of the specific, quantized energy levels that an electron can occupy in an atom.

significant figures Those measured digits that are known with certainty plus one uncertain digit.

silicone A polymer whose chains consists of alternating silicon and oxygen atoms.

single bond A pair of electrons shared between two atoms.

SI units (International System of Units) A measuring system that is used by scientists worldwide and has seven base quantities with their multiples and submultiples.

skin protection factor (SPF) The rating of a sunscreen's ability to absorb or block ultraviolet radiation.

slag A relatively low-melting product of the reaction of limestone with silicate impurities in iron ore.

slow-twitch fibers Muscle fibers suited for steady exercise of long duration.

smog The combination of smoke and fog; polluted air.

soap A salt (usually a sodium salt) of a long-chain carboxylic acid.

solar cell A device used for converting sunlight to electricity; a photoelectric cell.

solid A state of matter in which the substance has a definite shape and volume.

solute The substance that is dissolved in another substance (solvent) to form a solution; usually present in a smaller amount than the solvent.

solution A homogeneous mixture of two or more substances.

solvent The substance that dissolves another substance (solute) to form a solution; usually present in a larger amount than the solute.

specific heat The amount of heat required to raise the temperature of 1 g of a substance by 1 °C.

standard temperature and pressure (STP) Conditions of 0 °C and 1 atm pressure.

starch A polymer of glucose units joined by alpha linkages; a complex carbohydrate.

starvation The withholding of nutrition from the body, whether voluntary or involuntary.

steel An alloy of iron containing small amounts of carbon and usually another metal such as manganese, nickel, or chromium.

stereoisomers Isomers having the same formula but differing in the arrangement of atoms or groups of atoms in three-dimensional space.

steroid A molecule that has a four-ring skeletal structure, with one cyclopentane and three cyclohexane fused rings.

stimulant drug A drug that increases alertness, speeds up mental processes, and generally elevates the mood.

stoichiometric factor A factor that relates the numbers of moles of two substances through their coefficients in a chemical equation.

stoichiometry The quantitative relationship between reactants and products in a chemical reaction.

strong acid An acid that ionizes completely in water; a potent proton donor.

strong base A base that dissociates completely in water; a potent proton acceptor.

structural formula A chemical formula that shows how the atoms of a molecule are arranged, to which other atom(s) they are bonded, and the kinds of bonds.

sublevel See **subshell**.

sublimation Conversion of a solid directly to the gaseous state without going through the liquid state.

subshell A set of orbitals in an atom that are in the same shell and have the same energy; also called a *sublevel*.

substance A sample of matter that always has the same composition, no matter how it is made or where it is found.

substituent An atom or group of atoms substituted for a hydrogen atom on a hydrocarbon.

substrate The substance that attaches to the active site of an enzyme and is then acted upon.

sulfurous smog See **industrial smog**.

sunscreen A substance or mixture that blocks or absorbs ultraviolet (UV) radiation.

supercritical fluid An intermediate state having properties of both gases and liquids.

surface-active agent (surfactant) Any substance that stabilizes the suspension in water of a nonpolar substance such as oil.

surroundings Everything that is not part of the system being observed in a thermochemical study.

sustainable agriculture Farming practices that can produce food and fiber indefinitely, without causing irreparable damage to the ecosystem.

sustainable chemistry An approach designed to meet the needs of the present generation without compromising the needs of future generations.

synapse A tiny gap between nerve cells.

synergistic effect An effect greater than the sum of the effects expected from two or more phenomena.

system The part of the universe under consideration in a thermochemical study.

tar sands Sands that contain bitumen, a thick hydrocarbon material.

technology The practical application of knowledge by which humans modify the materials of nature to better satisfy their needs and wants.

temperature A measure of heat intensity, or how energetic the particles of a sample are.

temperature inversion A warm layer of air above a cool, stagnant lower layer.

teratogen A substance that causes birth defects when introduced into the body of a pregnant female.

tertiary structure The folding pattern of a protein.

tetracyclines Antibacterial drugs with four fused rings.

theory A detailed explanation of a phenomenon that is based on experimentation and may be revised if new data warrant.

thermochemistry The study of energy changes that occur during chemical reactions.

thermonuclear reactions Nuclear fusion reactions that require extremely high temperatures and pressures.

thermoplastic polymer A kind of polymer that can be heated and reshaped.

thermosetting polymer A kind of polymer that cannot be softened and remolded.

top note The fraction of a perfume that vaporizes most quickly, is composed of relatively small molecules, and is responsible for the odor when the perfume is first applied.

toxicology The branch of pharmacology that deals with the effects of poisons on the body, their identification and detection, and remedies for them.

toxic waste A waste that contains or releases poisonous substances in amounts large enough to threaten human health or the environment.

toxin A poisonous substance produced by a living organism.

tracers Radioisotopes used to trace the movement of substances or locate the sites of activity in physical, chemical, and biological systems.

transcription The process by which a segment of DNA transfers its information to a messenger RNA (mRNA) molecule during protein synthesis.

transfer RNA (tRNA) A small molecule that contains anticodon nucleotides; the RNA molecule that bonds to and carries an amino acid.

transition elements Metallic elements in the B groups of the customary U.S. arrangement of the periodic table or in groups 3–12 of the IUPAC-recommended table.

translation The process by which the information contained in the codon of an mRNA molecule is converted to a protein structure.

transmutation The conversion of one element into another.

triglyceride An ester of glycerol with three fatty-acid units; also called a triacylglycerol.

triple bond The sharing of three pairs of electrons between two atoms.

tritium A radioactive isotope of hydrogen with two neutrons and one proton in the nucleus (hydrogen-3).

unsaturated hydrocarbon An alkene, alkyne, or aromatic hydrocarbon; a hydrocarbon containing one or more double or triple bonds or aromatic rings.

valence electrons Electrons in the outermost shell of an atom.

valence shell electron pair repulsion theory (VSEPR theory) A theory of chemical bonding useful in determining the shapes of molecules; it states that valence shell electron pairs around a central atom locate themselves as far apart as possible.

vaporization The process by which a substance changes from the liquid to the gaseous (vapor) state.

variable A factor that changes during an experiment.

vitamin An organic compound that is required in the diet to protect against some diseases.

volatile organic compounds (VOCs) Compounds that cause pollution because they vaporize readily.

VSEPR theory See **valence shell electron pair repulsion theory**.

vulcanization The process of making naturally soft rubber harder by reacting it with sulfur.

wax An ester of a long-chain fatty acid with a long-chain alcohol.

weak acid An acid that ionizes only slightly in water; a poor proton donor.

weak base A base that ionizes only slightly in water; a poor proton acceptor.

weight A measure of the force of attraction between Earth (or another planet) and an object.

wet scrubber A pollution control device that uses water to remove pollutants from smokestack gases.

X-rays Radiation similar to visible light but of much higher energy and much more penetrating.

zwitterion A molecule that contains both a positive charge and a negative charge; a dipolar ion.

Index